Chula Vista Public Library
Chula Vista, CA 91910

W9-BMO-639

la luz que regresa
y otras historias

la luz que

regresa
y otras historias

delta3

CIDCLI

D.R. © CIDCLI, S.C.
Av. México No. 145-601
Col. Del Carmen Coyoacán
C.P. 04100, México, D.F.

www.cidcli.com.mx

D.R. © Herederos de Salvador Elizondo

Ilustraciones: Alejandro Luna
Coordinación editorial: Rocío Miranda
Cuidado de la edición: Elisa Castellanos
Diseño gráfico: Perla Luna

Primera edición, octubre 2007
ISBN: 978-968-494-218-9

La reproducción total o parcial de este
libro, en cualquier forma y por cualquier medio,
no autorizada por los editores, viola los
derechos reservados y constituye un delito.

Impreso en México / *Printed in Mexico*

CHULA VISTA PUBLIC LIBRARY

3 3650 01818 2074

índice

la **luz**
que regresa
Fábula crononáutica

Es más fácil prever el destino que escapar a él. Siempre pienso en esta sentencia con la que Plutarco comenta los últimos días de Julio César, cuando viene a mi mente el recuerdo, ahora ya lejano, de aquella velada memorable del 15 de marzo del 2027 que nos congregó en torno al profesor Moriarty y su asombroso invento. Muchos años han pasado ya desde entonces y sin embargo sus palabras y las enigmáticas visiones que nos mostró aquella noche en su aparato permanecen intactas, como si hubieran sido sustraídas al curso del tiempo y conservadas al margen de su paso. ¡Cómo tiembla todavía la espada en la mano de Casca antes de asestar el primer golpe! No así la voz ni los gestos de Moriarty. Todavía resuenan en mis oídos las palabras con las que inició aquella noche la demostración de su invento: el cronostatoscopio,

9

instrumento hoy llamado "cámara de Moriarty" y cuyo uso se ha generalizado entre los historiadores. De pie ante la consola de controles del enorme paralelogramo translúcido comenzó por explicarnos los principios generales de su teoría y del funcionamiento de la cámara cronostática. Acerca de la primera: "Se equivoca Heráclito al negar la posibilidad de bañarnos dos veces en el mismo río… Basta para ello sustraer una cantidad de agua suficiente para bañarnos dos veces…" Acerca del segundo: **"El tiempo es un sistema de cintas que corren en diversas direcciones y a diferentes velocidades…** es posible mediante mi invento pasar de una a otra, aumentar o disminuir su velocidad, detener su marcha, regresar su curso…"

Moriarty había trabajado toda su vida en dar una expresión real y sensible de la teoría que había ideado en su mente mediante fórmulas matemáticas. Le parecía que nada vale una teoría que no se puede demostrar en la práctica. Su empeño no fue en vano: con obstinado rigor dedicó los mejores años de su vida a lograr el objetivo que se había impuesto en su juventud: poder observar los acontecimientos de la historia en el momento y en el lugar que se producen. Su razonamiento era bastante simple y solía ilustrarlo con ejemplos sacados de la técnica del cine con la que es posible invertir el orden de los sucesos. Los romanos, convencidos de que Julio César era el más virtuoso entre ellos, pues había devuelto la paz a la República después de una larga serie de guerras civiles, consideraban la posibilidad de coronarlo rey.

A su regreso triunfal a Roma después de la batalla de Farsalia en que había derrotado a Pompeyo, el último de sus enemigos, algunos ciudadanos adeptos le ofrecieron, durante la fiesta de Lupercalia, la corona que en tres ocasiones rechazó en nombre de sus convicciones republicanas si bien tal vez aspiraba secretamente a ella. El Senado, movido por la inquebrantable lealtad republicana de César discute el asunto, pero César no se apresura a manifestarse ni en pro ni en contra. Más bien convoca al Senado en los idus de marzo.[1] Mientras tanto consulta los augurios y los signos, los mensajes enigmáticos, los presagios, interroga al destino... Éstos fueron, más o menos, los términos en que Moriarty resumió el material histórico que serviría para la demostración del cronostatoscopio. "Es bien sabido —agregó— que a su retorno triunfal a Roma, César fue enfrentado por un viejo adivino que le dijo que se guardara de los idus de marzo... Este hecho aparentemente pintoresco ha sido para nosotros de gran importancia, pues nos ha servido de punto de referencia para dirigir el rayo antitiempo hacia el punto en que su continuidad y su sucesión se rompen, hacia donde la cinta cronológica salta o se corta por la obra de la predicción del vidente o del presagio..."

Un enorme cubo, aparentemente de cristal translúcido, se alzaba a mitad del salón de conferencias. No era posible ver nada a través de esa

[1] En el antiguo calendario romano se daba el nombre de idus de marzo al día 15 del mes de Marte. Los idus eran días de buenos augurios. La fecha es famosa porque Julio César fue asesinado en los idus de marzo del año 44 a. C. Según el historiador griego Plutarco, César había sido advertido del peligro, pero desestimó el aviso.

luz que parecía contener en su interior, una luz inerte que no emanaba o traspasaba las paredes invisibles en que estaba encerrada. El doctor Moriarty dio la orden de apagar las luces principales y sentándose ante los controles dijo: "Guiándonos por la luz del cometa que apareció en aquellos días y del que hablan todos los historiadores, intentaremos retroceder dos mil setenta y un años hasta tal fecha como la de hoy, los idus de marzo del año 44 antes de Cristo…"

Moriarty oprimió el interruptor general. **La luz o la sustancia contenida en el cubo de la cámara se condensó tornándose negra e impenetrable,** como si fuera un enorme bloque de basalto. Un zumbido muy tenue, pero inquietante, se escuchaba venir del aparato. "Tarda en ponerse en movimiento…", —dijo Moriarty. Al cabo de unos instantes el zumbido se fue haciendo un poco más agudo.

"Ya se pone en marcha hacia el pasado, pero muy lentamente", dijo. Moriarty hacía girar las manivelas de la consola; las agujillas de los indicadores temblaban en los cuadrantes tenuemente iluminados; la cronobrújula que señalaba el rumbo de los tiempos giraba en el indicador principal. De pronto fue claramente visible, en el interior del cubo, una perturbación de esa luz líquida y como emitidas desde el centro mismo del bloque se escucharon, invertidas, las palabras que Moriarty acababa de decir: "Et nem at nel yum or ep od asap le ai sa ach ram ne enop es ay…"; como cuando se pasa una banda sonora al revés.

Luego apareció en el centro del aparato una mancha de luz muy tenue, de color azul, que se iba tornando gris, gris cada vez más opaco y a la vez más intenso. **"Se está condensando la luz que regresa...** —dijo Moriarty—. Esa mancha de luz gris que se está formando en el centro de la cámara cronostática es la primera señal que empezamos a captar del punto del tiempo hacia el que nos dirigimos… **es la luz del cometa..."** La masa de luz opaca contenida en el aparato se condensaba y difundía formando figuras vagas, turbias, sin contornos precisos, que por segundos semejaban objetos reales y cosas conocidas.

Sentado a la consola de mando, Moriarty piloteaba la nave en que surcábamos el mar del tiempo. En la víspera de los idus de marzo el sueño de César se rompió a medianoche por los gemidos lastimosos de su mujer, Calpurnia, que conmovida por el sueño que había soñado, despertó llorando.

—He visto en mis sueños cosas extrañas y tristes —dijo Calpurnia sollozando—; he visto caer, oh César, abatido por el rayo, el pináculo con que el Senado te honró a tu regreso victorioso de las Galias… —Calpurnia calló; después de un momento agregó con voz temblorosa—: Soñé también que yacías en mis brazos…¡muerto!…

La luz contenida en la cámara de Moriarty se animó de lentas transformaciones; vimos entonces, pero en sentido inverso, el sueño de Calpurnia: cómo los fragmentos dispersos en el sueño se reúnen para formar el pináculo que luego asciende por los aires hasta quedar colocado en la parte más alta de la casa y cómo la punta del relámpago retrocede y desaparece.

—Vayamos un poco más atrás, —dijo Moriarty, haciendo girar la manivela de control. La escena cambió bruscamente—. Ahora se puede ver —continuó— al hombre de puños de fuego y a los hombres que se elevan en llamas y luego caen… ah, hemos llegado a la fiesta de Lupercalia, es el momento en que César se encuentra por primera vez con el adivino, **es el punto de arranque de esta historia;** detengámosla allí; Moriarty oprimió el botón del interruptor. La imagen se detuvo. Como un bajorrelieve antiguo entrevisto en la bruma, se veía difuso e informe el momento en que el viejo adivino exclama: —¡Guárdate, oh César, de los idus de marzo!…

—Ahora vayamos unos días en dirección al presente, días después de la Lupercalia… —dijo Moriarty.

Vimos entonces aparecer en el interior del cubo opalino otra vez el pináculo; esta vez en el momento en que era tocado por la punta del rayo y caía al suelo rompiéndose en pedazos.

Ante la multitud de presagios nefastos y confundido por los sueños de Calpurnia, César dudó si acudir al Senado al día siguiente. Cediendo a los ruegos de su mujer, decide no hacerlo. En eso llega Decio Bruto, su amigo y heredero que secretamente se había unido a los conspiradores.

César le comunica su decisión de no concurrir al Senado. Decio le dice que los senadores le ofrecerán la dictadura de por vida y que si no va tal vez se sientan desairados y no le ofrezcan la corona hasta otra ocasión en que Calpurnia tenga sueños más felices. César accede finalmente y todos se dirigen al Senado.

Pero entonces, **las figuras vagas que componían la representación comenzaron a descomponerse y a borrarse.** El zumbido del aparato se hizo más agudo, apenas soportable. Moriarty oprimió el interruptor y dijo:

—Los electrodos que generan la luz antitiempo se han calentado; dejaremos que se enfríen unos minutos que podríamos aprovechar para discutir el desempeño de mi invento hasta ahora…

Alguien lo interpeló desde el fondo del salón. Ya no recuerdo quién, pues han pasado más de veinte años desde aquella velada memorable.

—Profesor Moriarty —dijo—, el funcionamiento de su aparato responde en todo a la lógica más sencilla y natural y por lo mismo más clara y más cierta, pero quisiera preguntarle si su teoría contempla la posibilidad de entrar en contacto directo con esos personajes que difusamente pueblan el interruptor de su aparto… si no es posible… ¿cómo diría yo?… *hablar* con ellos, prevenir a César de lo que le espera en el Senado, al pie de la estatua de Pompeyo…

—Yo mismo lo he intentado algunas veces —respondió Moriarty.

—¿Cómo, doctor Moriarty?

—Muy fácil: **basta encontrar un resquicio para colarse en la historia…**

—¿Un resquicio…?

—Sí, un vacío histórico que no esté ocupado por otro y que uno mismo puede ocupar, —dijo Moriarty. Tomó un respiro y luego continuó—: ¿Quién es el misterioso Artemidoro de Cnidos que advierte a César, a pocos pasos de la estatua de Pompeyo?

Artemidoro, que aparece en Shakespeare, es una mentira de Plutarco. Estrabón y Tito Livio lo niegan… Proyectaré ahora esa parte.

Las luces se apagaron. Confusas formas se movían en tumultuosas condensaciones y rarefacciones de la luz dentro del aparato. Va llegando el cortejo de César. Al fondo el pórtico del Senado y más allá la estatua de Pompeyo. La acción se detiene.

—Éste es el momento en que César vuelve a encontrarse con el adivino, —dijo Moriarty—; César le dice: "Y bien, los

idus de marzo han llegado…" Y el adivino le responde:
"Sí, César, pero no se han ido…" y sigue su camino hacia
el interior del Senado.

Cuando está a pocos pasos de la estatua de Pompeyo,
Moriarty interrumpe la acción nuevamente. Las figuras
desaparecen.

—Habrán notado ustedes —continuó diciendo Moriarty—,
que en todo el trayecto entre el encuentro con el adivino
y la entrada al Senado la figura de Artemidoro, llamado
"el sofista", no aparece por ningún lado… pero lo que
el arte agrega a la historia consigue en cierta medida
manifestarse sobre la imagen original—. Hizo girar la manivela
y la imagen se detuvo en el instante en que al lado de la
figura de César se advierte claramente un hueco o un vacío
negro. **—Esa mancha negra junto a César**
—siguió diciendo Moriarty— **es la ausencia o la
mentira** de Artemidoro que puede ser ocupada por
alguno de nosotros para llegar hasta César y entregarle
el mensaje… ¿Alguno de ustedes quisiera probar?…

Moriarty entonces se dirigió a un famoso latinista que se
hallaba presente (ya no recuerdo cómo se llamaba) y que
se limitó a decir que aun si conseguía llegar hasta César
ello no cambiaría el curso de la historia. El profesor Moriarty
llamó entonces a uno de sus asistentes para que tomara
su lugar en la consola de controles y penetró como por
ósmosis en el interior del enorme cubo luminoso que al
instante puso el aparato en marcha nuevamente. Apareció

entonces la misma escena de la llegada de César al Senado, sólo que en esta ocasión vemos, de espalda, a un hombre que trata de abrirse paso a codazos y empellones entre la multitud para llegar hasta César. Por fin logra acercarse y sigue a César unos pasos tendiéndole el mensaje. Cuando por fin podemos ver la cara de ese hombre nos damos cuenta de que bajo la larga cabellera y detrás de la venerable barba del mentido Artemidoro, el profesor Moriarty trata de prevenir a César.

—¡Es el profesor Moriarty! —exclama alguien desde el fondo de la sala en penumbra.

El intruso en la historia consigue al fin entregar el mensaje. Sin leerlo César lo guarda entre los pliegues de su túnica y sigue su camino entre las aclamaciones de la plebe romana.

El asistente oprimió entonces el botón de progresión hacia el presente y Moriarty emergió de la cámara como si fuera materializándose conforme iba saliendo de ella. Todos prorrumpimos en una calurosa ovación. Moriarty se pone otra vez al frente de los controles y echa andar el aparato. Ya asciende César por la escalinata del Senado; ya llega al estilobato; ya cruza el peristilo del pórtico y se dirige hacia la estatua de Pompeyo al pie del cual aguardan Decio Bruto, Casio, Trebonio y los demás conspiradores.

¡Cómo tiembla la espada en la mano de Casca cuando tira el primer golpe! ¡Cómo cae el César al pie de la estatua de su enemigo! ¡Venganza, fatalidad, destino!...

El profesor Moriarty no tuvo tiempo (murió unos años después de aquella reunión) de perfeccionar su invento al grado de poder penetrar y estudiar el futuro. Ahora que el cronostatoscopio es un instrumento de uso común y al alcance de cualquiera, en un sinnúmero de modelos de muy variados precios y que nuestro conocimiento y nuestra visión del pasado son perfectos, resta, como en los tiempos de Julio César, aprender a discernir el futuro. Te preguntarás, joven lector, cuál ha sido entonces el propósito y la finalidad o el destino de este relato. En mi pequeña cámara cronostática de modelo económico puedo verte leyendo este libro que ahora tienes ante los ojos; es allá por los primeros años del siglo veintiuno, muchos años antes de aquella memorable velada del 2027; puedo verte consultar en el diccionario las palabras ósmosis, estilobato, peristilo conforme lees. **Te preguntas cómo es que este escrito haya llegado a ti casi medio siglo antes de que yo lo escribiera** y veinte años antes de que sucedieran los hechos que narra.

Pues bien, todo es posible gracias a la prodigiosa invención de Moriarty.

el **hombre**
que llora

El Hospital General es gris por dentro y por fuera.
Opalescencias; brillos de quirófano a veces. Relámpagos
diagonales de acero pulido contra las concentraciones difusas
de la luz eléctrica espaciada a lo largo de los corredores.

Conforme se avanza por los últimos pasillos, **la luz
se va haciendo más lúgubre pero más
intensa**. Cada vez más triste. Tan triste que exhala esa luz
un olor antiséptico y atroz de tristeza. En el último cubículo,
el más luminoso de todos, por el que el sol penetra de lleno
a lo largo del pasillo hacia todo el hospital, está la figura que
llaman del hombre que llora.

Mucho se ha hablado de esta misteriosa figura que
conservan en el Hospital General. Mi abuela ha decidido
llevarme a verla, pues es grande la fama del hombre que
llora y dicen que a veces concede ciertas mercedes.

Mientras vamos por los corredores del hospital las enfermeras como bultos grises y blancos cuchichean a nuestro paso.

—Van a ver al hombre que llora —dice una monja a otra.

Todo es blanco en esa habitación olorosa a formol. El anciano que yace sobre la cama es tan blanco como la manta que lo cubre hasta la barbilla.

El viejecito llora como mujer. Eso dice mi abuela. Yo me quedo callado. Lo miro atentamente. Su boca se pliega como la de una máscara de teatro. Roja y húmeda chasquea una lengua larga y flaca como un verduguillo contra las encías desdentadas. Por sus mejillas agrietadas resbalan gruesos lagrimones desde sus ojos irritados y legañosos. Sólo su boca y sus ojos se mueven.

Dicen que es una pura cabeza y que no tiene cuerpo, pero esto yo no lo creo.

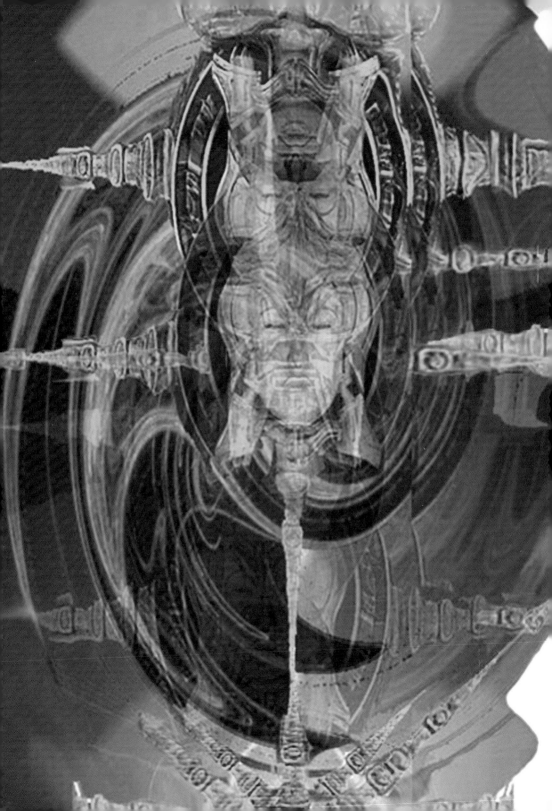

los indios verdes

Ya vienen otra vez los indios verdes. Por parejas las silenciosas avanzadas acampan en los aledaños de Mound City, un pequeño caserío de palos secos que conoció hace treinta años el pasajero auge de una veta que no tardó en agotarse. Los indios ofrecen pieles secas y palitos tallados con los dientes. **No saben contar;** solamente medir. Son adoradores —dicen— del sol verde de más allá del desierto y no saben hacer otra cosa que atar y desatar complicados nudos, para lo que se exhiben, a veces, en la terregosa y única calle de Mound. **No saben hablar,** pero algunos viejos gambusinos que se mueren lentamente en el lugar dicen que los indios verdes hablan por nudos, como los mudos que lo hacen a señas. Algunos vaqueros que acampan con sus manadas cerca del arroyo y que pasan por Mound camino del río Ancho, dicen que vienen del

Golfo de México en pequeños grupos y que la gente los cree sagrados porque propician la lluvia y la fecundidad de los animales benéficos y de las mujeres, y también pueden deshacer nudos que ningún cristiano podría desatar. Dicen también que son buenos comadrones de cerdos, de caballos y de vacas. **Todos sus conocimientos están en las manos y su religión consiste en ver el sol,** sabiduría que se confunde con monótonas y extrañas danzas por las que se preparan para un rito que practican a solas. Se dice que son afectos al ololiuqui, que guardan, durante sus largas migraciones en unas bolsitas hechas de escroto de toro seco que llevan colgadas al hombro con un tendón.

Otros dicen que a su paso van sembrando el locoweed que hace reventar a los caballos y a las mujeres las pone en brama como perras. Los que viven en Mound desde que el

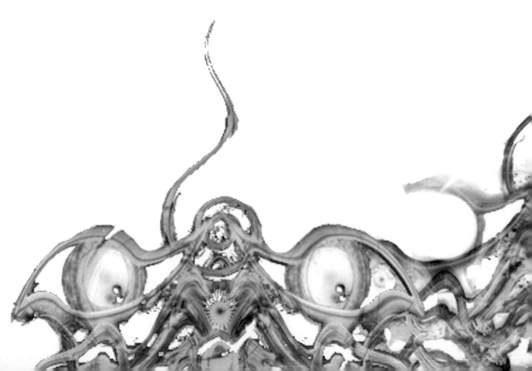

finado Bill McCoy fundó el pueblo hace unos treinta años, dan fe que desde entonces son siempre los mismos indios verdes los que pasan, cada cuatro años y que su número no ha aumentado ni disminuido en ese tiempo. Concluyen que como no proliferan deben de ser inmortales. Pero yo no estoy muy seguro, aunque ya los he visto pasar por aquí tres veces. Van desnudos y parecen hechos de cobre verdizo.

El viejo Buck Pringle que también los vio pasar por Realitos en 1876 dice que **no son inmortales, sino que están muertos** y que no hay nadie al sur del Colorado que esté más muerto que los indios verdes y que por eso no saben hablar ni entienden el lenguaje humano y que también por eso saben desatar cualquier nudo. Dice el viejo Buck que los mexicanos los mataron antes de la República y que **son las puras ánimas de los antiguos guerreros,** pero vaya usted a saber si es cierto.

sistema
de Babel

Ya va a hacer un año que decreté la instauración de un nuevo sistema del habla en mi casa. Todos somos considerablemente más felices desde entonces. No hay que pensar que lo hice porque el lenguaje que habíamos empleado hasta entonces no me pareciera eficaz y suficiente para comunicarnos. Prueba de ello es que lo estoy empleando aquí para comunicar, aunque sea en una medida remota e imprecisa, la naturaleza de esta nueva lengua. Además, su materia es esencialmente la misma de que estaba hecho el otro, ahora desechado y proscrito. Pero fueron, justamente esa eficacia y esa suficiencia del antiguo lenguaje las que me lo hicieron, al final, exacto, preciso y, sobre todo, extremadamente tedioso. ¡Qué estupidez trágica, me dije, **qué aberración tan tenaz de la especie es la de que las palabras correspondan siempre a la cosa** y que el gato se llame gato y no, por ejemplo, perro!

Pero basta con no llamar a las cosas por su nombre para que adquieran un nuevo, insospechado sentido que las amplifica o las recubre con el velo del misterio de las antiguas invocaciones sagradas. Se vuelven otras, como dicen. Llamadle flor a la mariposa y caracol a la flor; interpretad toda poesía o las cosas del mundo y encontraréis otro tanto de poesía y otro tanto de mundo en los términos de ese trastrocamiento o de esa exégesis; **cortad el ombligo serpentino que une a la palabra con la cosa** y encontraréis que comienza a crecer autónomamente, como un niño; florece luego y madura cuando adquiere un nuevo significado común y transmisible. Condenada, muere y traspone el umbral hacia nuevos avatares lógicos o reales. Digo reales porque **las metamorfosis de las palabras**

afectan a las cosas que ellas designan.

Para dar un ejemplo sencillo: un perro que ronronea es más
interesante que cualquier gato; a no ser que se trate de un
gato que ladre, claro. Pensemos, si no, un solo momento,
en esos tigres que revolotean en su jaulita colgada del muro,
junto al geranio.

Todos aquí ayudamos a difundir la nueva lengua.
**Concienzudamente nos afanamos en
decir una cosa por otra**. A veces la tarea es ardua.
Los niños tardan bastante en desaprender el significado
de las palabras. Diríase que nacen sabiéndolo todo. Otras
veces, especialmente cuando hablo con mi mujer de cosas
abstractas, llegan a pasar varias horas antes de que podamos
redondear una frase sin sentido perfecta.

la **historia**
según Pao Cheng

En un día de verano hace más de tres mil quinientos años, el filósofo Pao Cheng se sentó a la orilla de un arroyo a adivinar su destino en la caparazón de una tortuga. El calor y el murmullo del agua pronto hicieron, sin embargo, vagar sus pensamientos y olvidándose poco a poco de las manchas de carey, Pao Cheng comenzó a inferir la historia del mundo a partir de ese momento. **"Como las ondas de este arroyuelo, así corre el tiempo.** Este pequeño cauce crece conforme fluye, pronto se convierte en un caudal hasta que desemboca en el mar, cruza el océano, asciende en forma de vapor hacia las nubes, vuelve a caer sobre la montaña con la lluvia y baja, finalmente, otra vez convertido en el mismo arroyo…" Éste era, más o menos, el curso de su pensamiento y así, después de haber intuido la redondez de la tierra, su movimiento en torno al sol, la traslación de los demás astros y la propia rotación de la galaxia y del mundo. "¡Bah!" exclamó, "este modo de pensar me aleja de la Tierra de Han y de sus hombres que son el centro inamovible y el eje en torno al que giran todas las humanidades que en él habitan". Y pensando nuevamente en el hombre, Pao Cheng pensó en la historia. Desentrañó, como si estuvieran escritos en la caparazón de la tortuga, los grandes acontecimientos futuros, las guerras, las migraciones, las pestes y las epopeyas de todos los pueblos a lo largo de varios milenios. **Ante los ojos de su imaginación caían las grandes naciones y nacían las pequeñas** que después se hacían grandes y poderosas antes de ser abatidas a su vez. Surgieron también todas las razas y las ciudades habitadas por ellas que se alzaban un instante majestuosas y luego caían por tierra para confundirse con la ruina y la escoria de innumerables generaciones. Una de estas ciudades entre todas las que existían en ese futuro imaginado por Pao Cheng llamó poderosamente su atención y su divagación se hizo más precisa en cuanto a los detalles que la componían, como si en ella estuviera encerrado un enigma relacionado con su persona. Aguzó su mirada interior y trató de penetrar en los resquicios de esa topografía increada. La fuerza de su imaginación era tal que se sentía caminar por sus calles, levantando la vista azorado ante la grandeza de las construcciones y la belleza de los monumentos. Largo rato paseó Pao Cheng por aquella ciudad mezclándose a los hombres ataviados con extrañas vestiduras y que hablaban una lengua lentísima, incomprensible, hasta que de pronto se detuvo ante una casa en cuya fachada parecían estar inscritos los signos indescifrables de un misterio que lo atraía irresistiblemente. **A través de una de las ventanas pudo vislumbrar a un hombre que estaba escribiendo**. En ese mismo momento Pao Cheng sintió que allí se dirimía una cuestión que lo atañía íntimamente. Cerró los ojos y acariciándose la frente perlada de sudor con las puntas de sus dedos alargados trató de penetrar, con el pensamiento, en el interior de la habitación en la que el hombre estaba escribiendo. Se elevó volando del pavimento y su imaginación traspuso el reborde de la ventana que estaba abierta y por la que se colaba una ráfaga fresca que hacía temblar las **cuartillas, cubiertas de incomprensibles caracteres,** que yacían sobre la mesa. Pao Cheng se acercó cautelosamente al hombre y miró por encima de sus hombros, conteniendo la respiración para que éste no notara su presencia. El hombre no lo hubiera notado pues parecía absorto en su tarea de cubrir aquellas hojas de papel con esos signos cuyo contenido todavía escapaba al entendimiento de Pao Cheng. De vez en cuando el hombre se detenía, miraba pensativo por la ventana, aspiraba un pequeño cilindro blanco que ardía en un extremo y arrojaba una bocanada de humo azulado por la boca y por las narices, luego volvía a escribir.

Pao Cheng miró las cuartillas terminadas que yacían en desorden sobre un extremo de la mesa y conforme pudo ir descifrando el significado de las palabras que estaban escritas en ellas su rostro se fue nublando y un escalofrío de terror cruzó, como la reptación de una serpiente venenosa, el fondo de su cuerpo. **"Este hombre está escribiendo un cuento",** se dijo. Pao Cheng volvió a leer las palabras escritas sobre las cuartillas. El cuento se llamaba *La historia según Pao Cheng* y trata de un filósofo de la antigüedad que un día se sentó a la orilla de un arroyo y se puso a pensar en… **"¡Luego yo soy un recuerdo de ese hombre y si ese hombre me olvida moriré!..."**

El hombre, no bien había escrito sobre el papel las palabras "…si ese hombre me olvida moriré", se detuvo, volvió a aspirar el cigarrillo y mientras dejaba escapar el humo por la boca su mirada se ensombreció como si ante él cruzara una nube cargada de lluvia. Comprendió, en ese momento, que se había condenado a sí mismo, para toda la eternidad, a seguir escribiendo la historia de Pao Cheng, pues si su personaje era olvidado y moría, él, que no era más que un pensamiento de Pao Cheng, también desaparecería.

el grafógrafo

A Octavio Paz

Escribo. **Escribo que escribo.** Mentalmente me veo escribir que escribo y también puedo verme ver que escribo. Me recuerdo escribiendo ya y también viéndome que escribía. Y me veo recordando que me veo escribir y me recuerdo viéndome recordar que escribía y escribo viéndome escribir que recuerdo haberme visto escribir que me veía escribir que recordaba haberme visto escribir que escribía y **que escribía** que escribo que escribía. También puedo imaginarme escribiendo **que ya había escrito** que me imaginaría escribiendo que había escrito que me imaginaba escribiendo que me veo **escribir que escribo.**

en la playa

Cuando ya estaba cerca de donde se rompían las olas cesó de remar y dejó que la lancha bogara hacia la orilla con el impulso de la marejada. Estaba empapado de sudor y el sucio traje de lino blanco se le adhería a la gordura del cuerpo impidiendo o dificultando sus movimientos. **Había remado durante varias horas tratando de escapar de sus perseguidores.** Su impericia lo había llevado costeando hasta esa extensa playa que con sus dunas se metía en el mar hasta donde la lancha estaba ahora. Se limpió con la mano el sudor que le corría por la frente y miró hacia tierra. Luego se volvió y vio a lo lejos, como un punto diminuto sobre las aguas, la lancha de Van Guld que lo venía siguiendo. "Si logro pasar al otro lado de la duna estoy a salvo", pensó acariciando la Luger que había sacado del bolsillo de la chaqueta para cerciorarse de que no la había perdido. Volvió a guardar la pistola, esta vez en el bolsillo trasero del pantalón y trató de dar otro golpe de remo para dirigir la lancha hacia la playa, pero la gordura dificultaba sus movimientos y no consiguió cambiar el rumbo del bote. Encolerizado, arrojó el remo hacia la costa. Estaba tan cerca que pudo oír el golpe seco que produjo sobre la arena húmeda, pero la lancha se deslizaba de largo sin encallar. Había pozas y no sabía nadar. Por eso no se tiró al agua para llegar a la orilla por su propio pie. Una vez más se volvió hacia sus perseguidores. El punto había crecido.

Si la lancha no encallaba en la arena de la playa, le darían alcance. Tomó el otro remo y decidió utilizarlo como timón apoyándolo sobre la borda y haciendo contrapeso con toda la fuerza de su gordura. Pero se había equivocado y la lancha viró mar adentro. Entonces sacó rápidamente el remo del agua y repitió la misma operación en el lado opuesto. La lancha recibía allí el embate de la corriente y viró con tanta velocidad que el gordo perdió el equilibrio y por no caer sobre la borda soltó el remo que se alejó flotado suavemente en la estela. La lancha bogaba paralela a la costa y daba tumbos sobre las olas que reventaban contra su casco. Iba asido a la borda. De vez en cuando miraba hacia atrás. La lancha de su perseguidor seguía creciendo ante su mirada llena de angustia. Cerró los ojos y dio de puñetazos sobre el asiento, pero esto le produjo un vivo dolor, un dolor físico que se agregaba al miedo como un acento maléfico. Abrió las manos regordetas, manicuradas, y las miró durante un segundo. Sangraban de remar. Las metió en el agua y las volvió a mirar. Su aspecto era más siniestro ahora. La piel, desprendida de sus raíces de sangre, tenía una apariencia cadavérica. Volvió a cerrar los puños esperando que sangraran nuevamente y luego apoyó las palmas contra los muslos hinchados que distendían la tela del pantalón. Vio las manchas que habían dejado sobre el lino sucio y miró hacia atrás, pero no pudo estimar el crecimiento del bote perseguidor porque en ese momento un golpe de agua ladeó la lancha y haciéndola virar la impulsó de costado, a toda velocidad, hacia la playa. La quilla rasgó la superficie tersa y nítida de la arena con un zumbido agudo y seco. El gordo apoyó fuertemente las manos contra la borda, inclinando el cuerpo hacia atrás, pero al primer tumbo se fue de bruces contra el fondo de la lancha. **Sintió que la sangre le corría por la cara y apretó la Luger contra sus caderas obesas.**

Van Guld iba apoyado en la popa, detrás de los cuatro mulatos que remaban rítmicamente. Gobernaba el vástago del timón con las piernas y había podido ver todas las peripecias del gordo a través de la mira telescópica del Purdey. Cuando el gordo dio los puñetazos de desesperación sobre el asiento, Van Guld sonrió e hizo que la cruz de la mira quedara centrada sobre su enorme trasero, pero no hubiera disparado porque todavía estaba fuera del alcance del Purdey, un arma para matar elefantes a menos de cincuenta metros.

—¡Más aprisa, remen! —gritó Van Guld y luego pensó para sí—: "Tenemos que llegar antes de que cruce la duna".

Los negros alzaron más que antes los remos fuera del agua y, jadeando, emitiendo un gemido entrecortado a cada golpe, comenzaron a remar a doble cuenta. **El bote se deslizaba ágil sobre el agua casi quieta,** bajo el sol violento que caía a plomo del cielo límpido, azul. De la selva, más allá de la duna que estaba más lejana de lo que se la imaginaba viéndola desde el mar, el chillido de los monos y de los loros llegaba a veces como un murmullo hasta la lancha, mezclado con el tumbo de las olas sobre la arena, con el fragor de la espuma que se rompía en esquirlas luminosas, blanquísimas, a un costado de la barca.

Con un movimiento horizontal de la carabina, Van Guld siguió el trayecto de la barca del gordo cuando ésta encallaba sobre la arena. Apuntó durante algunos instantes la cruz de la mira sobre la calva perlada de sudor de su presa que yacía boca abajo junto a la lancha volcada. Las enormes caderas del gordo, entalladas en el lino mugriento de su traje, eran como un montículo de espuma sobre la arena. Apuntó luego el Purdey hacia la selva que asomaba por encima del punto más alto de la duna. Las copas de las palmeras y de las ceibas se agitaban silenciosas en su retina, pero Van Guld adivinaba el chillido de los monos, los gritos de los loros, mezclándose a la jadeante respiración del gordo, tendido con el rostro y las manos sangrantes sobre la arena ardiente.

—¡Vamos, vamos! ¡Más aprisa! —les dijo a los mulatos. Éstos sudaban copiosamente y sus torsos desnudos se arqueaban, tirantes como la cuerda de un arco, a cada golpe de remo. Su impulso movía la barca a espasmos, marcados por el jadeo de su respiración y no se atrevían a mirar hacia la costa donde estaba el gordo, sino que se tenían con la mirada al frente, como autómatas.

—¡Más aprisa!, ¡más aprisa! —volvió a gritar Van Guld. Su voz era diáfana como el grito de un ave marina y se destacaba de las olas, de la brisa, como algo de metal, sin resonancia y sin eco.

El gordo se palpaba el bolsillo del pantalón nerviosamente, dejándose unas difusas manotadas de sangre en el trasero.

Allí estaba la Luger. Si le daban alcance en el interior de la selva tendría que servirse de ella aunque era un tirador inexperto. Trató de incorporarse, pero no lo consiguió al primer intento. La quilla del bote había caído sobre su pie, aprisionándolo contra la arena. Pataleó violentamente hasta que logró zafarlo para ponerse en cuatro patas y así poder incorporarse con mayor facilidad. Pero luego pensó que puesto de pie, ofrecía un blanco mucho más seguro a la carabina de Van Guld. Si se arrastraba por la playa hasta ascender la duna, su cuerpo se confundiría, tal vez, con la arena para esquivar las balas que le dispararía su perseguidor.

Parapetado en la borda de la lancha miró en dirección de Van Guld. La lancha había crecido en sus ojos considerablemente. **Casi podía distinguir la silueta de Van Guld erguida en la popa,** escudriñando la blanca extensión de la playa, tratando de apuntar con toda precisión el rifle sobre su cuerpo. Esto era una figuración pues Van Guld estaba en realidad demasiado lejos. El bote seguía siendo un punto informe en el horizonte. Se incorporó pensando que tendría tiempo de llegar hasta la duna. Echó a correr, pero no bien había dado unos pasos, sus pies se hundieron y dio un traspié; cayó de cara sobre la arena que le escocía la herida que se había hecho en la frente.

A Van Guld le pareció enormemente cómico el gesto del gordo, visto a través del anteojo, **sobándose el trasero con la mano ensangrentada.**

Los pantalones blancos le habían quedado manchados de rojo. "Como las nalgas de un mandril", pensó Van Guld bajando sonriente el rifle y apoyando pacientemente la barbilla sobre sus manos cruzadas que descansaban en la boca del grueso cañón del Purdey. Estuvo así un momento y luego volvió a empuñar el rifle para seguir los movimientos del gordo. **Cuando lo vio caer de boca en la arena lanzó una carcajada.**

Después, el gordo se incorporó con dificultad y se sentó respirando fatigosamente. Su cara estaba cubierta de sudor. Con las mangas se enjugó la boca y la frente. Miró un instante la chaqueta manchada de sudor y de sangre y luego notó que uno de sus zapatos se había desatado. Alargó el brazo tratando de alcanzar las agujetas pero no logró asirlas por más que dobló el tronco. Tomó entonces la pierna entre sus manos y empezó a jalarla hacia sí. Una vez que había conseguido poner el zapato al alcance de sus manos las agujetas quedaban debajo del pie y por más esfuerzos que hacía por atarlas, no podía pues sus dedos además de estar heridos, eran demasiado cortos y demasiado torpes para retener fijamente las cintas y anudarlas. Trató entonces de quitarse el zapato, pero tampoco lo consiguió ya que sus brazos arqueados sobre el vientre voluminoso no eran lo suficientemente largos para ejercer una presión efectiva sobre el zapato. Se echó boca arriba y, ayudándose con el otro pie, trató de sacar el zapato haciendo presión sobre

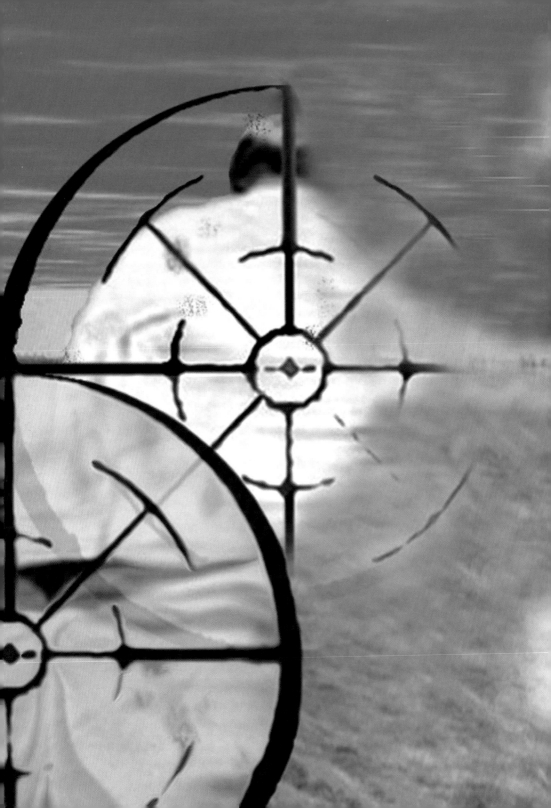

él con el tacón. Al fin logró sacar el talón. Levantó la pierna en el aire y agitando el pie violentamente al cabo de un momento hizo caer el zapato en la arena.

Ese pie, enfundado en un diminuto zapato puntiagudo de cuero blanco y negro primero y en un grueso calcetín de lana blanca después, con la punta y el talón luidos y manchados por el sudor y el contacto amarillento del cuero, agitándose temblorosamente, doblando y distendiendo coquetamente los dedos regordetes dentro del calcetín, producía una sensación grotesca, ridícula, cómica, cruzado como estaba por los dos hilos de araña milimétricamente graduados de la mira del Purdey.

Apoyándose con las manos, el gordo levantó el trasero y luego, doblando las piernas hasta poner los pies debajo del cuerpo, se puso de pie. Introdujo la mano en el bolsillo para sacar la pistola. Esto le produjo fuertes dolores en los dedos descarnados, pero una vez que tenía asida la Luger por la cacha los dolores se calmaron al contacto liso, acerado, frío, del arma. La sacó y después de frotarla contra el pecho de la chaqueta para secarla, la amartilló volviéndose en dirección de la costa, hacia la lancha de Van Guld. Pudo distinguir a los cuatro negros que se inclinaban simultáneamente al remar. La cabeza rubia e inmóvil de Van Guld se destacaba claramente por encima de las cabezas oscilantes y negras de los remeros.

El gordo estaba de espaldas a él. Van Guld vio cómo sacaba la pistola del bolsillo del pantalón y cómo agitaba el brazo mientras la secaba contra la chaqueta, pero no vio cómo la amartillaba. "No sabe usar la pistola", pensó Van Guld cuando vio que el gordo se dirigía cojeando hacia la duna con la pistola tenida en alto, con el cañón apuntando hacia arriba, casi tocándole el hombro y con la línea de fuego rozándole la cara.

Le faltaban unos cuarenta metros para llegar a la falda de la duna. Si se arrastraba

hasta allí no podría desplazarse con suficiente rapidez y daría tiempo a sus perseguidores de llegar por la costa hasta situarse frente a él. Consciente de su obesidad, pensó que si corría su cuerpo ofrecería durante el tiempo necesario un blanco móvil, lo suficientemente lento para ser alcanzado con facilidad. Se volvió hacia la barca de Van Guld. Calculó mentalmente todas sus posibilidades. La velocidad con que se acercaba le permitiría quizá llegar a tiempo a la cuesta de la duna arrastrándose. Se echó a tierra, pero no bien lo había hecho se le ocurrió que al llegar a la duna y para ascender la cuesta que lo pondría a salvo, tendría que ofrecerse, de todos modos, erguido al fuego de Van Guld.

—¡Paren! —dijo Van Guld a los remeros bajando el rifle. Los negros se arquearon sobre los remos conteniendo la fuerza de la corriente que ellos mismos habían provocado con el último golpe de remo. Los músculos de sus brazos y de sus hombros se hinchaban con el esfuerzo de parar el bote. Van Guld escupió sobre la borda para cerciorarse de que el bote se había detenido. Un pájaro salvaje aleteó rompiendo el silencio. **Van Guld clavó la vista delante de sí, en dirección del gordo,** luego, humedeciéndose los labios con la lengua volvió la cara mar adentro. Con la vista fija en el horizonte volvió a humedecerse los labios y se quedó así unos instantes hasta que la brisa secó su saliva. Tomó luego el Purdey y lo apuntó hacia el gordo —una mancha diminuta, blanca, informe—, mirando a través del anteojo. "Hasta la brisa nos ayuda —pensó—; bastará con ponerle la cruz en el pecho, y si va corriendo la brisa se encargará de llevar el plomo hasta donde él esté". La vertical no importaba; a la orilla del mar el aire corre en capas extendidas. "A veces tiende a subir en la playa; medio grado hacia abajo, por si acaso. Si está quieto, un grado a la izquierda para aprovechar la brisa", reflexionó y bajando el rifle nuevamente se dirigió a los remeros:

—¡Vamos, a toda prisa! —les dijo mirando fijamente el punto de la playa en donde se encontraba el gordo.

"Se han detenido", pensó el gordo mientras estaba calculando su salvación. Echó a correr. No había dado tres pasos cuando volvió a caer, pues como le faltaba un zapato se le había torcido un tobillo y el pie descalzo se le había hundido en la arena. Su situación era ahora más expuesta ya que no podía parapetarse en la lancha y todavía estaba demasiado lejos de la duna. Boqueó tratando de recobrar el aliento. **El corazón le golpeaba las costillas y a través de todas las capas de su grasa escuchaba el rumor agitado del pulso.** Se puso la mano en el pecho tratando de contener esos latidos, pero como sólo estaba apoyado, con todo su peso sobre un codo, los brazos le empezaron a temblar. Apoyó entonces las dos manos sobre la arena y trató de incorporarse. Haciendo presión con los pies sobre el suelo, consiguió, al cabo de un gran esfuerzo, ponerse en pie y se volvió hacia la lancha de sus perseguidores.

Sin servirse de la mira telescópica, Van Guld pudo darse cuenta de que el gordo se había vuelto hacia ellos. Los mulatos remaban rítmicamente y la lancha se acercaba inexorablemente.

—¡Más aprisa! —volvió a decir Van Guld.

Su voz llegó difusa hasta los oídos del gordo que tuvo un sobresalto en cuanto la oyó y echó a correr hacia la duna. A cada paso se hundía en la arena por su propio peso y le costaba un gran esfuerzo avanzar.

Van Guld vio con toda claridad cómo el gordo corría dando traspiés en la arena. Había cubierto la mitad del trayecto hacia la duna. Un mono lanzó un chillido agudísimo y corto, como un disparo. El gordo se detuvo volviéndose angustiado hacia la lancha de Van Guld. Con los brazos extendidos y las manos colgándole de las muñecas como dos hilachos se quedó quieto en mitad de la playa. Se percató de que en su mano derecha llevaba la Luger. La acercó para verla mejor y se volvió nuevamente hacia la lancha de Van Guld, luego extendió el brazo con la pistola en dirección de sus perseguidores. **Oprimió el gatillo.** Nada. Volvió a apoyar el dedo regordete con todas sus fuerzas pero el gatillo no cedía. Cortó otro cartucho apresuradamente y la bala saltó de la recámara rozándole la cara. Extendió entonces el brazo y oprimió el gatillo con todas sus fuerzas.

"Tiene el seguro puesto", pensó Van Guld para sí.
　—¡Imbécil! —dijo después en voz alta.
　Los negros siguieron remando impasibles.

El gordo examinó cuidadosamente la pistola. Con las manos temblantes comenzó a manipularle todos los mecanismos. **Volvió a cortar cartucho y otra bala le saltó a la cara.** Oprimió un botón y el cargador salió de la cacha. Apresuradamente volvió a ponerlo en su lugar; luego oprimió otro botón que estaba en la guarda del gatillo. Era el seguro de la aguja. Como al mismo tiempo estaba oprimiendo el gatillo, la pistola se disparó en dirección de la duna produciendo una nubecilla de pólvora quemada y un pequeño remolino de arena en la duna. A lo lejos entre las copas de los árboles, se produjo un murmullo nervioso. El gordo se asustó al oír la detonación, pero no se había dado cuenta cabal de que el tiro había partido de su propia arma. Se volvió hacia Van Guld. Podía distinguir todos los rasgos de su rostro impasible, mirándole fijamente desde la popa de la lancha. Echó a correr. De pronto se detuvo y empuñando la Luger la apuntó nuevamente hacia Van Guld. Tiró del gatillo, pero el arma no disparó. Se acordó entonces del botoncito que estaba en la guarda del gatillo y lo apretó. Oprimió el gatillo varias veces.

Las balas pasaron lejos de Van Guld y de su lancha. La brisa que les iba en contra las había desviado y las detonaciones no llegaron a sus oídos sino después de unos instantes. El gordo se había quedado inmóvil. Tres volutas de humo blanco lo rodeaban, deshaciéndose lentamente en el viento. La lancha siguió avanzando hasta quedar colocada directamente frente al gordo.

Volvió a oprimir el gatillo. La Luger hizo un clic diminuto. Se había agotado el cargador. Arrojó la pistola y echó a correr, pero no en dirección de la duna, sino en dirección contraria a la de la lancha de Van Guld. Cuando se dio cuenta de que su huida era errada se detuvo. Vaciló. Luego corrió en dirección de la duna. Cuando llegó a la cuesta se fue de bruces y cayó rodando en la arena. Se incorporó rápidamente e intentó nuevamente ascender la duna.

Van Guld empuñó el Purdey y encañonó al gordo, pero no tenía intención de disparar todavía. Miraba a través del telescopio cómo trataba de subir por la duna, resbalando entre la arena, rascando para asirse a ese muro que siempre **se desvanecía entre sus dedos sangrantes.**

El gordo cayó sentado al pie de la duna. Primero corrió a cuatro patas a lo largo del montículo, alejándose de Van Guld, pero a cada momento volvía a caer de cara. Finalmente logró avanzar corriendo con los brazos extendidos para guardar el equilibrio.

Van Guld ordenó a los mulatos que lo siguieran desde el mar. Se pusieron a remar y la lancha avanzaba suavemente sobre las olas, paralela al gordo que corría dando tumbos. La cruz del Purdey se encontraba un grado a la izquierda y medio grado abajo del pecho del gordo.

Se había adelantado a la lancha que ahora bogaba más lentamente pues había entrado en esa faja de mar donde las olas se rompen y donde la fuerza de los remos se dispersa en la marejada. El gordo se detuvo, apoyado contra el túmulo de arena que se alzaba tras él. Respiraba con dificultad y no podía seguir corriendo.

La lancha de Van Guld pasó lentamente ante él. Por primera vez se encontraron sus miradas. Al pasar frente al gordo Van Guld levantó la vista del telescopio y se quedó mirando fijamente al gordo que, también, lo miraba pasar ante él, resollando pesadamente, indefenso.

Una vez que Van Guld había pasado de largo, el gordo se volvió y empezó a escalar la duna, pero avanzaba muy lentamente porque todos los apoyos se desmoronaban bajo su peso. **Sus manos cavaban en la arena tratando de encontrar un punto fijo al cual asirse.**

Van Guld hizo virar la lancha en redondo.

Mientras la lancha volvía sobre su estela y los perseguidores le daban la espalda, el gordo ascendió considerablemente y su mano casi logró asirse al borde de la duna. Trataba de empujarse con los pies, pero se le deslizaban hacia abajo.

Van Guld quedó colocado frente a él. Sonriente, lo miraba patalear y levantar nubecillas de arena con los pies. Volvió a encañonarlo y a través de la mira pudo adivinar con toda certeza el rostro sudoroso, sangrante del gordo que jadeaba congestionado.

Hubo un momento en que sus pies, a fuerza de cavar furiosamente, encontraron un punto de apoyo. Su cuerpo se irguió tratando de alcanzar con las manos la cresta de la duna y por fin lo consiguió. Entonces pataleó más fuerte, tratando de elevar las rodillas a la altura de sus brazos, pero la arena se desvanecía siempre bajo su cuerpo. Logró sin embargo retener la altura que había alcanzado sobre la duna. Deseaba entonces que más allá de esta prominencia hubiera otra hondonada para poderse ocultar y ganar tiempo.

Van Guld había centrado la mira sobre la espalda del gordo. Acerrojó el Purdey haciendo entrar un casquillo en la recámara, amartillando la aguja al mismo tiempo.

Cuando llegó a la cima vio que la arena se extendía en una planicie nivelada hasta donde comenzaba la selva. Estaba perdido. Se quedó unos instantes tendido sobre el borde de arena y miró sobre sus hombros en dirección de Van Guld que lo tenía encañonado. Estaba liquidado, pero no sabía si dejarse deslizar nuevamente hacia la playa o seguir avanzando sobre la duna hacia la selva. Eran unos cien metros hasta los primeros árboles. Para llegar a ellos daría a Van Guld el tiempo suficiente de apuntarle con toda certeza, igual que si se quedaba ahí mismo.

Van Guld bajó el rifle medio grado de la cruz. Pensó que sobre todo en la cresta de la duna la capa de aire extendido tendería a subir. La corrección horizontal era ahora deleznable ya que se encontraba directamente enfrente del gordo, con la brisa a su espalda.

Resignado, el gordo subió al borde y se puso de pie sobre la duna volviéndose hacia Van Guld.

La lancha producía un chapoteo lento sobre las olas débiles del mar apacible. A lo lejos se oían los gritos de los loros que se ajetreaban en el follaje de las ceibas. **Le tenía la cruz puesta en el cuello para darle en medio de los ojos**, pero luego bajó el rifle un poco más, hasta el sexo, para darle en el vientre, porque pensó que si le daba en la cabeza al gordo no sentiría su propia muerte y que si le daba en el pecho lo mataría demasiado rápidamente.

El gordo lo miraba con las manos colgantes, sangrantes, separadas del cuerpo, en una actitud afeminada y desvalida.

Cuando partió el disparo, la lancha dio un tumbo escueto, levísimo.

Sintió que las entrañas se le enfriaban y oyó un murmullo violento que venía de la selva. Se desplomó pesadamente y rodó por la duna hasta quedar despatarrado sobre la playa como un bañista tomando el sol. Boca arriba como estaba notó, por primera vez desde que había comenzado su huida, la limpidez magnífica del cielo.

Van Guld bajó el rifle. La brisa agitaba sus cabellos rubios. Todavía estuvo mirando unos instantes el cuerpo reventado al pie de la duna. Luego ordenó a los remeros partir. La barca se puso en marcha. Los mulatos jadeaban agobiados de sol, impulsando los remos fatigosamente. Van Guld apoyó el Purdey contra la borda y encendió un cigarrillo. Las bocanadas de humo se quedaban suspensas en la quietud del viento, como abandonadas de la lancha que se iba convirtiendo poco a poco en un punto lejano, imperceptible.

La luz que regresa y otras historias
Se acabó de imprimir en el mes de octubre de 2007
en los talleres de Reproducciones Fotomecánicas, S.A. de C.V.
Democracias núm. 116, colonia San Miguel Amantla,
Azcapotzalco 02700, México, D.F.
El tiraje fue de 3 000 ejemplares

W9-CDH-275

25 6/21
CLEARANCE
$ 50

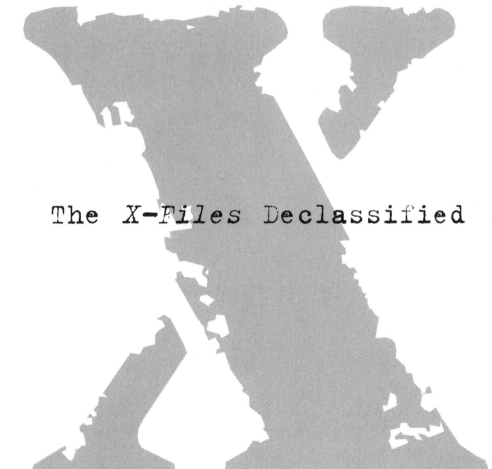

The *X-Files* Declassified

The X-Files Declassified

The Unauthorized Guide

Frank Lovece

A Citadel Press Book
Published by Carol Publishing Group

Copyright © 1996 Frank Lovece
All rights reserved. No part of this book may be reproduced in any
form, except by a newspaper or magazine reviewer who wishes to
quote brief passages in connection with a review.

A Citadel Press Book
Published by Carol Publishing Group
Citadel Press is a registered trademark of Carol Communications, Inc.

Editorial, sales and distrtibution, rights and permissions inquiries
should be addressed to Carol Publishing Group, 120 Enterprise Avenue,
Secaucus, N.J. 07094

In Canada: Canadian Manda Group, One Atlantic Avenue, Suite 105,
 Toronto, Ontario M6K 3E7

Carol Publishing Group books may be purchased in bulk at special
discounts for sales promotions, fund-raising, or educational purposes.
Special editions can be created to specifications. For details, contact
Special Sales Department, 120 Enterprise Avenue, Secaucus, N.J.
07094

Manufactured in the United States of America

10 9 8 7 6 5 4 3 2 1

Library of Congress Cataloging-in-Publication Data
Lovece, Frank.
    The X-files declassified : the unauthorized guide / Frank Lovece.
        p.   cm.
    "A Citadel Press book."
    ISBN 0-8065-1745-X
    1. X-files (Television program).   I. Title.
PN1992.77.X22L68   1996
791.45'72—dc20   95-26390
                                                                CIP

PHOTOGRAPH ACKNOWLEDGMENTS: FOX Broadcasting Company: 151; Michael
Grecco/FOX: 2, 5; Gillian Lefkowitz/Showtime: 17; MGM/USA: 45; Barry
Peake/HBO: 191; Showtime Networks Inc.: 57; Simon Film Productions Inc.:
118; South Gate Entertainment: 13; Suzanne Tenner/Paramount Pictures: 39.

For Maitland, whom I love

CONTENTS

ACKNOWLEDGMENTS

This volume is the result of months of research and writing—for which time, like Mulder, I had no life. I'd like to thank my friends and family profusely for putting up with my late nights, unreturned phone calls, and canceled invitations and appointments. I'd especially like to thank my light-of-my-life kids, Vincent and Erik Lovece.

I also extend my greatest thanks to Maitland McDonagh, who helped to track down facts, look for pictures, and subsidize my endless online research. My agent, Chris Calhoun, and my editor, Kevin McDonough, are understanding friends with great patience, who in the schism of "You want it fast or you want it good?" didn't push for fast. Kevin is as generous and genial an editor as a writer could hope for.

For their personal help in various capacities, I also thank Peter Berg, Mike Lackey—two godsends—as well as Renata Somogyi, Andy Edelstein, Craig Miller, Toni Cohen, and the ever-helpful staffs of the Lincoln Center Rose Theater Collection and Jerry Ohlinger's memorabilia shop. Fans might like to check out Miller's *Twin Peaks/X-Files* 'Zine, *Wrapped in Plastic*, 1912 E. Timberview Lane, Arlington, TX 76014.

I thank the countless journalists worldwide who have reported on *The X-Files*. And of course, my great thanks go to all those *X-Files* fans whose admiration and enthusiasm for the show have made this book possible.

X-GENESIS

Chris Carter and the Creation of *The X-Files*

Chris Carter wanted to make a scary show. "I don't mean scary in the horror-genre sense, but scary in the way that speculation pushes beyond scientific credibility to enter a realm of 'extreme possibility,'" he describes. "Films like *Coma* and *The Andromeda Strain* have that quality: It's the idea that shakes up you and your beliefs, not some hideous Frankenstein monster or a hand clasping the heroine's shoulder. We're all more interested in modern phenomena, which has a way of really shaking up that segment of our society that's come to believe in aliens and UFOs."

Add to this growing fear of conspiracies and suspicions about the U.S. government, particularly tales of the unaccountable, heavily armed, "black budget" secret part—from the CIA to the NSA. Real-life events like Waco, Ruby Ridge, and Oliver North's secret paramilitaries have made many people suspicious and fearful of their government. In the post-Watergate era, our longstanding suspicions about government have turned into distrust and even fear. And with the element of forensic science (popularized in *The Silence of the Lambs*) you've the basis for modern ghost stories to tell those huddled around the modern electronic campfire.

Yet a lot of writer-producers might have come up with something similar to *The X-Files*, it took Chris Carter's off-kilter talent and particular quirks and influences to envision and create a show that ranks with television's greatest.

Carter was born Oct. 13, 1957 in Bellflower, California. His earliest major television influence was the show *Kolchak: The Night Stalker* (ABC 1974–75), the series spin-off of the hit TV-movies *The Night Stalker* (1972) and *The Night Strangler* (1973). Each version starred Darren McGavin as rumpled reporter Carl Kolchak, who kept running across supernatural entities but could never convince editor Tony Vincenzo (Simon Oakland) of their existence.

"When I saw *Stalker*, it really shook me up to think there might be a twilight world of bloodsucking creatures," Carter recalls. "I probably remember only two scenes from the series [but] it was a scary show. That made a big impression on me when I was a kid."

1

In 1979 Carter graduated from California State University, Long Beach, with a journalism degree. That and his interest in surfing led to a job writing for *Surfing* magazine, based in nearby San Clemente. In a few years Carter became *Surfing*'s editor, and in 1983 he began a committed relationship with future wife Dori Pierson, a screenwriter. (She later wrote several TV-movies, starting with *The Imposter* [*sic*] in 1984, as well as the 1988 feature film *Big Business*.) With Pierson's encouragement and contacts, Carter began writing and pitching his own scripts as well; in 1985, one of them came to the attention of Jeffrey Katzenberg, then chairman of Walt Disney Studios, who decided to give Carter a try with a standard development contract.

That led to his first production effort, the "Disney Sunday Movie" *The B.R.A.T. Patrol* (ABC 1986), cowritten with Michael Patrick Goodman. Carter also wrote for NBC Productions, where he created and produced an unsold adventure-drama pilot, *Cameo by Night*, which aired in August 1987. Also around this time, for the Disney Channel, Carter developed an unsold sitcom called *The Nanny*—which, he hastens to add, "wasn't THAT *Nanny*, [starring Fran Drescher]."

In 1987 he wrote two episodes of the musical sitcom *Rags to Riches*, and coproduced that show during its two-month-long second season in 1988. In between, he and Pierson—who married in 1987—cowrote and served as coexecutive producers of a one-hour "Disney Sunday Movie" (and apparent pilot) *Meet the Munceys* (ABC 1988). Then Carter created and served as executive producer of NBC Productions' *Brand New Life*, an updated *Brady Bunch* starring Barbara Eden and Don Murray. The following year, Carter briefly served as a writer and story editor on the Gary Cole series *Midnight Caller*.

Throughout all these vagaries, Carter gained a reputation as a good writer and promising TV producer. In 1992, Fox Broadcasting's new president of TV production, Peter Roth, took a chance and signed Carter to a standard three-year development deal. He finally had the chance to do his scary show.

"If you look at my resume, you'll never find any clear connection between my old work and *The X-Files*," Carter observes. "I just wanted to do something as scary as I remember *The Night Stalker* was when I was in my teens."

But *Night Stalker* was only one influence. Carter was also aware of an increasing public belief in the paranormal. He met a psychology professor who said he'd served as a consultant on *Intruders* (CBS, May 1992), a two-part TV-movie about alien abductions. The consultant "told me that three percent [*sic*] of the public believed in this syndrome. I was astounded. I realized there was a topicality to this theme of the unknown, and *X-Files* grew out of that fascination."

Another *X-Files* influence was the cult-classic '60s TV show *The Avengers*. "I loved that relationship," Carter's says of the witty, mutually respectful

3

but nonromantic interplay between suave British spy Jonathan Steed (Patrick Macnee) and his primary female partner, Emma Peel (Diana Rigg). "I think it was the intensity of the stories there. It's the way I sort of instinctively write, so that was also fed into my ultimate concept of the show," which he'd always planned as having male and female coleads.

What didn't feed into Carter's vision, ironically, was science fiction. "I was never what you would call a science fiction devotee," Carter says. "I've never read the classic science fiction novels, except maybe one of each by Ursula Le Guin and Robert Heinlein a long time ago, and I've never watched an episode of *Star Trek*!"

Fox executives did not jump at Carter's proposal. "They turned it down at first," Carter remembers. "They didn't know what it was. And then I went back with Peter Roth, and we were able to sell it to them. . . . They reluctantly bought the idea but it took two pitch meetings to convince them that we had something worth proceeding on and to okay a script and pilot."

By May 21, 1993, *The X-Files* had made it to series, with David Duchovny and Gillian Anderson costarring as FBI agents investigating unsolved cases called the X-Files. Fox tentatively placed it in its Tuesday night lineup, following the tongue-in-cheek, 1890s western *The Adventures of Brisco County, Jr.* Both were soon afterward rescheduled to Friday, often considered a dead night for ratings. The series premiered strongly, on September 10. "If succeeding chapters can keep the pace," reviewed the trade magazine *Variety*, "the well-produced entry could be this season's UFO high-flier." Fox sister-magazine *TV Guide*, in its Fall Preview issue, opined that, "If you can overlook a credibility gap the size of the Milky Way—and many viewers *will* overlook it—the show is actually well-done. Whether you believe these stories or not, they're first-rate entertainment . . . a well produced, suspenseful mystery series that draws you in and keeps you hooked. *The X-Files*'s Nielsen ratings were higher than anything else Fox aired on admittedly ratings-poor Friday night. Before September was out, Fox gave Carter a full-season, twenty-two-episode order, which would shortly be upped to twenty-four. In addition, the series attracted a high percentage of most advertisers' target audience: Urban, educated, eigthteen- to thirty-four-year-old viewers. While viewership did drop precipitously until a fan-following (self-described "X-Philes") and strong word-of-mouth attracted the curious, the series kept building until, by April, its ratings were beating that of its premiere. The season finale, "The Erlenmeyer Flask," was the highest-rated—and even it was consistently beaten throughout season two. While all this still amounted to *The X-Files* finishing in the Nielsen cellar, the series' critical and ad-sales success prompted Fox to renew it.

During the season, Carter, like any other executive producer, had had to wrestle with the network over issues of taste and content. Less typically, he

4

fought to preserve his show's loosely resolved (and sometimes muddily unre-solved) endings—rightly noting that you can't handcuff monsters and aliens and book 'em, Danno.

Carter also was insistent that, "I didn't want this to be another *Moon-lighting*. I didn't want the relationship to come before the cases. . . . I think the best kind of sexual tension is when you put a smart man and a smart woman in a room: You've got immediate sexual tension, no matter if it's romantic [or not]. There's a tension here. And I think that's what we have with Mulder and Scully. I think there's a mutual respect, a mutual passion to solve these cases. And I think that people have responded to that."

By summer's end, after gaining viewers during rerun season, *The X-Files* was the critics' darling, appearing on "best-of" lists and netting an endorse-ment by Viewers for Quality Television. Yet it was the second season (in which production began July 11, 1994) that truly fulfilled the network's, and Carter's, audience aspirations.

Once again, *TV Guide* gave the show a remarkable amount of coverage. When Carter and the stars took a late-spring trip, by invitation, to the FBI Academy in Quantico, Virginia, the magazine dutifully covered it; later *TV Guide* would even go so far as to publish an *X-Files* comic-book story from the companion Topps Comic series. Second-season production ended May 4, 1995, and the show was on a roll: Its year-end ratings put it well into the middle of the Nielsens—terrific for Fox, which otherwise had only a bare hand-ful of stalwarts like *The Simpsons* and *Beverly Hills, 90210* in that range. Con-tinuing its critical success, *The X-Files* scored an upset Golden Globe Award for Television Series, Drama, over such highly touted contenders as *ER* and *NYPD Blue*; this helped bring a new-viewer momentum through the spring and summer reruns, building a big foundation for the third-season return.

During the spring and summer came a parade of magazine cover stories—the great cult-fave turning into a trend. Official *X-Files* novels and comic books had appeared earlier in the year, as had an *Entertainment Weekly* cover story and a *Mad* magazine parody. There was a year-old official fan club, a blizzard of fanzines, and, in June, the first *X-Files*-dedicated convention.

Duchovny hosted the 1995 season finale of *Saturday Night Live*. And soon he would appear on Jay Leno, Tom Snyder, and David Letterman, as well as the covers of *Details* and (again, but solo this time) *Entertainment Weekly*. Anderson did the talk-show circuit, particularly in the U.K., where *The X-Files* was a modest hit (and for a time the highest-rated show on BBC2).

The 1995–95 season premiere was Fox's top-rated program that week. By mid-season, *The X-Files* was Fox's highest-rated show, outpacing the net-work's established hits, and 20th Century–Fox Television sold the fall 1997 rerun rights to sister cable-network FX for a reported $600,000 each—the most ever paid by a cable network for an hour-long drama series, topping the record $475,000 each that USA Network had paid for *Murder, She Wrote*.

Carter himself had broken from the ranks of semianonymous TV-show creators to become a household name. That's not a bad accomplishment. After all, how many viewers know who created *Friends?*

In fall 1995, when his original three-year deal with Fox expired, Carter re-upped for five more years in a contract brokered by his agents, Elliott Webb and Bob Broder of Broder, Kurland, Webb, Uffner, and attorneys Larry Rose and Bruce Ramer. Its provisions include a commitment for a science-fiction drama series (set in the year 2000, with the working title *Millennium*) and for the development of an *X-Files* feature film (which he'd long discussed informally and at fan conventions, but which was only put into contractual terms now; Duchovny and Anderson would star, and Carter might direct).

As for the future—and whether Mulder and Scully will ever find the truth or just get lives outside their work—it's only sketchily mapped out. "I know basically where I am going with the series," Carter asserts. "I know what the final episodes will entail."

BIOGRAPHIES AND FILMOGRAPHIES

• David Duchovny •

David Duchovny was born August 7, 1960, in New York City, and grew up on East 11th Street and 2nd Avenue, near the famed 2nd Avenue Deli and hard across the old Dutch graveyard at St. Mark's Church.

"We used to play baseball [there]," he reminisces, "except the gravestones were flat, they weren't the kind that stick up—and since we didn't have bases! . . ." He smiles at the ironic morbidity. "It was like . . . 'He's rounding Stuyvesant! He's going to Van Dyke! He slides into Van Dyke! He's safe! He's safe! He's in there!' So once you made it into Van Dyke," he dryly jokes, "a sacrifice fly can pull you safely into Van Heuson."

His father is Amram (Marty) Ducovny, a Brooklyn-

Duchovny, in a rare, smiling promotional still.

born Russian Jew who is fifty-eight years old in 1996, and who "took the *h* out of our last name because he was tired of having it mispronounced," Duchovny explains. "But when my parents divorced, my mother put the *h* back in, as a show of solidarity with how a family member spelled the name. I spell it with the *h*; my brother doesn't use the *h*. My sister goes back and forth, depending on her mood."

Dad was a writer. He worked as a publicist for the ninety-year-old human-rights and cultural organization, the American Jewish Committee. But he also wrote three books: the in-retrospect wince-inducing *The Wisdom of Spiro T. Agnew*; *David Ben-Gurion in His Own Words*, and *On With the Wind*, a bestseller about the colorful Washington, D.C., gadfly and Watergate figure Martha Mitchell. Amram also wrote the off-Broadway play, *The Trial of Lee Harvey Oswald* (1967) which starred Ralph Meeker (1920–88). Amram moved to Paris after his 1972 divorce, and reportedly writes novels, but none have come out.

Duchovny's mom, Margaret (Meg) Duchovny (fifty-six years old in 1996), was born and raised in Scotland. She presently runs the lower grades at Grace Church School in New York City's East Village. David's older brother, Daniel, is now a TV commercial director in Los Angeles; their younger sister Laurie, an Audrey Hepburnesque beauty who's twenty-nine in 1996, teaches at the St. Anne's parochial school in Brooklyn.

After the divorce, mom was "afraid we'd all end up in the gutter," Duchovny remembers. For Duchovny, "The divorce was probably the most important emotional moment of my life. I don't think you ever recover from something like that. You are forced into an adult world of emotions that you aren't prepared to deal with."

Duchovny had been a shy kid who spoke so little that when he was young, his brother Daniel used to tell friends David was retarded. By fifth grade, however, David had overcome his reticence enough to play one of the three magi in a Christmas production. In fact, he did well enough in both school and sports that at thirteen, he won an academic scholarship to the Upper West Side's elite Collegiate prep school—where a spectrum from the likes of John F. Kennedy, Jr. to actor Zach Galligan (*Gremlins*) has been educated. One classmate was actor Jason Beghe, a lifelong friend who appeared in *The X-Files* episode "Darkness Falls." "I was the gregarious one," Beghe remembers. "David was the one who applied himself."

David, nicknamed Duke, was a star on the collegiate baseball and basketball teams. When he went on to prestigious Princeton University (where he was renicknamed Doggie), he spent a year playing guard on the basketball team and two seasons playing center field on the baseball team. Yet after "I got fed up with my coach or he got fed up with me," Duchovny and varsity sports parted ways, and the studious student hunkered down to earn a 1982 bachelor of arts in English literature—with grades good enough to get him into Yale.

"I was really a tight-assed kind of student," Duchovny says of his Princeton days. When he discovered that one roommate wanted to be an actor, Duchovny scoffed at him, "You came to Princeton—why are you acting?" Yet on reflection today, "I wish I'd had a little more fun. I didn't have those wild

Duchovny and Sheryl Lee, in the "Jake's Story" episode of *Zalman King's Red Shoe Diaries*.

and crazy college years that people seem to try to recapture the rest of their lives. In fact, it's kind of *good* I had such a miserable time in college, because I spent no time trying to recapture it. I can just move on."

"Miserable" is relative, of course; aside from playing varsity sports and acing his classes, "I had a girlfriend I met in December of my first year. She was my girlfriend for four years and a year after we graduated. If I'd met her a little later we'd probably have stayed together. I think I was in love before that, but she was my first really long-term relationship."

He had a long-term relationship with English lit as well by now, and with a Mellon Fellowship, went to Yale and earned his master's degree in the field. Studying under such literary stars as Harold Bloom, John Hollander, Jay Hillis Miller, and Geofrey Hartman, he continued on as a Ph.D. candidate. That involved, among other things, being a teaching assistant and outlining his doctoral dissertation. He was on a career path to professorship—but eventually realized, "I would have been a failed academic, because I was good at it but it was insincere. I spoke the language, but underneath I was thinking, 'Somebody's going to find out that I really don't care.'"

In the fall of 1985, buddy Beghe suggested Duchovny take acting classes. Duchovny was already spending time hanging out with students at Yale's famous drama school—they seemed to be fun and jolly sorts—and he thought Beghe's suggestions "made sense, because I was twenty-six years old and didn't feel like spending the rest of my life teaching."

Dropping out to become an actor wasn't a conscious part of that plan, so Duchovny—thinking about becoming a playwright and screenwriter—"thought I should find out what kind of dialogue fits." He took a playwriting course, and when Beghe's agent offered to represent him if he were willing to pursue acting seriously, Duchovny began commuting twice a week from New Haven to New York to study with Marsha Haufrecht of the Actors Studio.

"I learned from her that basically anything goes: I learned to tell the truth, show whatever you're feeling at the moment, even if it seems to be wrong. If you're in a funeral [scene] and you feel like giggling, you have to go ahead and giggle. . . . And if you don't do that, you may be doing the correct thing for the scene, but you're going to be doing it as a liar."

The transition from seeing acting as a research tool for writing to acting for the sake of acting was not without some dissonance and guilt. "I was going from one endeavor considered by the people who do it as the deepest intellectual and most spiritual endeavor you can do—to spend your life with books—to something where the parts might be superficial, and I might not be any good at it. So I had a lot of shame about the fact that I wanted it." On the other hand, after the long history of emotional repression and need to please others that he'd endured up to then, acting gave him "an emotional life really for the first time. It was great. I could scream, yell, and cry on stage without consequences. I could have a full life; nobody would arrest or leave me for [behaving] like that." Describing that emotional freedom more tellingly, "You can have the woman you're not supposed to have, and there are no repercussions and nobody doesn't love you afterward."

Throughout all this, he continued teaching at Yale. But after having auditioned for a TV-commercial casting agent, he wound up with his first paying role, earning $9,000—twice his teaching-assistant stipend—for playing a bar patron in a Lowenbrau beer spot reportedly airing in 1987. "I was terrified," he remembers—but he pulled it off and decided to pursue other acting jobs.

At the urging of actress-girlfriend Maggie Jakobson (who as Maggie Wheeler appeared in *The X-Files* episode "Born Again"), Duchovny played her womanizing boyfriend in the low-budget, independent movie *New Year's Day*, directed by the idiosyncratic writer-director Henry Jaglom. Like everyone else, in this improvisational film Duchovny essentially played himself. "I wasn't as good an actor with scripts as I am now," he recalls. "At that point I was afraid that I couldn't make somebody else's words on a page come alive as well as I could my own words." Shot in 1987, *New Year's Day* remained unreleased until 1989.

After his Jaglom experience, Duchovny was flown to Los Angeles during a Christmas break, to test for three TV pilots, with the full limo treatment

12

and a room at the Sunset Marquis hotel. Discovering that he wouldn't make it back to Yale in time for the start of next semester, he phoned in sick—reportedly from poolside. He didn't, however, land a series, and returned East to take a small role in megadirector Mike Nichols's hit seriocomedy *Working Girl* (1988), which began shooting in February 1988.

Duchovny permanently relocated to Los Angeles in time for *New Year's Day*'s December 1989 debut at the influential AFI Los Angeles International Film Festival. Yale and his dissertation had been eclipsed by his acting career. "My agent thought I should move to California in case there was any 'heat' when *New Year's Day* opened. And there *was* a little heat, but the only thing that happened was that I changed agents." *New Year's Day* opened theatrically months later, on December 13, by which time Duchovny had already filmed a blink-and-miss-it part as a club-goer in the Rob Lowe–James Spader film *Bad Influence* (1990), shot in Los Angeles from June to August.

He quickly followed up with a lead role in the extremely low-budget erotic psychodrama *Julia Has Two Lovers* (1991), which shot from August 3 to October 13, 1989, and played virtually nowhere outside of L.A. and New York.

His income was not enhanced by being in Jaglom's virtually no-budget, glorified home movie *Venice/Venice* (1992), which began shooting in September 1989. And afterward, it would be a long several months before he got a supporting role in *Don't Tell Mom the Babysitter's Dead* (1991), shot from May to July 1990 under director Stephen Herek (*Bill & Ted's Excellent Adven-*

13

With David Charles in *Julia Has Two Lovers.*

A cross-tressed Duchovny in *Twin Peaks.*

14

ture, *The Mighty Ducks*). Though independently financed, this likable and surprisingly successful Christina Applegate comedy became Duchovny's first film released through a major studio, Warner Bros.

Later in 1990, Duchovny shot his most significant part yet, as the male lead in writer-director Mel Tolkin's acclaimed apocalyptic drama, *The Rapture* (1991), starring Mimi Rogers.

Before *The Rapture* was released, however, Duchovny found himself a pop-culture shooting star on the TV series *Twin Peaks* (ABC, April 8, 1990–June 10, 1991). For three consecutive episodes, Duchovny played what would seem the plum role of DEA Agent Dennis Bryson—an old friend of FBI Agent Dale Cooper (Kyle MacLachlan). Except Cooper hadn't seem him in a while, and in the interim, Dennis had begun cross-dressing.

There was "nothing special about the part," Duchovny insists. "I remember showing up on the set and thinking, 'Well, here I am wearing a dress and pantyhose' and wondering, 'Is this the beginning *and* end of my career?'" But he also felt as if he had nothing to lose. As for what his family thought of him in the showy if, well, untraditional male role, "Mom, she actually thought I looked thin. . . . 'Are you getting enough to eat?'"

For all its oddities, the part *was* a terrific career move, since millions of people who hadn't heard of him before were suddenly aware of this gutsy David Duchovny guy. But his next acting gig wouldn't be for six months. During that time, he says, he was "leeching off people pretty much." He reportedly wrote a couple of articles and did a commercial or two, and worked for a caterer. And as an outlet for his creativity, he began reading his poetry at a joint called the Largo Pub.

When things finally came home, however, they came in through all the doors. Spring 1991 found Duchovny committed to three projects almost at once. First, there was the canine comedy *Beethoven* (1992), shot from May 1 to July 26. In this hit (slapstick farce, coscripted by a pseudonymous John Hughes, Duchovny and Patricia Heaton play venal yuppies, Brad and Brie, who in a subplot try to trick the beleaguered head of Beethoven's family (Charles Grodin) into signing away his air-freshener factory. Of Beethoven

Duchovny says, "He had a lot of saliva. Saint Bernard saliva is sticky and nasty. If you can imagine bad-smelling maple sap, that's what it's like to work with that dog."

At roughly the same time as the *Beethoven* deal came *Ruby*, a fictionalized dramatization of Lee Harvey Oswald's killer Jack Ruby, which filmed from June 13 to August 13. Duchovny played J. D. Tippit, whom Oswald shot and killed the day of the Kennedy assassination. Duchovny quickly followed that up with what his signature role: Jake Winters, protagonist of the steamy Showtime cable TV-movie *Red Shoe Diaries* (1992), shot from August 26 to October 8, 1991, and the narrator-linking device of the spin-off anthology series *Zalman King's Red Shoe Diaries*.

Less than a week after *Red Shoe Diaries* finished shooting, production on *Chaplin* (1992) began, and stretched on until late February 1992. Duchovny spent a little time in the American portion of the U.S.–U.K. shoot, in the small but notable role of Charlie Chaplin's longtime cameraperson, Rollie Totheroh.

After playing a supporting role as a married boyfriend in the Veronica Hamel–Nancy McKeon TV-movie *Baby Snatcher*, which shot in February and March 1992, Duchovny got his next big break: costarring in the ensemble

15

With, left to right, Brad Pitt, Juliette Lewis, and Michelle Forbes in *Kalifornia*.

Duchovny with, left to right, Stephen King and Lynn Redgrave on *Jeopardy*.

16

cast of the moderately low-budget ($9 million) but high-profile *Kalifornia* (1993), with the up-and-coming Brad Pitt, the equally emergent Juliette Lewis, and Michelle Forbes, who'd played Ensign Ro Laren on the 1991–92 season of *Star Trek: The Next Generation*. While *Kalifornia*, which shot from May 11 to July 14 in Georgia and Los Angeles, got only middling reviews, it drew attention for its initial NC-17 rating.

At that time, Duchovny now asserts, he wasn't much interested in television, feeling he was just one more good break away from a leading-man movie career. As a result, he says, he wasn't much nervous or concerned when he went to audition for *The X-Files*. In fact, Duchovny appeared to consider it just a few more weeks of work and a free trip—he was well aware of the odds against any particular pilot making it to series, or, once making it, of surviving. "I didn't see that you could do a show about aliens every week," he says. "Little did I know there were other things in store."

A respectable second-place tally, behind King.

What made him right for the part? "I was chosen for *The X-Files* because of previous experience playing an FBI agent—although it's the first time I'm doing it in a suit," he answers jokingly. "Fortunately, I don't have to use J. Edgar Hoover as a role model this time around." He was evidently equally flip when he auditioned for Chris Carter. "I told him to wear a tie," Carter remembers. "He showed up in a tie with pink pigs all over it. I think that got him the job."

Workdays on *The X-Files* average about twelve to fourteen hours each, with Duchovny and costar Gillian Anderson each appearing in almost every scene. "Working with Gillian under these circumstances tends to make the working relationship more like a marriage," he muses. "We have our good days and our bad days and we just have to work through it."

Duchovny recently renegotiated a new contract for a reported $100,000 per episode, and now that the show—Fox's highest-rated—is guaranteed a long run and lucrative syndication, he's financially set for life. On the creative end, aside from his acting, he's gotten back to Life Plan A: Writing. Unusually for a TV star, he's gotten to cowrite four episodes, including "Colony" and "Anasazi" with Chris Carter. "First of all," Carter says, "we're friends, so it was nice to work together. Second of all, he's very smart about the story side of things and it adds to the show. It invests

With Brigitte Bako in the cable-movie *Red Shoe Diaries*.

17

Duchovny, not being bumped from *The Late Show With David Letterman.*

him in the show in an interesting way, too. I'm very happy with the shows on which we collaborated."

"He has a good eye," Gillian Anderson agrees. "He's very good at picking apart a script, because he has quite a background." As an actor, Duchovny says of himself, "The way I approach every character is that nobody wants to be in pain. So they do things to combat the pain. But there are always a few moments in a script or an episode where the pain comes through, regardless of how much the character tries to keep it down. That's the way I approach the drama." His low-key style, he says, drives from his feeling that, "I'm the kind of actor you have to watch closely. I don't run out to get you. You kind of have to come to me. Luckily, enough people looked closely."

With luck, they'll be looking closely at him as the star of the feature film *Playing God*, a crime-thriller scheduled for production in 1996. In it, Duchovny plays a Miami mob doctor—an on-call gunshot-wound specialist—who finds himself falling in love with a Miami cop. Independently produced by a company called Beacon, it's scheduled to be released by Columbia Pictures.

It all sounds promising. Duchovny isn't always so sure, though. "I wish I had the life people think I have," he muses, staring at the abyss. And as for the abyss that stares back at him, "People don't have to like *me*," he declares, "they just have to like the show."

• David Duchovny •
FILMOGRAPHY

MOVIES:	ROLE:
• *Working Girl* (December 1988) dir. Mike Nichols	Tess's birthday party friend
• *New Year's Day* (filmed 1987, released December 1989) dir. Henry Jaglom	Billy
• *Bad Influence* (March 1990) dir. Curtis Hanson	Club-goer
• *Julia Has Two Lovers* (March 1991) dir. Bashar Shbib	Daniel
• *Don't Tell Mom the Babysitter's Dead* (June 1991; working title: The Real World) dir. Stephen Herek	Bruce
• *The Rapture* (October 1991) dir. Mel Tolkin	Randy
• *Ruby* (March 1992) dir. John MacKenzie	Officer J. D. Tippit
• *Beethoven* (April 1992) dir. Brian Levant (replaced Steven Rash)	Brad

18

- *Baby Snatcher* (CBS TV-movie May 3, 1992)   David
  dir. Joyce Chopra
- *Red Shoe Diaries* (Showtime TV-movie   Jake Winters
  May 16, 1992)
  dir. Zalman King
  Unrated version released on video October 1992
- *Venice/Venice* (filmed beginning 1989,   Dylan (Italy segment)
  released October 1992)
  dir. Henry Jaglom
- *Chaplin* (December 1992)   Rollie Totheroh
  dir. Richard Attenborough
- *Kalifornia* (September 1993)   Brian Kessler
  dir. Dominic Sena
  Unrated version released on video February 1994

TV-SHOW APPEARANCES INCLUDE:

- *Twin Peaks* (ABC) (scripts untitled; episodes 11–13 of the season)
  episode of December 15, 1990
  episode of January 12, 1991
  episode of January 19, 1991
- *Zalman King's Red Shoe Diaries* (Showtime)
  narrator; framing appearances 6/92-7/92
  narrator; framing appearances 4/93–present
  "Jake's Story" July 10, 1993
- *The Late Show With David Letterman* (CBS)
  interview, January 17, 1995 (previously scheduled for January 16)
  interview, May 18, 1995 (previously scheduled for May 17)*
- *Sci-Fi Buzz* (Sci-Fi Channel)
  interview, magazine-format series, February 19, 1995
- *Q&E* (E! Entertainment)
  interview, March 3, 1995
- *Saturday Night Live* (NBC)
  host, May 13, 1995
- *The Late Show With Tom Snyder* (CBS)
  interview, July 7, 1995
- *The Tonight Show With Jay Leno* (NBC)
  interview, May 26, 1995
  interview, June 27, 1995
- *The Larry Sanders Show* (HBO)
  "The Bump"; played himself, in episode telecast throughout August 1995
- *Jeopardy* (syndicated)
  celebrity panelist, week of November 6, 1995**
- *47th Annual Primetime Emmy Awards* (Fox)
  presenter, September 10, 1995

19

'Latter show taped in England; per the New York *Daily News*, this made Duchovny "the first *Late Show* guest to be bumped from the show on both sides of the Atlantic."

"with guests Stephen King and Lynn Redgrave; Duchovny's charity: The Children's Defense Fund

Duchovny also reportedly provided a guest voice on an episode of the USA Network animated series *Duckman*.

• Gillian Anderson •

"I used to not like myself," Gillian Anderson reflects. "I spent time over-weight, underweight, wearing black, hiding. In the past couple of years, I've started to open up." Gone are the days of a hinted-at eating disorder; now, as an interviewer has told her, normally staid British fans are gaga over "the thinking man's crumpet"—to which she could only reply, "Well, it's more flat-tering than being a lobotomized man's crumpet, I suppose!"

Yet who are those fans really thinking of? Gillian Anderson? Or Dana Scully? In contrast to the pragmatic and phlegmatic Scully, "I am one of the least straight-laced people you will ever meet," Anderson says. "I'm a full-fledged believer" in the supernatural, alien visitation, and other paranormal paradigms.

Gillian Anderson was born August 9, 1968, in Chicago, Illinois. The eldest child of Edward and Rosemary (each fifty-two years old in 1996), she has a several-years younger brother, Aaron, and an even younger sister, Zoe. When Gillian herself was very young, her family moved to London, England, where "I spent nine years of my childhood," living in the Crouch End neigh-borhood and elsewhere. Dad was studying production at the London Film School, and the family stayed on afterward. When Anderson was ten or eleven, they relocated to Grand Rapids, Michigan, where Edward now runs a film post-production company and Rosemary is a computer analyst.

Anderson attended Grand Rapids' Fountain Elementary School, followed by City High, a small, exclusive magnet school for the academically gifted, with only about thirty to fifty students in each graduating class. In this rar-efied and privileged environment, Anderson (class of '86) had room for typ-ical high school rebelliousness. "I was a bad girl," she says. "My grades were bad. I was daydreaming, pulling pranks. I got into a heavy punk scene—I had a nose ring and my hair was purple and black and blue." Yet that's all fairly mild stuff, and when she talks about being "in the principal's office every other day [for] talking . . . stealing papers, throwing paper airplanes," it seems downright Jughead-and-Archie innocent.

On the other hand, she took a seriously wayward cue from *Lolita*. "I was in a relationship with a man ten years older than me when I was fourteen," she recalls. "He was in a punk band, and I used to give him cans of food from our house and buy him Big Gulps and cigarettes. I was terrible." A few years later, amazingly, Anderson heard that her Mr. Wrong "was studying to become an entertainment lawyer—which scares the hell out of me," she adds, laughing, "because he was a pathological liar."

Anderson herself was a pathological actress, appearing early in her high school career as Police Officer no. 2 in the venerable *Arsenic and Old Lace*. Sometime after that, when she was a junior, "I decided to audition for a community theater play and I got the part, and then I felt extremely happy, like I had found my place. My grades went up and I was voted most improved student." Her previous what-I-want-to-be-when-I-grow-up notion of becoming a marine biologist sank without a trace.

Anderson attended Goodman Theater School of DePaul University and excelled there. She graduated with a bachelor of fine arts degree in 1990, having also studied with the National Theatre of Great Britain's summer program at Cornell University in Ithaca, New York.

A New York City showcase performance for an audience of agents was arranged for Anderson's graduating class. Anderson's monologue prompted a William Morris agent to offer her representation if she would move to New York. And around August 1990, she did. "The car was packed so high that I couldn't see out the rear-view mirror," she remembers. "And when I stopped to sleep, I had to crouch up in a fetal position."

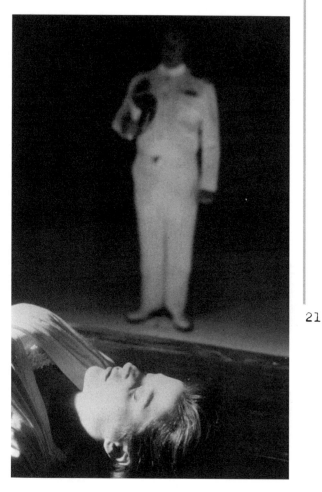

Anderson (with Don Davis, background), post-partum, in "One Breath."

21

She found an apartment in Greenwich Village; between auditions, she waitressed at the Dojo restaurant, on St. Mark's Place in the funky East Village (just three short blocks from where Duchovny grew up). Then six months after hitting New York, she got what seemed a major break—a limited run of the challenging Alan Ayckbourn black comedy *Absent Friends*, at the prestigious Manhattan Theater Club. Mary Louise Parker had dropped out at the last minute—"officially" due to illness, but also reportedly to be in the film *Grand Canyon* (1991)—and Anderson's agent sent her to audition for the role of Evelyn, a moody young mom attending a living-room reunion of old friends. First performed in London in 1975, the play opened off-Broadway with Anderson on February 12, and was successful enough to be extended a week past its prescheduled March 17 closing.

Remarkably, Anderson's first New York stage role got the fledgling actress and her veteran British cast mate, Brenda Blethyn, a big write-up in the *New York Times*. Anderson won a 1990–91 Theatre World Award for Outstanding New Talent.

Yet after these accolades, she was back to waitressing throughout the spring and summer. Then, she was offered the opportunity to appear in another off-Broadway play, a movie, and a play with the celebrated Long Wharf Theater in nearby New Haven, Connecticut—often the last and most important tryout site before bringing a play to Broadway. She accepted the latter two offers, she says, since the off-Broadway play would've conflicted with both.

The movie, a very low-budget adaptation of Chris Ceraso's play *Home Fires Burning*, shot from November 4 to December 1, 1991, in Pocahontas, Virginia, but was never released theatrically or on video. It was a potentially engrossing drama about a twenty-two-year-old, Cliff Harnish (Michael Dolan), who returns to his family's bleak mining town after getting involved with the Klan and neo-Nazis. His mother (Tess Harper) has become a drunk; his father (Raymond J. Barry, later to play Sen. Matheson in *X-Files* 2.01, "Little Green Men") has taken up with another woman (Karen Allen). Anderson plays Cliff's childhood sweetheart, April; *Variety*, reviewing it at the non-competition section of the 1992 Cannes Film Festival, called her work "an attractive debut." Directed, coproduced and coadapted by first-time feature filmmaker Lou Puopolo, it was retitled *The Turning* sometime after Cannes—possibly to avoid confusion with the 1989 Hallmark Hall of Fame TV-movie *Home Fires Burning*, starring Barnard Hughes, Neil Patrick Harris, Elizabeth Berridge, and Brad Sullivan.

Shortly after putting out *Home Fires*, Anderson played the role of Celia onstage in a limited run of Christopher Hampton's *The Philanthropist*, in a production with Tim Choate, Margaret Gibson, Ronald Guttman, Lily Knight, Don Reilly, and Sam Tsoutsouvas. A nice, respectable, but relatively small credit, the play wound up having more impact than Anderson could have imagined—for very soon afterward, "I came out to L.A. to visit a man I'd met in a play in New Haven. I was going to stay for two weeks, and I got here and sold my return ticket."

Yet Los Angeles, careerwise, was even chillier. "I moved to Los Angeles, and did nothing," Anderson remembers. "Basically all I did for almost a year was audition for different things." She was still with William Morris, which certainly helped. Yet it took forever to land even an episode of *Class of '96*, the short-lived Fox prime-time soap set at an Ivy League college; Anderson played a guest role as Rachel in the March 9, 1993, episode, "The Accused," directed by Peter Horton (*thirtysomething*). Some time previously, she also provided the voice of Lisa Kelly on the audiocassette abridgment of Anne Rice's erotic diary-entry novel, *Exit to Eden.*

Her exit to *X-Files* came just in time. "I didn't have any money and I was relying on my boyfriend to help me out financially," Anderson recalls. "The day I got the pilot episode, my last unemployment check arrived."

On *Late Night With Conan O'Brien.*

The X-Files script had been was a real page turner—"I couldn't put it down"—but the audition process was a head-turner. According to Anderson, Fox "wanted someone taller, leggier, and bustier" for Dana Scully. "I guess they were going to make this '*The XXX-Files.*'"

According to Duchovny, "I played the [audition] scene in a kind of sarcastic way—much more sarcastic than it was written—and Gillian was just completely thrown by it. I was toying with this person, because Mulder doesn't really care if she stays or goes. And she was shocked that anybody would talk to her that way. That's exactly how she should have reacted. It was perfect."

"I was terrified," Anderson remembers. "When we first started *X-Files*, I was so green. It was only my second time in front of the camera." Worse, she had had only two days to prepare, reporting for work just two days after being cast. "David helped me out when he could, teaching me the ropes. But basically, it was a sink or swim situation." Anderson and Duchovny found their groove almost immediately, once the nervous Anderson learned to stop flubbing her complicated, often jargon-filled lines. But she felt ambivalence within herself. "In the beginning, it created a lot of friction inside of me and some anger: 'I want to have a life; I want to have my own time,' I thought. But then you've got to accept it."

Once in Vancouver, Anderson developed a mutual attraction with Errol Clyde Klotz, the series' Canadian-born assistant art director. They married four months after meeting, on New Year's Day, 1994, while on vacation together in Hawaii. "It was just the two of us and a Buddhist priest on the 17th Hole of this golf course in Hawaii," Anderson explains. "That was the most beautiful place we could find on short notice."

Then *The X-Files*'s subtext got uncomfortably—if miraculously—real. At a Fox Broadcasting party for the show in Burbank, California, just weeks later, paranormal-believer Anderson sat down with psychic Debi Becker, and then proceeded to not believe. "You're going to have a little girl," said Becker,

23

who'd been hired by Fox to help give the party an appropriately otherworldly edge. Anderson replied, "No, I'm not. I just got this show." Two months later, she discovered that the psychic was either real (the Mulder explanation) or hit a 50/50 chance on the sex of a baby, which a young married woman would very likely have at *some* point in her life (the Scully explanation).

Having a baby when you're suddenly the costar of a struggling but promising new TV series can be problematic, though hardly disastrous. Ever since *I Love Lucy*, pregnancies have either been incorporated into TV story lines or shot around, as was done on *Cheers* and *Seinfeld*. Yet unlike those shows, *The X-Files* depends on the two stars' presence in most scenes—imagine *Dragnet* without Joe Friday. Anderson was flatly afraid of being fired. "Those were stressful times," she says, with great understatement.

Looking to her costar's greater experience with showbiz, Anderson told Duchovny weeks before telling anyone else on *The X-Files*. "I went into his trailer and I said, 'David, I'm pregnant.' It looked like his knees buckled. I think he said, 'Oh, my God.' And he asked me if it was a good thing. I said, 'Yeah, it is.'"

When she finally felt able to tell series creator Chris Carter, "He was shocked. Understandably. I mean, everybody was." *TV Guide* reported Carter "went ballistic." Carter later asserted, "Ballistic is not something I go."

Much to Carter's credit, he found a way to work around Anderson's pregnancy. His solution also provided a huge creative shot-in-the-arm: After what Anderson described as "a lot of shooting from the neck up," Carter had Scully abducted by entities unknown—creating a tense dynamism by casting Mulder out in the desert, after having had a taste of true partnership, and a single person he could trust. Some of the resultant episodes—"Duane Barry," "Ascension," and "One Breath,"—are among the series' best.

Anderson and Klotz's daughter, Piper, was delivered by caesarean operation on September 25, 1994. Anderson missed only one show, the vampire-themed episode "3," and the producers devised a creative way to give her a break on her first show back ("One Breath")—Scully mysteriously returns after her abduction and spends most of the show lying comatose in bed. "I actually fell asleep during the coma scenes," Anderson says. "I was in hospital for six days, and then I was back to work four days later." Anderson and Klotz named Carter as Piper's godfather, and the baby, Anderson says, has made her "a much happier person since she came along. Nothing is quite so important anymore."

The key to Anderson's *X-Files* success is treating her relationship with Duchovny as a marathon and not a sprint, to avoid the acrimony that can arise between two chained-together costars of a high-pressure hit. During Duchovny's fall 1995 flurry of magazine covers, "I felt like, This is *our* show. It wasn't just his show," Anderson says. "But I learned not to care so much."

"It's a lot of work to work with someone as intensely as we do on a daily basis," Anderson explains. "Our relationship shifts and changes, and on the weekends we don't hang out because we're sick of seeing each other all week!" She describes their relationship was having "evolved, in that we respect each other and we like each other, and we show up on set and we work, and we leave." Of course, as she acknowledges, "There are times when I think we wish the other one didn't exist."

Despite her legions of fans and her celebrity status, Anderson remains philosophical about her stardom. "I had a very good feeling that this show would be successful," Anderson says, "but I don't think it's really even hit me yet. Once in a while I'll be driving down the street in Canada and think, 'I'm in Canada. How did I get here?'"

• Gillian Anderson •

FILMOGRAPHY

MOVIES: ROLE:

- *Home Fires Burning* a.k.a. *The Turning*   April Cavanaugh
  (filmed 1991; unreleased)
  dir. Lous Puopolo

TV-SHOW APPEARANCES INCLUDE:

- *Class Of '96* (Fox)   Rachel
  "The Accused" March 9, 1993
- *Sci-Fi Buzz* (Sci-Fi Channel)
  interview, magazine-format series, February 19, 1995
- *Q&E* (E! Entertainment)
  interview, March 3, 1995
- *Live With Regis & Kathie Lee* (ABC)
  interview, May 18, 1995
- *The Jon Stewart Show*
  interview, May 18, 1995
- *Late Night With Conan O'Brien* (NBC)
  interview, May 22, 1995
- *Steve Wright's People Show* (U.K.; BBC1)
  interview, June 3, 1995
- *47th Annual Primetime Emmy Awards* (Fox)
  presenter, September 10, 1995
- *ReBoot* (ABC Saturday-morning computer-animated series)
  "Trust No One" December 30, 1995
  voice of Data Nully, in *X-Files* parody

Other credits include:
Exit to Eden audiocassette (Random House AudioBooks, 1993)
As character Lisa Kelly; with actor Gil Bellows; abridged adaptation of book by Anne Rice, written under pseudonym Anne Rampling.
CBC RealTime (Canada; late November 1994)
interview, call-in radio show

• Mitch Pileggi •

How does a bald, glowering bureaucrat brought in for a brief guest spot somehow become a TV sex symbol? For the hearty and easygoing Mitch Pileggi—a journeyman who's slogged through muddy trenches of telefilms, direct-to-video dreck, and even *It's Pat*—the events are no less welcome for being unexplainable.

"I don't know," says Pileggi, the forceful actor who plays Mulder and Scully's immediate FBI superior, Assistant Director Walter S. Skinner. (The *S* stands for Sergei.) "I mean, I watch shows, and I watch the character, and it's like, 'Boy, he sure is grumpy. . . . What would appeal to anybody?'" Pileggi—born April 5, 1952, in Portland, Oregon, and raised all over the world—made his movie debut in the forgettable horror flick *Mongrel* (filmed 1982), followed by the little-seen *Rio Abajo,* a.k.a. *On the Line,* an English-language U.S.–Spain coproduction about American border guards; top-lined by David Carradine and Victoria Abril, it was filmed in 1984, and played virtually nowhere but Los Angeles three years later before going straight to video.

Shortly afterward, however, Pileggi began landing roles in TV-movies and in such episodic series as *The A-Team*, *Hooperman*, and the short-lived Michael Nouri–Blair Underwood police drama *Downtown*. Things began to pick up, yet the muscular, 6'2" Pileggi found himself getting progressively stuck in a character niche where he was playing security goons (*It's Pat*), psychotic supernatural killers (Wes Craven's *Shocker*, his sole film lead to date), and guys with names like Sarge (*Return of the Living Dead Part II*) and Bull (*Three on a Match*).

One reason he got the role of Skinner was that the producers wanted to play against type, and introduce a quietly dynamic bureaucrat rather than the stereotypical paper-pusher. "I had gone in and read for Chris several times before for other episodes, different characters," Pileggi remembers. "And at the time I was shaving my head. . . . So I came in for this [Skinner] and my hair had grown back, or what hair I have had grown back, and you know, it just clicked."

Pileggi, unintentionally and after-the-fact, discovered that his portrayal of Skinner had its foundation in his father. "My family—my brothers, sisters, and my mom—watched the show, and they said, 'My God, that's Dad,'" he recalls. "He was an operations manager and had a lot of people accountable to him. He was very tough on his employees, but he also cared about them a lot, too." Like Skinner, "He wore glasses, he was bald, he always wore a suit." And in what's probably the ultimate tribute, "My mom cries when she sees Skinner, because he reminds her of my dad."

• Jerry Hardin •

Venerable and versatile Jerry Hardin—the enigmatic advisor Deep Throat of several key episodes of *The X-Files*—has made probably hundreds of TV appearances since the 1950s. He also managed to amass over seventy-five stock and regional theatrical credits by as early as 1961.

Hardin spent the 1970s and '80s appearing as a character actor in such films as *Mitchell* (1975), *Head Over Heels,* a.k.a. *Chilly Scenes of Winter* (1979), *Reds* (1981), and *Missing* (1982), as well as telefilms including *Guilty or Innocent: The Sam Sheppard Murder* (NBC 1975) and the mini-series *The Chisholms* (CBS 1979). He has some thirty theatrical-film credits to date, was an ensemble star of the 1982–83 CBS sitcom *Filthy Rich*, and had recurring roles on *L.A. Law*, *Melrose Place*, and the mid-'70s Brenda Vaccaro schoolmarm series, *Sara*.

Chris Carter had seen and liked Hardin's work in *The Firm* (1993), where Hardin played one of the deadly corporate mob lawyers pitted against Tom Cruise. The role had just the kind of three-piece-pinstripe, covert-conspiracy resonances that the character of Deep Throat needed.

"I really was not aware that they were going to recur the role, so it looked like a one-time trip to Vancouver," Hardin says. But he soon found himself

The prolific, beloved character actor Jerry Hardin, left.

a regular, albeit overnight, Vancouverite. "I often was only notified a week beforehand," he recalls. "The producers would call and ask, 'Are you available? We would like to include Deep Throat next week.' And you get on a plane and you go to Canada and you shoot."

"I enjoyed doing it," he adds. "I liked the elliptical way in which the character was presented. That's a nice, juicy kind of writing, and I thought that would be fun to do." Yet Hardin was also well aware of the need for the character to drop in, fit some plot points together, and keep the story moving quickly. "That's one of the acting problems of the character. How do you get all this information out in a way that sounds like it's interesting and fresh?"

As for who Deep Throat really was, Hardin's as much in the dark as anyone. He guesses that "this man was placed highly in government, perhaps not in an official position so much as an unofficial position—perhaps a member of the president's 'Kitchen Cabinet.' He had access to extraordinary amounts of information and high-placed friends, but he was less likely to be somebody who's highly placed in the CIA or somewhere else."

28

Some suggest Chris Carter didn't appreciate Hardin's nudging about making Deep Throat a regular. Carter says that's not true, and that with Deep Throat's death he wanted to impress upon the audience that virtually anything can happen to any character on the show. And he did indeed bring Hardin back twice, as a ghost/hallucination, and as an alien's morphed mask, making good on a promise Hardin described this way: "When we finished shooting the death scene of Deep Throat, just at dawn, they opened a little champagne, and the toast was, 'No one every really dies on *X-Files*!"

• Steven Williams •

Born January 7, 1949, Steven Williams, the actor playing steely-eyed Mr. X, is a former military man and model who broke from journeyman anonymity as an actor when he played Captain Adam Fuller from 1987–90 on *21 Jump Street,* Fox's first hit show. He reprised the role on two episodes of the spin-off series, *Booker,* where he got to know future *X-Files* co-executive producers Glen Morgan and James Wong; they would later suggest he play Mr. X, after an actress hired to play the character as Ms. X didn't work out. Yet despite Williams's long experience with series television, Morgan says, "At first, Steve wasn't going over all that well [either] and they were unhappy with him. I said, 'Jerry Hardin brought so much to Deep Throat and we're kind of giving Mr. X Jerry's lines.'" Carter remembers it differently, saying, "We wanted someone who had a much different persona than Deep Throat." Yet as Morgan recalls, it took time for that distinction to take hold. "That's why, later on, they didn't use X for awhile," he says. "But Steve is a good actor, which is why we could do the scene in 'One Breath' where he performs an execution. Deep Throat was a guy willing to lose his life for letting out the secret, whereas X is a guy who's still scared. He's somewhere between Mulder and Deep Throat."

Williams made his movie debut in the African-American teen drama *Cooley High* (1975), and little by little garnered work in TV-movies and episodic TV, as well as doing bit parts in movies such as *The Blues Brothers* (1980), *Doctor Detroit*

Williams, left, with Mitch Pileggi in "End Game."

29

(1983), *Twilight Zone: The Movie* (1983), and *Rambo: First Blood, Part II* (1985). Yet he worked steadily and continually, and after a stint as police Lt. Jefferson Burnett in the first several episodes of *The Equalizer*, began to get more serious attention.

And who is X? "I know very little about him," Williams confesses. "X is an enigma. I only know that Deep Throat was his friend and mentor, just as he was Mulder's friend and mentor. And X is obligated to Deep Throat, like he owed Deep Throat a favor." All we know is that enigmatic Mr. X will surely be around as long as Chris Carter—Mr. *X-Files*—has his say.

• William B. Davis •

"The Cigarette-Smoking Man" is the physical embodiment of the shadow government, of The Ones Who Run Things, in his role as the unnamed liaison between its "elders" and the FBI. Yet actor and acting teacher William B. Davis nonetheless describes his character "as the hero. The only way to play a villain is to think that you're right, that you're saving the world. It's the other people who are messing up. It's the Mulders who are really going to make a total mess of this thing, and I've got to fix it. So from my point of view, I believe that I'm doing what's necessary, what's best for the world." As for his lungs' point of view, the actor, who in reality gave up smoking seventeen years ago, uses clove cigarettes on the set.

Davis, born January 13, 1938, began his career as a child actor in Ontario; he studied acting at the University of Toronto and the London Academy of Music and Dramatic Art. Davis spent five years in England, as the director of several theaters, and worked at the prestigious National Theatre. By the late 1960s, he returned to Canada, as a theater artistic director and sometime CBC radio producer. After twenty years of teaching acting he returned to his craft and "was quite surprised that in twenty years of telling other people what to do, I'd actually learned something about how to do it myself."

That revelation prompted him to find an agent and move to Vancouver and a series of jobs in locally-based TV shows, TV-movies, and theatrical films, including *Look Who's Talking*.

• THE LONE GUNMEN •
Tom Braidwood
Dean Haglund
Bruce Harwood

Byers, Langly, and Frohike, who've appeared in about a dozen episodes to date, made their debut in the episode "EBE." Known collectively as The Lone Gunmen, they're a group of conspiracy theorists who publish a small-press magazine, *The Lone Gunman* (a name based on the "lone gunman" school of thought in the assassinations of Kennedy, et al.).

Here's their dossier. You can read it, but then we'd have to kill you.

Tom Braidwood, born September 27, 1948, earned a bachelor's degree in theater and a master's in film from the University of British Columbia. Pursuing a dual path of both stage acting and production, he landed small roles in such Canadian films as *Harry Tracy* (1981), starring Bruce Dern and Gordon Lightfoot and directed by future *X-Files* helmer William A. Graham; the Canadian hit *My American Cousin* (1986); and the partly Canadian-shot John Travolta film *Eyes of an Angel* (1991). He often worked both in front of and behind the camera. On *The X-Files*, he's one of a handful of rotating first assistant directors.

Braidwood is married with two daughters; in the commercially unreleased 1992 film *The Portrait*, which he produced and in which he has a small role, he appears with Kate and Jessica Braidwood (as well as future *X*-guests Gabrielle Rose and Alex Diakun).

Dean Haglund, born July 29, 1965, is a popular Vancouver stand-up comic who performs with the improvisational troupe TheatreSports. [cq] Since at least 1992, he's gotten the occasional role on such locally filmed series as *The Commish, Sliders,* and *Lonesome Dove: The Series.* When he auditioned for the role of *uber*-hacker Langly, he based his take on a refreshing approach: real life, not stereotype. "From my university days I know a bunch of computer guys who are Ph.D. types in the upper end of computer theory research," he says, noting they "all know really good rock bands—they're certainly not the pocket-protector types." As for Langley's metamorphosing eyewear, "The prop guy keeps pulling a different pair out of the bag. He's got a bag of all these glasses and we can never remember which one we used on the show before!" The name "Langly" is of course a reference to the Virginia home of CIA headquarters.

Bruce Harwood, born April 29, 1963, is a British Columbia actor whose most prominent earlier role was that of the environmental expert Willis in the 1990–91 season of *MacGyver*. He also appeared as a scientist in the supporting cast of the "Disney Sunday Movie" TV-movie/pilot *Earth*Star Voyager*.

Hardwood's said he conceives of the primly suit-and-tie-wearing Byers as "a university professor, and in his spare time on the weekends and the evenings, he goes down to this little office which moves once a month. The Lone Gunmen have to keep moving, because they haven't got enough money and because they're worried about being bugged."

31

Bruce Harwood, left, as Byers.

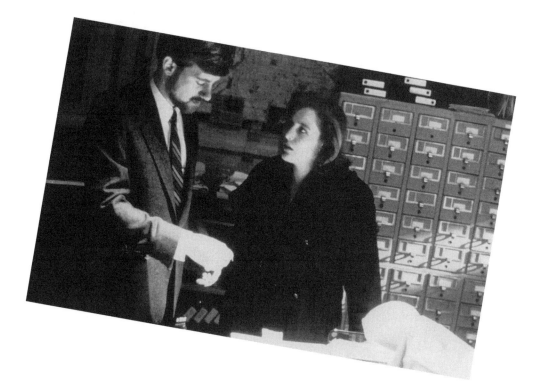

• Nicholas Lea •

He is not now, nor has he ever been, Ratboy. That's the fan-nickname for his character, Alex Krycek—or, perhaps, "Alex Krycek"—the shadow-government assassin sent by the Smoking Man to kill Mulder's father (successfully), Scully (unsuccessfully, killing her sister Melissa instead) and Mulder (also unsuccessfully).

"I love playing those kind of characters," Lea has enthused. "Hopefully I'm [playing] not just a guy who's bad, but a guy who's doing something for a particular reason. I don't think anybody who does bad things really thinks they're bad. They just think they're doing what they should be doing. And it's either bad guys who are doing wrong and not knowing it, or good guys doing wrong and trying to do good."

Born June 22, 1962, Lea has served in the Canadian Navy, fronted an alternative-rock band called Beau Monde for five years, and worked in a clothing store. While his good looks helped get him roles in Vancouver-shot TV series such as *The Hat Squad*, he's conceded it took awhile for his acting skills to equal his screen presence.

Lea's first big break came with the Vancouver-filmed series *The Commish* (ABC 1991–95) playing Officer Enrico "Ricky" Caruso. During his run on the show, he met one-time girlfriend Melinda McGraw, who played Chief of Detectives Cyd Madison during two seasons and who went on to play Melissa Scully on *The X-Files*.

Before playing Krycek, Lea had previously played a different character on *The X-Files*—a handsome but hapless nightclubber picked up by the pheromone-spewing apparent alien, Marty, in "Genderbender." Director Rob Bowman remembered being much taken with Lea's work in the scene where a cop breaks up the couple's coupling in a steamy-windowed car. "During that last shot in the car, when he sees that the girl has now become a guy, I thought Nick did a beautiful job walking the line in conveying a turning point in his life," Bowman says. "He'll never be the same again for the rest of his life, after seeing that. And I thought he found just the right level to play that."

When Bowman went on to direct "Sleepless," he suggested Lea read for Krycek—a major role that normally would have gone to a Los Angeles actor. But, Bowman says, "Nick was the best of all. He earned the role."

PRODUCTION STAFF CREDITS

The X-Files

• The Pilot •

Ten Thirteen Productions
Twentieth Television

Creator-Executive Producer: Chris Carter
Coexecutive Producers: R. W. Goodwin, James Wong, Glen Morgan
Supervising Producer: Daniel Sackheim
Director of Photography: Thomas Del Ruth, ASC
Editor: Stephen Mark
Casting: Randy Stone, CSA
Vancouver Casting: Sid Kozak
Music: Mark Snow
Production Designer: Michael Nemirsky
Production Manager: Lisa Richardson
First Assistant Director: Anthony Atkins
Second Assistant Director: Craig Matheson
Set Decorator: Shirley Inget
Art Director: Sheila Haley
Script Director: Portia Jacox
Costume Designer (L.A.): Deborah Everton
Costume Designer (Van.): Sheila Bingham

Hairstylist: Malcolm Marsden
Make-Up: Fern Levin
Property Master: Kent Johnson
Location Manager: Louisa Gradnitzer
Production Coordinator: Gretchen Goode
Chief Lighting Technician: David Anderson
Key Grip: Rick Allen
Special Effects: Rory Cutler
Special Effects Producer: Mat Beck
Sound Mixer: Michael Williamson
Stunt Coordinator: Ken Kirzinger
Production Services: Pacific Motion Pictures Corporation
Processing: Gastown Film Labs
Telecine: Gastown Post and Transfer
Electronic Assembly: Encore Video
Postproduction Sound: West Productions, Inc.
Supervising Sound Editors: David Rawlinson, David Elliot
Music Editor: Jeff Charbonneau
Assistant Editor: J. J. Rogers

• First Season •

Episode numbers in parentheses.

Ten Thirteen Productions
Twentieth Television

Creator-Executive Producer: Chris Carter
Coexecutive Producers: R. W. Goodwin, James Wong, Glen Morgan

Supervising Producers: Howard Gordon, Alex Gansa
Coproducer: Paul Rabwin
Line Producer: Joseph Patrick Finn
Executive Script Consultant: Chris Ruppenthal (1.21–1.23)
Casting: Rick Millikan, CSA
Vancouver Casting: Lynne Carrow, CSA

Original Casting: Randy Stone, CSA
Music: Mark Snow
Director of Photography: John S. Bartley CSC
Art Director:
  Mickael Nemirsky (1.02–1.06)
  Graeme Murray (1.07–on)
Editor:
  Stephen Mark (1.02, 1.05, 1.11, 1.14, 1.17, 1.20, 1.22–1.23)
  Heather MacDougall (1.03, 1.06, 1.09, 1.12, 1.18, 1.21, 1.24)
  James Coblentz (1.04, 1.07, 1.10, 1.13, 1.16, 1.19)
Production Manager: J. P. Finn
First Assistant Director:
  Brian Giddens (1.02–1.04, then even-numbered through 1.14)
  Tom Braidwood (odd-numbered beginning 1.05)
  Vladimir Stefoff (even-numbered beginning 1.16)
Second Assistant Director: Collin Leadley (per on-screen spelling, 1.02–1.19), Collin Leadlay (per on-screen spelling 1.20–on)
Set Decorator: Shirley Inget
Assistant Art Director:
  Clyde Klotz (1.02–1.09, 1.11, 1.13, 1.15)
  Gary P. Allen (1.10, 1.12, 1.14, 1.16, 1.18, 1.20, 1.22, 1.24)
  Greg Loewen (1.17, 1.19, 1.21, 1.23)
Script Supervisor:
  Wendy Mclean (all except 1.20, 1.22)
  Terry Murray (episode 1.20, 1.22)
Costume Designer: Larry Wells
Costume Supervisor (credit, earlier part of season) / Assistant Costume Designer (credit, later part of season): Jenni Gullet
Property Master: Ken Hawryliw
Transportation Coordinator: Bob Bowe
Construction Coordinator (1.05–on): Rob Maier
Hairstylist:
  Malcolm Marsden (1.02–1.20)
  Julie McHaffie (1.21–1.24)
Make-Up: Fern Levin

Special Make-Up Effects (1.18–on): Toby Lindala
Location Manager:
  Todd Pittson (even-numbered beginning 1.02)
  Louisa Gradnitzer (odd-numbered beginning 1.03)
Camera Operator: Rod Pridy
Focus Puller: Marty McInally
Production Coordinator:
  Roberta Sheehy (1.02–1.10), Robert Henricksen (1.11–on)
Assistant Production Coordinator: Anita Truelove
Chief Lighting Technician: David Tickell
Key Grip:
  Rick Allen (1.02–1.03)
  Al Campbell (1.04–on)
Special Effects: David Gauthier
Visual Effects Producer:
  Mat Beck (with 1.05, credit moved to immediately after Assistant Production Coordinator)
Sound Mixer: Michael Williamson
Stunt Coordinator:
  Ken Kirzinger (all except 1.24)
  Tony Morelli (1.24)
Assistant Editor:
  J. J. Rogers (1.02, 1.04, 1.09–1.10, 1.13, 1.16, 1.19, 1.22)
  Shannon Leigh Olds (1.03)
  Ron South (1.05, 1.08, 1.11, 1.14, 1.17, 1.20, 1.23)
  Jeff Cahn (1.06–1.07, 1.12, 1.15, 1.18, 1.21)
Postproduction Coordinator (1.07–on): G. R. Potter
Main Title Sequence:
  Castle/Bryant/Johnsen
Processing: Gastown Film Labs
Telecine: Gastown Post and Transfer
Electronic Assembly: Encore Video
Postproduction Sound: West Productions, Inc.
Supervising Sound Editor: Thierry Courturier
Music Editor: Jeff Charbonneau

• Second Season •

Episode numbers in parentheses.

Ten Thirteen Productions
Twentieth Television

Creator-Executive Producer: Chris Carter
Coexecutive Producers: R. W. Goodwin,
James Wong, Glen Morgan (latter two
2.01–2.14)
Supervising Producer: Howard Gordon
Producers: Paul Brown (2.01–2.09),
Joseph Patrick Finn (2.04–on), David
Nutter (2.04–2.13), Rob Bowman
(2.14–on), Kim Manners (2.19–on)
Coproducer: Paul Rabwin
Line Producer: Joseph Patrick Finn
(2.01–2.03)
Associate Producer: Crawford Hawkins
Director of Photography: John S. Bartley,
CSC
Music: Mark Snow
Casting: Rick Millikan, CSA
Vancouver Casting: Lynne Carrow, CSA
Original Casting: Randy Stone, CSA
Art Director: Graeme Murray
Editor:
    Stephen Mark (every third beginning
    2.01)
    James Coblentz (every third beginning
    2.02)
    Heather MacDougall (every third
    beginning 2.03)
Production Manager: J. P. Finn
First Assistant Director:
    Tom Braidwood (odd-numbered
    beginning 2.01)
    Vladimir Stefoff (even-numbered
    beginning 2.02)
Second Assistant Director:
    Collin Leadlay
Visual Effects Producer: Mat Beck
Creative Consultant (2.12–2.14):
    Steve DeJarnatt
Set Decorator: Shirley Inget
Assistant Art Director:
    Greg Loewen (odd-numbered beginning
    2.01)

Gary P. Allen (even-numbered
    beginning 2.02)
Script Supervisor:
    Wendy Mclean (all except below)
    Barry Patricia (2.09–2.10)
    Helga Ungerait (2.12, 2.14, 2.20,
    2.22)
Costume Designer: Larry Wells
Assistant Costume Designer:
    Jenni Gullet
Property Master: Ken Hawryliw
Key/Hairstylist: Malcolm Marsden
Make-Up (credit 2.01–2.04): Fern Levin
Key & Special Make-Up (credit 2.05–on):
    Fern Levin
Special Effects Make-Up (credit moved to
    here, beginning 2.05; previously below
    postproduction supervisor): Toby
    Lindala
Location Manager (credit moved to below
    property master, beginning 2.04)
    Louisa Gradnitzer (odd-numbered
    beginning 2.01)
    Todd Pittson (even-numbered
    beginning 2.02)
Camera Operator:
    Rod Pridy (2.01–2.19)
    John Clothier (2.20–2.24)
Focus Puller: Marty McInally
Production Coordinator: Anita Truelove
Assistant Production Coordinator: Joanne
    Service
Chief Lighting Technician: David Tickell
Key Grip: Al Campbell
Special Effects: David Gauthier
Stunt Coordinator: Ken Kirzinger
Casting Associate (Van.): Coreen Mayrs
Transportation Coordinator: Bob Bowe
Construction Coordinator: Rob Maier
Head Painter (2.25): Louis Solyom
Postproduction Supervisor: Kenneth
    Dennis
Assistant Editor (credit moved to below
    music editor, beginning 2.04):
    Ron South (2.01)
    J. J. Rogers (2.02, 2.05, 2.08, 2.11,
    2.14, 2.17, 2.20, 2.23)

35

Jeff Cahn (2.03–2.04, 2.06, 2.10, 2.12, 2.15, 2.16, 2.18, 2.21, 2.24)
Sue Kesler (2.07, 2.09, 2.13, 2.19, 2.22, 2.25)
Sound Mixer (credit moved to below construction coordinator, beginning 2.04): Michael Williamson
Postproduction Sound: West Productions, Inc.
Rerecording Mixers:
    David John West, MPSE; Torri Nello; Craig Hunter (all except below)
    David John West, MPSE; Marti Humphrey; Gary D. Rogers (2.02, 2.06, 2.20, 2.24)
Supervising Sound Editor (credit moved to below postproduction sound, 2.04): Thierry J. Courturier
Scoring Mixer: Larhold Rebhun
Music Editor: Jeff Charbonneau
Main Title Sequence: Castle/Bryant/Johnsen
Processing: Gastown Film Labs
Telecine: Gastown Post and Transfer
Visual Effects Supervisor (2.10–2.11): Roger Dorney
Electronic Assembly: Encore Video
Computer Graphics: (2.01–2.02): Northwest Imaging & FX
Footage (2.11/boxing): FA Productions
Animal Trainer (2.19): Frank Welker
Creature Effects (2.20): K.N.B. EFX Group, Inc.

• Third Season •
To Episode 3.10

36

Episode numbers in parentheses.

Ten Thirteen Productions
Twentieth Television

Creator-Executive Producer: Chris Carter
Coexecutive Producers: R. W. Goodwin, Howard Gordon
Supervising Producer: Charles Grant Craig (3.01–3.08)
Producers: Joseph Patrick Finn, Rob Bowman, Kim Manners
Coproducer: Paul Rabwin
Associate Producer: Crawford Hawkins
Director of Photography: John S. Bartley, CSC
Music: Mark Snow
Art Director: Graeme Murray
Editor:
    Stephen Mark (3.01, 3.04, 3.07)
    Heather MacDougall (3.02, 3.05)
    Jim Gross (3.03, 3.06, 3.09)
Story Editors: Darin Morgan, Frank Spotnitz, Jeffrey Vlaming
Creative Consultant (3.10): Vince Gilligan
Casting: Rick Millikan, CSA
Vancouver Casting: Lynne Carrow, CSA
Original Casting: Randy Stone, CSA
Production Manager: J. P. Finn
First Assistant Director:
    Vladimir Stefoff (odd-numbered beginning 3.01)
    Tom Braidwood (even-numbered beginning 3.02)
Second Assistant Director: Collin Leadlay
Unit Manager: Bretty Dowler
Visual Effects Producer: Mat Beck
Set Decorator: Shirley Inget
Assistant Art Director:
    Gary P. Allen (odd-numbered beginning 3.01)
    Greg Loewen (even-numbered beginning 3.02)
Script Supervisor:
    Wendy Mclean (odd-numbered beginning 3.01)
    Helga Ungerait (even-numbered beginning 3.02)
Costume Designer:
    Larry Wells (3.01–3.02)
    Jenni Gullet (3.03–on)
Assistant Costume Designer: Jenni Gullet (3.01–3.02)
Costume Supervisor: Gillian Kieft (3.03–on)

Location Manager:
Todd Pittson (odd-numbered beginning 3.01)
Louisa Gradnitzer (even-numbered beginning 3.02)
Key Hairstylist:
Malcolm Marsden (3.01–3.03)
Robert A. Pandoni (3.04–on)
Key Make-Up: Fern Levin
Special Effects Make-Up: Toby Lindala
Casting Associate (Vanc.): Wendy O'Brien Livingstone
Casting Associate (L.A.): Stacy Wise
Extras Casting: Lisa Ratke
Chief Lighting Technician: David Tickell
Key Grip: Al Campbell
Special Effects: David Gauthier
Stunt Coordinator: Tony Morelli
Transportation Coordinator: Bob Bowe
Construction Coordinator: Rob "Stroby" Maier
Property Master: Ken Hawryliw
Second Unit D.P. (3.03–on): Jon Joffin
Camera Operator: Nathaniel Massey
Focus Puller: Patrick Stepien
Production Coordinator: Anita Meehan Truelove

Assistant Production Coordinator: Susan Crawford
Sound Mixer: Michael Williamson
Postproduction Supervisor: Lori Jo Nemhauser
Assistant Editors: Sue Kesler; Jeff Cahn
Scoring Mixer: Larhold Rebhun
Music Editor: Jeff Charbonneau
Time Lapse Photography (3.02–3.03): Simon Kerwin Carroll
Postproduction Sound: West Productions, Inc.
Supervising Sound Editor: Thierry J. Couturier
Rerecording Mixers:
Jim Williams; Todd Orr; Don MacDougall (3.01, 3.03)
David John West, MPSE; Torri Nello; Douglas E. Turner (3.02, 3.04–3.10)
Main Title Sequence: Castle/Bryant/Johnsen
Processing: Gastown Film Labs
Telecine: Gastown Post and Transfer
Electronic Assembly: Encore Video
Westlaw Provider: West Publishing Company

37

X-CELLENCE: AWARDS

• THE PRIMETIME EMMY •

1993–1994: 46th Annual Primetime Emmy Awards
 Outstanding Individual Achievement in Graphic Design and Title Sequences:
James Castle, Bruce Bryant, Carol Johnsen, title designers

C.C.H. Pounder, Emmy-Nominated for
Outstanding Guest Actress in a Drama
Series, for "Duane Barry."

• THE GOLDEN GLOBE •

1994: 52nd Annual Golden Globe Awards (presented February 1995)
Series, Drama

• MISCELLANEOUS AWARDS •

1994: Environmental Media Award
TV, Episodic, Drama: for "Darkness Falls"

1994: Academy of Science Fiction, Fantasy and Horror Saturn Award
Outstanding Television Series

1995: Environmental Media Award
TV, Episodic, Drama: for "Fearful Symmetry"

1996: Screen Actors Guild (SAG) Award
Actress, (TV) Drama: Gillian Anderson, *The X-Files*

Anderson at the Emmy Awards in 1995,
presenting the award for Supporting Actress
in a Drama Series.

X-POSITION

The Annotated Episode Guide

• An Explanatory Note •

Each episode synopsis opens with title, airdate and writer/director credits, as well as an episode number in the widely accepted form: Season/dot/airdate-order number. Thus, episode 2.14 is the fourteenth episode of the second season.

Nearly every episode title-sequence ends with a flash and the onscreen motto The Truth Is Out There. We've noted those rare occasions when a different motto is used, as well as any other onscreen pronouncements.

After each synopsis we have provided two areas of annotation:

X-actitude: Numbers, names, facts, and figures from the episode, in list form.

X-otica: Everything else, from background anecdotes by the stars and producers themselves, to the minutiae of which towns in each episode are real and which fictional, as well as brief notes on any interesting, real-life locales where episodes were shot. Also, on occasion, we give clearly presented conclusions, extrapolations, and attempts to point out—and iron out—continuity issues.

Following are cast lists. With front-credit performers's whose character names aren't printed onscreen, and so have to be deduced from dialogue or other artifacts, such as nameplates. End-credit performers's character names are printed on-screen. For the end-credit guests, we've noted where their listed character name is incomplete (with a fuller name given in the episode) or otherwise at odds with the script.

A note about names: The X-Files, stylistically, often chooses to forgo the TV-series convention of somehow working guest-characters' names into their initial scenes; sometimes, we never learn important characters' names at all. In the synopses, we've generally identified character and place-names at first appearance, even if the name isn't mentioned until later in the episode. We consider them named in an episode if their name appears in either dialogue or in a clearly visible artifact, such as a name tag or an office nameplate.

Common abbreviations used in the synopses include

- APB
  All-Points Bulletin
- CDC
  The Centers for Disease Control and Prevention
- CIA
  Central Intelligence Agency
- DOD
  Department of Defense
- EMS
  Emergency Medical Services
- FBI
  Federal Bureau of Investigation
- ME
  Medical examiner
- MO
  Modus operandi (Latin), a standard legal phrase for a criminal's pattern of operation.
- NSA
  National Security Agency
- OPR
  Office of Professional Responsibility

Performers are listed in the order of their onscreen credits. The only exception is when a front-credited actor is listed last but with the special notation "and [whomever]." Since this is a contractual way of distinguishing special guest stars, we've listed such performers first in those cases.

[N] in a synopsis indicates a plot-point discussed in *X-humation: The Nitpick File*

Also: "FBI headquarters" and "the J. Edgar Hoover Building" refer to the same place and the terms are used interchangeably.

When a synopses records Mulder's assertion that, say, the real-life explorers Lewis and Clark wrote in their journals of Indians turning into werewolves, we're *not* stating this as fact, but merely reporting what's in the episode.

1.01 PILOT "THE X-FILES"   September 10, 1993
Writer: Chris Carter
Director: Robert Mandel

Opening text: "The following story is inspired by actual documented accounts.

COLLUM NATIONAL FOREST, NORTHWEST OREGON: Twenty-one-year-old Karen Swenson, in her nightclothes, runs for her life—to no avail. She meets her doom in the form of an eerie white light, and a silhouetted figure from atop a ridge. The next day, as local police examine the corpse, a coroner, John Truitt, tells Detective Miles of the county sheriff's office that the young woman has been dead eight to twelve hours, with no visible cause of death, or any sign of foul play—except, perhaps, for a nosebleed and two small pink, circular bumps on her lower back. Miles recognizes the victim—she'd gone to high school with his son. A shocked Truitt wonders if a past terror is now happening again.

FBI HEADQUARTERS, WASHINGTON, D.C., MARCH 6: Agent Dana Scully reports to Division Chief Scott Blevins and two other men—one of whom is tall and basset-faced and is smoking. The conversation reveals Scully's past experience, personally and with the Bureau. Blevins assigns her to team with Agent Fox Mulder (whose reputation she is already aware of) and to report on his investigations of his highly unorthodox "X-File" cases.

Scully finds Mulder's office (in what's later confirmed to be in the basement level). "Sorry, nobody here but the FBI's most unwanted," Mulder quips. He's sure Scully is here only to spy on him, and so has checked up on her.

Testing her, Mulder shows Scully a slide of a chemical chart for a substance found in the tissue around Karen Swenson's marks. Scully says it's unknown, but organic—synthetic protein, perhaps? Mulder doesn't know, but notes it's shown up in similar, previous deaths in Sturgis, South Dakota, and Shamrock, Texas, and that Swenson is the fourth of her high school graduating class to die in such circumstances. Mulder's gotten permission to exhume the body of the third victim, twenty-year-old schizophrenic Ray Soames, and to take tissue samples for comparison. Soames had confessed to the first two murders and was confined to a mental hospital, but then went missing for seven hours one day, and died of exposure in the middle of July.

Later, in their rented car on their way to the town of Bellefleur, Oregon, Scully notes that the regular county medical examiner, Jay Nemman, hadn't done Swenson's autopsy—the only one for which tissue samples were taken. Suddenly, strange noises and a whacked-out radio prompt Mulder to pull over and spray-paint an orange *X* on the road. He won't say why. They arrive at the cemetery to meet Truitt, the fill-in coroner. Suddenly, Nemman screeches up, saying he was away and hadn't been notified of this, and demands to know what these FBI agents think they're doing. His bluster is cut short by his worried daughter Theresa, who'd accompanied him and convinces him to leave.

43

Their first case together. Note Scully's long hair and Mulder's unimaginative tie.

Inside the coffin is a morbid surprise: something that looks like some alien dwarf carcass. Scully, at an autopsy commencing 10:56 P.M., tells Mulder it's a simian—"somebody's sick joke." But Mulder insists she take X-rays and do a full workup. At 4:37 A.M., in her motel room, Scully types up a report saying analysis reveals an "anomalous or possibly mutated mammalian physiology"—which doesn't account, she notes, for a small gray metallic implant she found in the nasal cavity and took with her.

NEXT DAY, RAYMON COUNTY STATE PSYCHIATRIC HOSPITAL: the agents speak with Soames's doctor, and then see live-in patients Billy Miles and Peggy O'Dell, two classmates of Soames's. They'd been in a car accident; Billy is now in a vegetative "waking coma," and the mentally unhinged Peggy is in a wheelchair. She also has, the agents note, the same marks on her back as Swenson. Later, searching in the forest where the victims had been found, Scully hears rumbling and sees a strange light over a ridge and a menacing figure brandishing a rifle. Saying he's with the county sheriff's department, he tells them they're on private property and orders them at gunpoint to leave.

They do so, driving into a sudden storm. Then, while Scully is showing Mulder a handful of unusual ash she found all over the woods, the same strange disturbance as before starts up again. Mulder checks his watch, 9:03 P.M., as a blinding light envelops them. When it ends, seemingly a moment later, the car is without power and the time is now 9:12. Scully can't accept that they "lost" nine minutes; time, she says, is "a universal invariant." [N] The car now mysteriously works.

In her motel room, Scully's typing a report when the electricity goes out. Deciding to bathe by candlelight, she strips to bra and panties, and panics when she finds three marks like those on the victims. Rushing to Mulder's room in her bathrobe, she shows him the marks—which to her relief prove to be mosquito bites.

Her relief gets them to talking. Mulder tells about his sister disappearing from their room when he was twelve and she eight; it tore his family apart. He went on to school in England, then found himself in the FBI with a knack for applying behavioral models to cases. He'd stumbled upon the X-Files, which looked at first "like a garbage dump for UFO sightings, alien abduction reports. . . ." Yet he became intrigued and read up on hundreds of cases. Then he found his access to classified data being blocked "somewhere at a higher level of power. The only reason I've been allowed to continue with my work is because I've made connections in Congress." Opening up, he reveals he underwent deep-regression hypnosis with a Dr. Heitz Werber (pronounced VER-ber), in which he remembered his sister disappearing in a flash of light, and of his being paralyzed and unable to help.

44

A woman phones to say Peggy O'Dell is dead. The agents rush to Rural Highway 133, where amid a police scene, a trucker explains the girl ran in front of him. Mulder's suspicious, since Peggy was confined to a wheelchair, and Scully finds Peggy's watch stopped at 9:03, the time of the odd storm. Then Mulder's informed that the examination lab has been trashed and Soames's body stolen, and when the agents return to their motel, it's on fire, destroying all their evidence.

Theresa Nemman, more fearful than ever, asks Scully and Mulder for protection. At a diner, she tells them that ever since graduation, she's been finding herself mysteriously in the woods, and she has the marks and the nosebleeds. She was the one who'd phoned them. But before she can say more, her father arrives to take her home. Accompanying him is Detective Miles, whom the agents now recognize as the threatening man in the forest— and, Mulder realizes, Billy Miles' father.

On a hunch, Mulder and Scully return to the cemetery and find the first two victims' graves empty. Mulder, for some reason, believes the vegetative Billy is committing the murders. With nothing to lose, the agents go to his bedside and find the ash-like substance on Billy's feet. Returning to the forest for a comparative sample, they're waylaid by Detective Miles, who knocks down Scully and is about to shoot Mulder when they hear a woman

45

Charles Cioffi, right, in a 1971 signature role, with the cat who won't cop out when there's danger all about . . . *Shaft.*

scream. Miles sees Billy menacing Theresa in a clearing, and raises his rifle to shoot his son. Mulder tackles him and then the eerie light reappears, as Billy holds Theresa like a sacrifice. Yet when it vanishes, they're fine—with their marks gone, and Billy back to normal.

FBI HEADQUARTERS, MARCH 22: Billy testifies under hypnosis as the agents, Blevins, and the two men watch. He says at a party in the woods, an eerie light took him to a "testing place," where he was told to gather others for tests. "But the test didn't work," he says. "They wanted everything destroyed" (evidently including Mulder and Scully's data).

Afterward, Scully concedes to Blevins she has no proof for Mulder's hypothesis of alien abduction—although, she professionally but pointedly adds, there *is* that metal object removed from Soames, which she'd kept with her. She's had it tested—and the object is made of some unknown material.

That night, Mulder phones to tell Scully all the files on Billy are gone. Elsewhere, a somber man in a black suit—the Smoking Man from Blevins's office—saunters down a storage corridor. He places Scully's unknown-metal object into a box with similar objects. Then he leaves and closes the door— a door identifying this place as the Pentagon.

46

Charles Cioffi	Division Chief Scott Blevins*
Cliff DeYoung	Dr. Jay Nemman
Sarah Koskoff	Theresa Nemman
Leon Russom	Detective Miles
Zachary Ansley	Billy Miles
Stephen E. Miller	Coroner (John) Truitt
Malcolm Stewart	Dr. Glass (unnamed in episode)
Alexandra Berlin	Orderly
Jim Jansen	Dr. Heitz Werber (Billy's interviewer; unnamed in episode)
Ken Camroux	Third Man (in Blevins's office)
Doug Abrams	Patrolman #1
William B. Davis	Smoking Man
Katya Gardener	Peggy O'Dell
Ric Reid	Assistant Coroner
Lesley Ewen	FBI Receptionist
J. B. Bivens	Truck Driver

The actress who played Karen Swenson, who had no lines, is uncredited.

*Identified per door nameplate near end of episode; other sources give title as "Section Chief."

X-actitude: This episode marks the first time we see Mulder popping his (and creator Chris Carter's) favorite snack, sunflower seeds.

Agents' rental-car license plate: RL1-670

Nemman's Jeep license plate: IEC-1K8

Box in which Smoking Man stores unknown metal object: no. 100041

X-otica: *The X-Files* pilot episode was shot in Vancouver over fourteen days in March 1993; post-production (the editing and addition of music, sound effects, and special effects) was finished by early May. The one-hour pilot's budget was a respectable $2 million.

While Washington, D.C., stock shots were often used the first season for what are called "establishing exteriors," the FBI's J. Edgar Hoover Building has to date had a specially shot stand-in: Simon Fraser University, in Burnaby, B.C., about four miles east of downtown Vancouver.

Some hospital locations were shot at the abandoned Riverview Mental Institution in nearby Coquitlam (not to be confused with the neighboring town of Port Coquitlam).

Collum National Forest, Raymon County, and Bellefleur, OR are all fictional. Sturgis, SD, and Shamrock, TX are real.

Anderson says she didn't want to do the bra-and-panties scene, but as a fledgling actress felt she had no choice. "There really wasn't a reason for it," she says. "The [mosquito] bites could have been on my shoulder or something."

Veteran actor Charles Cioffi is best known as Lt. Vic Androzzi, the NYPD contact for the title character of *Shaft*.

47

1.02 "DEEP THROAT" September 17, 1993

Writer: Chris Carter

Director: Daniel Sackheim

X-File case no.: DF101364

OUTSIDE ELLENS AIR FORCE BASE, SOUTHWEST IDAHO: Test-pilot Lt. Col. Robert Budahas has barricaded himself in his house. Soldiers find him hunkered down, seemingly insane.

Four months later at an upscale Washington bar, Mulder tells Scully the military is stonewalling about Budahas's psychosis and even his location. His desperate wife, Anita, finally reported his disappearance to the FBI as a kidnapping—but the case was shelved. Mulder reveals that since 1963, six pilots from this base have been listed as MIA.

In the restroom, Mulder's approached by a mysterious man. (His eventual designation as "Deep Throat" isn't given in dialog or onscreen credits this episode.) He calmly advises Mulder away from the case, yet offers to be of help since he admits to a certain interest in Mulder's work, adding "You have much work to do, Agent Mulder." Later, as a piqued Scully calls Mulder wondering if he knew Ellens was a UFO–sighting mecca, Mulder realizes his home phone is tapped and an unmarked blue van is outside.

Later in Idaho, Mrs. Budahas tells the agents her husband's strange behavior began two years before. Her friend, Verna McLennen's husband, had the same symptoms.

Mulder finds the base director, Colonel Kissel, hard to approach. The two agents learn from local reporter Paul Mossinger that UFO buffs gather at The Flying Saucer restaurant. There the agents get a hand-drawn map to Ellens (curiously unlisted on official maps) and by evening are driving alongside the restricted installation. In the early morning, they witness two airborne balls of light.

Suddenly, a menacing helicopter approaches, apparently chasing a teenage couple, whom Mulder and Scully help to escape. At a restaurant, the teens brag to the agents that they sneak through a fence-hole to neck and "watch the air show." They've also heard of someplace called The Yellow Base, where UFO parts are supposedly stored. A shadowy man code-named Redbird watches from a car. Later, Mulder tells Scully that Ellens is one of six bases where the supposed wreckage of the famous alleged 1947 Roswell flying-saucer crash is stored. He suggests the military is building aircraft using UFO high-technology.

The agents visit Budahas, who was returned home the night before. His memories of all things aeronautical have been erased. Scully suspects amnesia; Mulder suggests the stress of flying an aircraft at near-impossible speeds and maneuvers. Driving back, Mulder and Scully are waylaid by two ominous-looking cars. Black-suited characters ransack their vehicle, punch Mulder, and order them to leave for "national security" reasons—or else.

Yet Mulder later returns to the classified installation, guided by the teens to the fence-hole. That night, he emerges onto a runway to see a beautiful ball of light that splits into four. Then he finally sees a triangular aircraft hovering overhead with spotlights, which accelerates impossibly away. MPs capture Mulder, whisk him away, and drug him.

Early in the morning, Scully can't get a long-distance phone line; neither can the motel manager at his desk. Scully returns to find Mossinger snooping in her room. Hearing a walkie-talkie in his car, she leaps inside to find his gun and Airbase Security ID—he's Redbird. At gunpoint, she forces him to drive her to the base—where a woozy Mulder stumbles out, unable to remember recent events. One week later at FBI headquarters, Scully reports Budahas was returned to his family—and while Mulder's "alien technology" scenario is inconclusive, she herself is a corroborating witness to the UFO lights.

At a running track, Mulder is met by the mysterious man. He'll continue to provide them information, "so long as it's in my best interest." Which is? "The truth."

"They're here, aren't they?" Mulder asks.

"Mr. Mulder, they've been here for a long, long time."

Jerry Hardin	Deep Throat
Michael Bryan French	Paul Mossinger
Seth Green	Emil (teen boy; unnamed in episode)
Gabrielle Rose	Anita Budahas
Monica Parker	Ladonna (Flying Saucer restaurant owner; unnamed in episode)
Sheila Moore	Verla McLennen
Lalainia Lindbjerg	Zoe (teen girl; unnamed in episode)
Andrew Johnston	Lieutenant Colonel (Robert) Budahas
Jon Cuthbert	Commanding Officer
Vince Metcalfe	Kissell
Michael Puttonen	Motel Manager
Brian Furlong	Lead Officer
Doc Harris	Mr. McLennen

The children playing Josh and Leslie Budahas, who have no lines, are uncredited.
Note: The official Fox *X-Files* website erroneously lists Charles Cioffi in the episode cast.

49

X-actitude: Idaho airport at which the agents arrive: Marriette Field
The agents' hotel: The Beach Grove Motel
The restaurant where the agents speak with the teens: The Flying Saucer
License plate of the agents' car: 8216
License plate of one car of the black-suited men: Idaho CC1356
Mulder's sweatshirt logo: Georgetown University
Secret Defense Department suborbital-spycraft project Scully mentions: Aurora Project
Mr. McLennen's brother: Hank

X-otica: The fictional Ellens Air Force runway and Marriette Field are actually the small Boundary Bay Airport in Ladner, B.C.

Inspiration Alert: The scene where Scully mysteriously can't get a phone line out recalls a similar one in the classic *Bad Day at Black Rock* (1955), starring Spencer Tracy.

1.03 "SQUEEZE" September 24, 1993
Writers: Glen Morgan & James Wong
Director: Harry Longstreet

X-File case no.: X129202

BALTIMORE, MARYLAND, 8:30 P.M.: Businessperson George Usher is killed in his office by what sounds like a wild animal. The killer escapes through a six-by-eighteen-inch air vent.

WASHINGTON, D.C., THREE DAYS LATER: Scully lunches with old Academy classmate Tom Colton, a rising star in the Violent Crimes section, and reminisces with her about fellow classmate Marty Neil. Colton worries that Scully is hindering her career by associating with the eccentric Mulder. Then Colton asks for her help on a make-or-break case—that of three Baltimore serial killings in six months, with Usher's the most recent. Each victim's liver was ripped out with bare hands.

After Scully agrees to help, Mulder tells her that the recent killings echo ten similar Baltimore-area murders in 1933 and 1963. Since this particular X-File includes a related 1903 murder, Mulder talks his way onto the case by claiming earlier jurisdiction. At the crime scene, he lifts fingerprints off the high-up air vent—fingerprints that match several from the 1933 and 1963 killings. With a pattern of five murders every thirty years, Mulder predicts there'll soon be two more.

Mulder shows up at the parking garage below the Usher crime scene, telling Scully the killer won't return. He's apparently wrong. Noticing movement in the air vents, they and other agents arrest a Eugene Tooms. At the FBI's Richmond, Virginia, office, Tooms passes a polygraph test confirming he works for Baltimore Municipal Animal Control, was in the vent removing a dead cat, was once enrolled in college, has killed no one—and is not, despite the fingerprint evidence, 100-plus years old. Mulder is unconvinced. That night, Tooms crawls into a suburban home's air vent by elongating his body like rubber and kills again.

Mulder, checking the 1903 census, finds a Eugene Victor Tooms who resided at 66 Exeter Street, Room 103. Scully, in the meantime, has found Tooms's current address is merely a cover, and that Tooms hasn't been at work since the arrest. Then Mulder discovers that the first 1933 victim also lived at 66 Exeter Street, Room 203—right above Tooms. The agents then interview Frank, the officer who investigated the 1933 crime. Frank gives Mulder and Scully all the official and unofficial evidence he's collected. They check on 66 Exeter Street, now an abandoned wreck, and break into the deserted Room 103, where they discover a hole in the wall leading to the basement. There they find a shrine adorned with trophies from kills. They also find an odd "nest," leading Mulder to speculate that Tooms is a mutant who hibernates for thirty years, and that perhaps eating five livers can sustain him for that time. Scully leaves to call for a surveillance team—but not before Tooms, hiding in the darkened ceiling, snatches a bracelet from her.

Though two other agents do begin a stakeout, Colton angrily calls them off and insinuates Scully's a loser for sticking with Mulder. Scully goes home and leaves Mulder a phone message saying what's happened—unaware that she's being stalked by Tooms. Mulder, arriving at Exeter and finding the agents gone, searches Tooms's lair and finds Scully's bracelet. Racing to her home, he breaks in during Tooms's attack, and the two agents trap and arrest the killer.

Newspapers later report on a serial-killer suspect being caught, and Scully tells Mulder she's ordered genetic tests. Preliminary results show a highly abnormal muscle and skeletal system, and a rapidly declining metabolic rate. Tooms, in a mental-patient cell, methodically builds another nest out of paper and, seeing the tiny food-tray slot in his door, breaks into a demented grin.

Doug Hutchison	Eugene Victor Tooms
Donal Logue	Agent Tom Colton
Henry Beckman	Detective Frank Briggs (last name revealed in episode 1.21, "Tooms")
Kevin McNulty	Fuller (unnamed in episode)
Terence Kelly	(George) Usher
Colleen Winton	Examiner
James Bell	Detective Johnson (unnamed in episode)
Gary Hetherington	Kennedy (unnamed in episode)
Rob Morton	Kramer (unnamed in episode)
Paul Joyce	Mr. Werner (unnamed in episode)

51

X-actitude: Scully's apartment number: 35

Site of two of 1933 murders: Baltimore suburb Powhattan Mill

Frank Briggs's background: lives in the Lynne Acres Retirement Home; retired in 1968

Building sign at 66 Exeter St.: "Pierre Paris & Sons"

Background on Scully and Colton's classmate, Marty Neil: Worked the World Trade Center bombing; now, two years out of the Academy, is a supervisor in the Foreign Counterintelligence Office of the FBI's New York City bureau.

Per the police report seen in the sequel (episode 1.21, "Tooms"), Tooms was arrested July 23, 1993, at 107 E. Cordova. However, this address for Scully's apartment house is at odds with the building number seen in 2.06, "Ascension," which is 1419, a brownstone with stone steps.

X-otica: Director Harry Longstreet "had no respect for the script," according to James Wong; among other things, Longstreet didn't shoot "coverage" (multiple angles on a scene, to give the editor more choices), as is typical to do. Wong and Michael Katleman (who would direct episode 1.06, "Shadows") "had to go back up and reshoot some coverage, shoot a scene they didn't shoot, and add a lot of inserts to try to make it work."

Detroit-born Doug Hutchison recalls that at his audition, director Longstreet had instructed him to play Tooms emotionlessly. "And afterwards he said 'Okay, that's very good, and now I'd like you to show me that you can be this serial killer. Pretend that you're stalking your victims. I just want to see your potential for evil.' And I'm thinking, 'What is this? This is ridiculous! What does he want me to do? Make a face, or what?' So I sat and I pondered this direction . . . and he said, 'Do you understand what I'm saying?' And it just jumped out of me before I knew it came out, but I said, 'Yeah, I got it, you want me to stalk you, you motherfucker.' " That took Longstreet aback, but coexecutive producers James Wong and Glen Morgan loved it.

1.04 "CONDUIT" October 1, 1993
Writers: Alex Gansa & Howard Gordon
Director: Daniel Sackheim

CAMPSITE 53, LAKE OKOBOGEE NATIONAL PARK, NEAR SIOUX CITY, IOWA: A camper-trailer shakes violently—and eight-year-old Kevin Morris screams to his mother, Darlene, that his teenaged sister Ruby has vanished.

Sometime later, at FBI headquarters, Blevins informs Scully that Mulder has requested travel expenses to Sioux City—based, apparently, on a tabloid UFO–abduction headline. Blevins suspects Mulder has a personal reason, and shows Scully a file on Mulder's sister Samantha, who by Mulder's account was similarly abducted twenty-one years ago, when she was eight and Mulder was twelve. Blevins wants to disallow the request, but Scully asks if she can talk to Mulder about it first. Mulder tells her that this lake had four UFO sightings in August 1967—one by a Girl Scout troop of which Darlene Morris was a member.

The two agents arrive at Darlene's door, where Darlene introduces them to Kevin, who's watching TV static and drawing weirdly shaped zeros and ones. Mulder says they know of her Girl Scout UFO sighting, since her name is on file at the Center for UFO Studies in Evansville, Illinois.

At the sheriff's department, Mulder phones a friend, Danny, at FBI headquarters, to ask for analysis of Kevin's zeros and ones—evidently, binary code. The sheriff tells the agents Ruby is a problem girl and likely just ran away. Outside, on the agents's car, a note reads, "Across the street. Follow me." There, in the public library, Ruby's friend Tessa Sears tells them Ruby's boyfriend, Greg Randall, was to run away with Ruby that night, since he'd gotten her pregnant. The agents look for Greg at a biker bar where he works, but the bartender hasn't heard from him since he called in sick three weeks ago. Then the bartender suggests the agents nose around Lake Okobogee.

Before they can do so, some black-suited government goons demand to know where Mulder got "the documents" (Kevin's binary-code pages). One, named Holtzman, threatens Mulder with obstructing justice, but Mulder calls his bluff. Compromising, Holtzman explains the pages are a classified fragment of a Defense Department satellite transmission—and when Mulder still demurs, Scully tells them about Kevin. The goons trash Kevin's room looking for evidence, and spirit away Kevin and Darlene. At the FBI's Sioux City office, an Agent Atsumi tells Mulder and Scully there was nothing affecting national security in Kevin's code: When loaded into a computer, it formed snatches of music, artwork, and other things.

Later at her home, Darlene tells Mulder and Scully to stay away. At the lakeside abduction scene, Mulder finds the sand has turned to glass—a feat which requires 2500°F of heat. Mulder follows a white wolf to a pile of rocks, and scares away it and two others with warning shots. The rocks hide a shallow grave with Greg Randall's body. A handwritten note in his wallet indicates a doctor's appointment; the handwriting is the same as on Tessa Sears's note. They discover it was Tessa—not Ruby—whom Greg had gotten pregnant. In the sheriff's interrogation room, Tessa says Greg was meeting

Uncovering Greg
Randall's body.

53

Ruby behind her back, and she confesses to murdering Greg when he saw the two of them at the lake—though *then* she switches gears to say Ruby wasn't there.

That night, Mulder and Scully walk into Darlene's unlocked house. From a second-floor vantage point, they see that the spread-out pages of Kevin's binary code form a picture of Ruby. The agents rush back to the lake and find the camper. They find Darlene in the woods, saying Kevin ran in and she couldn't keep up. Mulder finds Kevin approaching an orange glow and saves him from roaring motorcyclists who almost run them over. Scully and Darlene have found the comatose Ruby, who in the hospital afterward shows signs of prolonged weightlessness. When the agents ask what happened, she merely replies, "They told me not to say." And Darlene? She bitterly declares, "The truth has brought me nothing but heartache," and says she'll claim Ruby fell off the back of a Harley.

Later, back at home, Scully listens to a tape of one of Mulder's old hypnotic-regression sessions; he's saying a voice has told him that no harm will come to his sister, and that she'll return someday—a voiceover that segues to a somberly contemplative Mulder, who breaks down sobbing.

54

Carrie Snodgrass	Darlene Morris
Michael Cavanaugh	Sheriff
Don Gibb	Bartender
Joel Palmer	Kevin Morris
Charles Cioffi	Division Chief Scott Blevins
Shelly Owens	Tessa (Sears)
Don Thompson	Holtzman
Akiko Morison	Leza Atsumi (first name not given in episode)
Taunya Dee	Ruby (Morris)
Anthony Harrison	Fourth Man
Glen Roald	ME Worker
Mauricio Mercado	Coroner

X-actitude: Per police report, Samantha T. Mulder was born Jan. 22, 1964, Chilmarc [*sic*], MA; lived at 2790 Vine St. in that town until her disappearance. Her medical records in episode 3.02, "Paper Clip," give middle name Ann and birthdate Nov. 21, 1965.

FBI travel-expenses request form no.: 302

Protocol channels: Mulder to Mulder's ASAC (Assistant Special Agent in Charge), to the district G-14, to Division Chief Blevins

Darlene's ex-husband: John

Greg's biker bar: The Pennsylvania Pub

Greg and Tessa's appointment: Dr. Jack Fowler, August 7, 2:30 P.M.

Mulder's hypnotic-regression tape: Session no. 2B, June 16

Mulder's friend at FBI: Daniel Bernstow, Cryptology Section (per fax cover sheet)

***X*-otica:** This episode makes the first mention of "Danny," Mulder's ever-helpful, unseen Bureau pal who expedites fingerprint searches, test results, and other such quantitative data.

Substituting for the fictional Lake Okobogee is B.C.'s Buntzen Lake, in the town of Port Coquitlam southeast of Vancouver.

The "zero and one" portrait of Ruby that Kevin draws was hand printed by art staffer Vivian Nishi with felt pens, tracing over wall-mounted sheets of paper onto which a too-perfect-looking computer printout was projected. Her hand-drawn numerals gave it the necessary childlike feel.

Carrie Snodgress garnered an Oscar nomination and Golden Globe Award for her title role in *Diary of a Mad Housewife* (1970). The one-time companion to rock star Neil Young, she then retired for eight years until *The Fury.*

1.05 "THE JERSEY DEVIL"   October 8, 1993
Writer: Chris Carter
Director: Joe Napolitano

NEW JERSEY, 1947: While fixing a flat tire on a road, Paul, a family man, three miles from Atlantic City, is snatched away by a creature. A manhunt at dawn finds his corpse, with one leg eaten off, and in a nearby cave, a huge, hairy humanoid whom the officers immediately kill.

PRESENT DAY, FRIDAY: At the office, Scully brings news of a body found in New Jersey missing an arm and a leg—possibly eaten off by a human. Mulder pulls an X-File on the 1947 case, and says police then killed what they reported to be a naked cannibal, whose autopsy report vanished from the Paterson, New Jersey, police file a few years later. At the Atlantic City morgue, the coroner, Glenna, confirms that the recent victim, vagrant Roger Crockett, was cannibalized. A Detective Thompson enters and throws the busybody FBI agents out.

Scully leaves to get to her godson's birthday party. Mulder remains. A Parks Service ranger, Peter Brouillet, shows Mulder the crime scene, and confesses that four years ago, he may have seen the Bigfoot-like "Jersey Devil." At her godson Trent's party, Scully laments the lack of men in her life. Trent's mom, Ellen, reminds her she's called her FBI partner "cute." Scully reflexively replies, "He's a jerk." She reconsiders: "He's not a jerk—he's obsessed with his work." Then Scully meets Rob, the attractive divorced dad of party-guest Scotty.

Later, near the Mercy Mission, Mulder asks the homeless about Crockett. One vagrant, in exchange for a few bucks, shows him a drawing of a beast-person. Later, Mulder, asleep in the alley on his unofficial stakeout, is awakened by the sound of something rummaging through the trash. He sees the shadowy being and gives chase, but the arriving police think he's a crazy vagrant and arrest him. Thompson, awakened at 3 A.M., lambastes Mulder at the jail and arranges things so he can't get out of the drunk tank until after the weekend, when charges are dropped and Scully picks him up. She has to be back in Washington by 7:30 P.M. for a date with Rob, but on the way back, she stops at her alma mater, the University of Maryland, to introduce Mulder to Dr. Diamond, a professor and an expert on wildman myths.

That night, at 7:55 P.M., Brouillet calls Mulder to say he's found a wildman-like, long-haired male who's been dead six to eight months; the body's at the coroner's office now. Next morning, the two agents, Brouillet, and Diamond join an astonished Glenna. Mulder suggests the creature's mate must be foraging in Atlantic City, where, he contends, the authorities want to hush up the killings for tourism's sake.

The three men and Scully investigate an abandoned building near the vagrant area. Thompson, driving by, notices the Ranger vehicle and, asserting jurisdiction, calls in a SWAT team—one that may or may not be trying to "accidentally" kill Mulder. Mulder escapes, following the creature into another abandoned building. There the beast, a female, slashes Mulder and runs away.

Shortly afterward, word comes that the beast-woman's been cornered in the woods. Mulder, Scully, Diamond, and Brouillet arrive at the same time as police. Brouillet gets to her first, with a sedative dart gun, yet before he can reach her, she's killed by two police gunshots.

One week later in Washington, autopsy results indicate the Jane Doe's age as twenty-five to thirty years old, and the male's as about forty. There's a human bone in the beast-woman's digestive tract. Diamond, allowed to do a medical exam of the female's body, found no prehistoric bone structure or physiology. The female's uterus indicated she may have given birth; Mulder theorizes she may have been trying to protect and feed her young. He leaves for the Smithsonian to tell an ethnobiologist about these findings, as Rob phones Scully to invite her and Trent to the Cirque du Soleil with him and Scotty. Yet moments later, we find her joining Mulder on his Smithsonian jaunt. And in the woods outside Atlantic City, a young but capable-looking beast-boy peers out through the underbrush.

Claire Stansfield	The Creature
Wayne Tippit	Detective Thompson
Gregory Sierra	Dr. Diamond
Michael MacRae	Ranger Peter Brouillet (Spelling per closed captioning; the Lowry book spells it "Boulle," though a definite "Br" sound is heard.)
Jill Teed	Glenna
Tasmin Kelsey	Ellen

Beast-turned-beauty Claire Stansfield (with Ron Marquette) in "The Bounty Hunter" episode of *Zalman King's Red Shoe Diaries*.

Andrew Airlie	Rod (*sic*; Rob, per both dialog and closed-captioning)
Bill Dow	Dad (Paul)
Hrothgar Mathews	Jack (the vagrant; unnamed in episode)
Jayme Knox	Mom
Scott Swanson	First Officer
Sean O'Byrne	Second Officer
David Lewis	Young Officer
D. Neil Mark	SWAT Team Officer

The FBI woman who tells Scully that Mulder's on line 3 is uncredited.

X-actitude: Mulder's Atlantic City hotel: Galaxy Gateway, Room 756

Brouillet's years on the force: 32

Atlantic City morgue file on Roger Crockett: Case no. 2242, Aug. 9, 1993, found New Jersey State Park

Unseen FBI employees handling car requisitions this episode: Lorraine and Fran

X-otica: Mulder here exhibits the first trace we see of his apparent enjoyment of men's magazines and adult video. In his office, no less, he examines a *Playboy*-type magazine in which the centerfold claims to have been abducted by aliens. Scully, looking at the unseen woman's evident breast implants, makes a calmly cutting remark about "antigravity."

The "Jersey Devil" is an actual folkloric figure, and the title inspiration for the New Jersey Devils hockey team.

Gregory Sierra is best-known as Julio Fuentes on *Sanford and Son*, Detective Sgt. Chano Amenguale on *Barney Miller*, and the original vice-squad commander, Lt. Lou Rodriguez, on *Miami Vice*. Six-footer Claire Stansfield has appeared on *Frasier*, *Twin Peaks* and "The Bounty Hunter" episode of Duchovny's *Red Shoe Diaries*.

1.06 "SHADOWS"   October 23, 1993
Writers: Glen Morgan & James Wong
Director: Michael Katleman

MILITARY CONTRACTOR HTG INDUSTRIAL TECHNOLOGIES, PHILADELPHIA: Secretary Lauren Kyte is packing up an office; her boss, Howard Graves, committed suicide two weeks ago. A desk plaque, unbeknownst to her, mysteriously slides across the desktop by itself. Later, Lauren is attacked by two robbers at an ATM; two hours after this, a teenaged couple looking for an abandoned building in which to crash finds two bodies on a fire escape.

BETHESDA NAVAL HOSPITAL: Mulder and Scully have been called to the morgue by an unnamed official-looking pair and a pathologist. Two bodies dead for six hours are still somehow warm, showing postmortem muscle reflex and a high level of electrostatic charge—with the larynx, esophagus, and hyoid bone all apparently crushed from the *inside*. Expert-on-the-unusual Mulder says he's unfamiliar with this—yet afterward, tells Scully it's psychokinetic manipulation. He also shows her his eyeglasses, on which he's surreptitiously gotten the corpses' thumbprints.

The next morning at HTG, Lauren gives Graves's successor, Robert Dorlund, her two weeks' notice. Dorlund tries to talk her out of it, saying she was like a daughter to Graves, and when he grasps her to emphasize his point, some unseen force shoves him away.

FBI HEADQUARTERS: Mulder ID's one of the bodies as that of Mohammed ah Malachi, a terrorist with ties to the exiled, Philadelphia-based Isfahan. Later, on Philly's Broad Street, a cop tells Mulder he'd found the bodies last Wednesday around 10 P.M. That gives Mulder and Scully a time frame for viewing ATM security-camera videos—which show a spectral blur behind the terrorists as they attempt to mug a woman whose bank records identify her as Lauren.

At her house, packing to move, Lauren denies contact with the men—until the agents show her a video frame-grab. She then says she'd run from them and didn't want to bother with police involvement. When the stonewalled agents get into their car, it starts by itself—peeling rubber backwards until broadsided by another. At a garage, Mulder's told the car hasn't been tampered with, yet the switched-off headlights shine nonetheless, due to massive levels of electrostatic charge in the filaments. Scully suspects sabotage.

They stake out Lauren, watching as she arrives at work to yell at a painter restenciling the name on Graves's old parking space. They later find an obit [N] for Howard Thomas Graves, fifty-three, found dead one Tuesday in his hot tub, his wrists slit. He left no survivors. An FBI expert digitally enhances the surveillance photos, bringing out an image of Graves. That night, Lauren hears anguished, muffled voices—including Graves's—and finds her bathtub filled with bloody water; she concludes it's a message that Graves was murdered.

Scully thinks Graves faked his death. ME Ellen Bledsoe confirms Graves's demise, but the only identification of the body came from Lauren—and the body was cremated after its organs were donated.

At the University of Pennsylvania Hospital Tissue Bank, a doctor tells the agents Graves's kidney was transplanted in Boston, his liver in Dallas, and his corneas in Portland; however, they've cryogenically preserved the dura mater of his spinal column and confirm it is, indeed, Graves's.

At HTG, Dorlund threatens Lauren over some sensitive matter she had discussed with Graves. Frightened, she later asks Mulder to meet her at her house. Yet before he and Scully can arrive, two assassins, a man and a woman, burst in, and an invisible force kills them. The agents bring Lauren in for questioning, but the mysterious, official-looking man and woman arrive; after some friction, they tell the agents HTG was suspected of illegally selling technology to the Isfahan. Then, after failing to get answers from Lauren themselves, they give Mulder another shot. He privately tells her he believes Graves is communicating from beyond. She relents and says she'd found him despondent since HTG was going under and Dorlund had brought the Isfahan in as customers. She's convinced Dorlund had Graves killed for fear he'd scuttle the deal.

The FBI ambushes HTG for evidence of the illegal sales. They find nothing incriminating, until Dorlund, in Graves's office, tries to stab Lauren with a letter opener, and the ghostly Graves snatches it and pierces the wall fabric, behind which evidence is hidden. Later, a relocated Lauren now works at Monroe Mutual Insurance Company in Omaha, Nebraska, where Graves may perhaps have followed.

Barry Primus	Robert Dorlund
Lisa Waltz	Lauren Kyte
Lorena Gale	Ellen Bledsoe
Veena Sood	Ms. Saunders (mysterious investigator, unnamed in episode)
Deryl Hayes	Webster (mysterious investigator, unnamed in episode)
Kelli Fox	Pathologist
Tom Pickett	Cop
Tom Heaton	Groundskeeper

Jamie Woods-Morris   Ms. Lange
Nora McLellan   Jane Morris (last name not given in episode)
Anna Ferguson   Ms. Winn

The actors playing the teen couple (who have lines), the assassin couple (who have significant screen time), and the two terrorist-muggers (who have brief screen time) are uncredited.

X-actitude: Lauren's address: 858 Franklin St., Bensalem (fictional town; a suburb either in Pennsylvania or nearby New Jersey)

Desk plaque: Benjamin Franklin quote: "One To-day is Worth Two To-morrows"

Number of miles on the rental car: 100

Lauren's total debt amount: $15,000

The dumpster by the fire escape with the bodies: no. 33425

Graves's background: Divorced 1970; wife left after their daughter, Sarah Lynn Graves (September 8, 1966–August 3, 1969, per gravestone), drowned in a pool to which he'd left the gate-latch open.

Name being stenciled onto Graves's parking space: Tom Braidwood

In-joke: Braidwood is the series' first assistant director, who later plays a recurring role as Frohike of the Lone Gunmen.

X-otica: Coexecutive producers Morgan and Wong have called this lackluster story a response to Fox, which wanted a poltergeist episode, as well as one with a "relatable" supporting character whom Mulder and Scully could help. "It was just a little too ordinary, like you have seen it before," said Morgan, "which is exactly what the network wanted at the time."

1.07 "GHOST IN THE MACHINE"   October 29, 1993

Writers: Alex Gansa & Howard Gordon
Director: Jerrold Freedman

EURISKO WORLD HEADQUARTERS, CRYSTAL CITY, VIRGINIA: Founder Brad Wilczek argues with CEO Benjamin Drake, who's terminating Wilczek's pet project, the Central Operating System (COS). That evening, Drake finds his office restroom overflowing with water; when he uses the phone seeking janitorial help, it merely gives the time (7:35 P.M.)—upon which the electronic door shuts, and Drake, applying a metal key to the lock, is electrocuted. COS's computer-voice announces, "File deleted."

FBI HEADQUARTERS: Agent Jerry Lamana, Mulder's old partner in Violent Crimes, surprises Mulder and Scully at the office food cart. With desperate joviality, he tells them about Drake: Building engineer Claude Peterson found the body twelve hours ago, and the investigation's being run by FBI Academy forensics instructor Nancy Spiller, "The Iron Maiden." Lamana begs for their help, since Drake was a friend of the attorney general's; Mulder relents.

At Eurisko, Mulder explains to Scully that Lamana wanted up the ladder. But Lamana, working hate crimes in Atlanta, derailed his career by losing critical evidence. Suddenly, their elevator jolts to a stop above the fourth floor; Scully intercoms for help, stating her name. The elevator reactivates— while COS looks up Scully's home phone number. Scully and Mulder meet Lamana and Peterson, who says any saboteur would have had to override COS. He'll provide a list of everyone with COS's access code.

Back at headquarters, Mulder can't find his killer-profile notes. But at a meeting with Spiller, Lamana, and at least three other agents, Mulder and Scully recognize Lamana's killer-profile as Mulder's work. Mulder afterward confronts Lamana, who pooh-poohs his theft. Scully and Mulder question Wilczek, the only person with COS access. He makes his hatred of Drake clear, yet Scully, writing in her field journal, doubts Wilczek's guilt. She goes to bed—whereupon her computer activates, its modem connects, and COS retrieves the file. [N]

The next day, Scully's speech-pattern analysis of tapes of Wilczek's Smithsonian lectures indicates it is Wilczek's disguised voice on the time-recording heard before Drake's death. Lamana volunteers to arrest Wilczek, who's leaving his house after unsuccessfully trying to access COS from home.

Lamana follows him to Eurisko, where Wilczek gains access—astonished to find COS speaking when he'd never installed voice synthesis. Then he watches in horror as Lamana, stuck in the elevator between the twenty-ninth and thirtieth floors, plummets to his death. Scully later tells Mulder Wilczek confessed to Lamana's murder. Mulder doesn't believe Wilczek. On arriving at Wilczek's house to investigate further, officials in black suits tell him his subpoena's no good and that unless he has "Code 5" clearance, to leave. Mulder demands of Deep Throat why the Defense Department is running a Code 5 investigation. Deep Throat says the rumor is Wilczek's developed an AI (artificial intelligence) "adaptive network"—a learning computer.

FEDERAL DETENTION CENTER, WASHINGTON, D.C.: Wilczek swears to Mulder he's not "protecting COS," but simply refusing to share anything with "an immoral government." Mulder wants Wilczek to destroy COS. He agrees, and will design a virus Mulder can use. Mulder smuggles a laptop into Wilczek's cell.

At 1:31 A.M., Scully finds someone remotely accessing her computer. The FBI traces the call to Eurisko. There Scully finds Mulder; they enter using Wilczek's license plate, which the computer scans—but partway in, a sharp-pronged gate slams down as if to smash their car. Taking the stairs, they find the twenty-ninth-floor door locked and booby-trapped. As Scully tries crawling through an air vent to the other side, Peterson finds Mulder on the landing, while Scully finds herself pulled by powerful air currents toward an industrial fan that slices up her flashlight. Desperately, she fires at it.

61

Mulder accesses COS at user level seven—at which point Peterson pulls a gun and says he's been trying to access COS for two years. He forces Mulder to hand over the viral disc—until Scully gets the drop on Peterson. The infected COS starts speaking gibberish, and "dies."

Later, Mulder tells Deep Throat he's checked with both the attorney general and a Congressman Klebanow of the Department of Corrections Subcommittee, but Wilczek has "disappeared." Deep Throat simply replies, "*They* can do anything they want." Wilczek may or may not break and give them his AI research—but COS, at least, is no longer a danger. At Eurisko, Peterson is given six more hours to revive COS before abandoning it for scrap. No one notices the computer momentarily sputtering to life.

Jerry Hardin	Deep Throat
Rob LaBelle	Brad Wilczek
Wayne Duvall	Agent Jerry Lamana
Blu Mankuma	Claude Peterson
Tom Butler	(Benjamin) Drake
Gillian Barber	Jane Spiller (*sic*; Nancy per episode)
Marc Baur	Man in Suit
Bill Finck	Sandwich Man (at FBI lunch cart)
Theodore Thomas	Clyde

The official Fox *X-Files* website erroneously lists the character Brad Wilczek as Steven Wilczek, and Claude Peterson as Clyde Peterson.

Caught between floors, Scully ID's herself to the computer's satisfaction.

X-actitude: Lamana's bill to treat Mulder and Scully to lunch: $8.50

Drake's weight: 180 pounds

Spectrograph Scully uses: Audio Spectrum Identisearch, borrowed from the Voice Biometrics Lab at Georgetown University

Source of Scully's warrant for Wilczek: Judge Benson in Washington Heights

Wilczek background: Founded Eurisko at age twenty-two in his parents' garage, after having spent years following the Grateful Dead in concert; Eurisko, he says, is Greek for "I discover things."

X-otica: Cowriter Howard Gordon has himself called this episode "easily and clearly our worst. It's basically uninteresting." He and Alex Gansa were admittedly not computer literate, and didn't have a feel for the material. "It's an old idea, a machine gaining intelligence. There may have been a more interesting way of doing it and we unfortunately don't feel that we licked the problem." His final analysis? "Well, it pretty much sucked."

This episode marks the first time Scully's fired her gun.

Crystal City, VA, is a real-life Washington, D.C., suburb, just over the Key Bridge from Georgetown.

63

1.08 "ICE"   November 5, 1993

Writers: Glen Morgan & James Wong

Director: David Nutter

ARCTIC ICE CORE PROJECT, ICY CAPE, ALASKA, 250 MILES NORTH OF THE ARCTIC CIRCLE. MORNING, FRIDAY, NOVEMBER 5, 1993: During a –33°F blizzard, a dog roots around for food. At 8:30 A.M., shambling team captain John Richter sends a video message: "We're not who we are." A second man, Campbell, attacks him. They each point a gun at the other—then as if by silent pact, each blows his own brains out.

FBI HEADQUARTERS: Scully and Mulder watch a tape of Richter's jubilant transmission when they set a depth record for ice-sheet drilling. A week later came Richter's final message. The Weather Service now predicts a three-day window before the next Arctic Storm, allowing the FBI to investigate.

DOOLITTLE AIRFIELD, NOME, ALASKA, WEDNESDAY: Mulder and Scully hook up with Dr. Denny Murphy, professor of geology at the University of California at San Diego; toxicologist Dr. Nancy Da Silva; physician Dr. Hodge; and bush pilot Bear.

The team finds the bodies of Richter and Campbell, plus a filing cabinet with soil and ice samples. The dog attacks Mulder and Bear but Hodge tranquilizes it and notes that though Bear is bleeding, the animal isn't rabid. Scully sees black nodules on the dog—a possible sign of bubonic plague—

and notices something squirming beneath some irritated flesh. Bear, in private, finds similar nodules on himself.

Scully's autopsies on Richter and Campbell show they died of gunshot wounds, and that three other corpses found at the ice station evidenced strangulation. But there's no evidence of nodules, which Hodge notes have disappeared from the dog. Murphy declares the drill site is concave—like, perhaps, a meteor crater. They find ammonium hydroxide in Richter's blood, and evidence of that toxin in the ice samples—along with a ratio of ammonia to water too high for Earth even 250,000 years ago. They also find a weird, single-celled creature in Richter's blood—possibly the larval stage of a larger organism.

Bear is anxious to leave, but Mulder says if the bodies are infected, they can't risk exposing the outside world, and since the dog attacked them, they must test themselves. Yet Bear declares he's leaving *now*, and when the agents restrain him, all see something scrambling beneath his skin. They surgically remove a wriggling organism. Mulder radios Doolittle for an airlift and quarantine; the radio operator oddly hesitates before saying a storm is blocking air traffic until tomorrow, and maybe the military base at Kotzebue can help.

Bear dies, and though all the victims have had the wormlike organism, only his remains alive; it slithers into the brain's hypothalamus gland, which secretes acetylocholine, which produces aggressive behavior. Mulder speculates to Scully that the "worm" lives in sub-zero ammonia—the same conditions as on other worlds. This area *is* over a meteor crater. They argue over whether to kill it or save it for study.

A suspicious Hodge is sure the agents knew about the creature. When Da Silva notes Hodge and Scully got splattered with Bear's blood, they all agree to check each other for nodules; none found, they retire to separate quarters. Mulder, investigating a noise later, finds Murphy dead—just as the others arrive. Accusations fly. Scully wants them all tested, but Mulder won't let Hodge touch him. It boils to a point where Scully and Mulder draw guns on each other—and when Mulder says for God's sake it's *him*, Scully tells him, "You may not be who you are." Mulder lets himself be locked into a storage room in case he's infected.

When Da Silva accidentally mixes two drops of infected blood on a microscope slide, Scully sees the two larvae kill each other, and when Scully places an ammonia jar with one live "worm" next to a jar with another [N], each tries in vain to attack the other. They place one in the ear of the infected dog, who later passes two dead "worms" in its stool. Introducing a "worm" to Mulder would thus either cure him . . . or needlessly infect him.

Hodge agrees to examine Mulder, but waylays him while Da Silva locks Scully in a storeroom. As Hodge prepares to drop a "worm" into Mulder's ear, he notices Da Silva's skin moving. Hodge throws Da Silva off Mulder, then he and Mulder free Scully. They put the "worm" in Da Silva's ear to cure her.

Later, at Doolittle, Da Silva and the dog are quarantined. Mulder says he's returning with proper equipment. Hodge is surprised—hasn't Mulder heard? Forty-five minutes after evacuation, someone torched the station. "The military?" wonders Hodge. "Centers for Disease Control? You ought to know," he tells Mulder bitterly and ironically, "they're *your* people."

Xander Berkeley	Dr. Hodge
Felicity Huffman	Dr. Nancy Da Silva
Steve Hynter	Dr. Denny Murphy
Jeff Kober	Bear
Ken Kerzinger	(John) Richter
Sonny Surowiec	Campbell

The animal performer is uncredited.

***X*-actitude:** Filing cabinet with soil/ice samples labeled: "Ice Cores 2,175–3,250"

Depth of ice-sheet: Per Murphy's analysis, 3,000 meters; Mulder, however, had said the team found it to be twice that.

***X*-otica:** A taut, tense episode—one of the series' best—with Scully and Mulder hurdling a critical juncture of mutual trust.

The dog in the episode is a parent of Duchovny's dog Blue.

Icy Cape is an actual locale on the northwest Alaskan Arctic coast, between the towns of Wainwright and Point Hope.

Jeff Kober costarred as Dodger on *China Beach.* Xander Berkeley is familiar from *Mommie Dearest*, *Terminator 2: Judgment Day*, and *Leaving Las Vegas*. Steve Hytner was in the series cast of *Disney Presents the 100 Lives of Black Jack Savage*, starring future "Mr. X" Steven Williams. Ken Kerzinger, the ice-core Team Captain, is *The X-Files*'s stunt coordinator.

65

1.09 "SPACE"　　　　　　　　　November 12, 1993
Writer: Chris Carter
Director: William Graham

PASADENA, CALIFORNIA, 1977: At the Jet Propulsion Laboratory, a TV correspondent for WXDL/Channel 11 reports on the first Viking Orbiter pictures of Mars, revealing a face-like land formation. Project director Lt. Col. Marcus Aurelius Belt calls it a trick of the light. But later, he flashes back years to his astronaut spacewalk, being attacked by "something out here!" Belt wakes in shock, engulfed by an image of the Martian face.

PRESENT DAY. SHUTTLE SPACE CENTER, CAPE CANAVERAL, FLORIDA: The space shuttle is T-minus 1 minute, 15 seconds to launch. At Houston Mission Control is Belt and Communications Commander Michelle Generoo. Florida aborts the takeoff at T-minus 3 seconds.

WASHINGTON D.C., TWO WEEKS LATER: Mulder tells Scully an anonymous letter-writer from NASA wants to speak with the FBI. It's Generoo, who approaches them to say she may have evidence of shuttle sabotage. An auxiliary power unit (APU) valve malfunctioned. Had the takeoff not been aborted, the shuttle would have exploded. Someone's anonymously mailed her X-rays and other documents showing deep-grooved marks on the APU—possible evidence of tampering. Tomorrow, a new launch is scheduled; her fiancée's the mission commander.

HOUSTON SPACE CENTER, NEXT DAY: Mulder tells Scully Belt nearly died on *Gemini 8*, making an emergency splashdown. When the agents show Belt a picture of the damaged valve, he calls it specious. Scully and Mulder speak with engineers, who confirm the agents have a picture of an anomalously scored APU valve. Mulder can't believe Belt would launch the shuttle with a bad part and yet, later, liftoff is indeed successful.

Then at their hotel some time later, Generoo tells them something's wrong. As the agents follow her car back to Mission Control, Generoo sees the Martian face appear in the foggy night and crashes. Mulder and Scully find the crashed car and pull her from the wreckage, and she insists they continue. At Mission Control, they learn that at two hours, eighteen minutes (2:18) after launch, Houston lost communication; now they can't rotate the shuttle away from the sun, and it's nearly 103°F in the cabin. When Generoo arrives, relatively unhurt, they isolate the problem to a digital processor in the Houston data banks. Generoo takes the agents there as the lights go out, but it's just a scientist checking since some sensors went off.

By 2:54 into the flight, communication is back but other systems are down. A minute later, Belt gives the astronauts complete control, though Generoo says that decision risks stranding them. The flight is successful and at a press conference, Belt lies, denying any problems. Mulder approaches Belt afterward, wondering whether he'd also lie to the FBI—and Belt sidesteps the question.

Over Canada, at 12:39 into the flight, the shuttle develops an oxygen leak, leaving the astronauts just thirty minutes of air. Scully and Mulder retrieve Belt from his high-rise apartment. At Mission Control, he orders the astronauts to stay in space suits, to prepare the emergency oxygen system, and to deploy the payload. As the astronauts do so, one reports, "There's someone outside the ship! Some kind of ghost!" Belt goes bonkers. Scully, meantime, finds a diagram of the faulty valve, and learns this analysis was

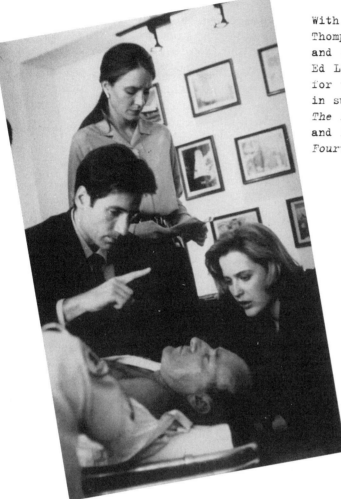

With Susanna
Thompson (standing)
and character-actor
Ed Lauter, known
for tough-guy roles
in such films as
The Longest Yard
and *Born on the
Fourth of July.*

67

ordered by Belt, whom they find cowering under his desk with "Help Me" written on his blotter.

EMS arrives. Generoo, the next in command, wants to bring the shuttle down immediately, but Belt yells no, "It's out there!" He confesses that while he didn't sabotage the shuttle, he didn't stop "them. They don't want us to know!" The agents, momentarily seeing the Martian in Belt's face, convince Belt to help bring the astronauts down safely. Belt tells Generoo to tell the astronauts to change reentry trajectory to thirty-five degrees. Generoo doesn't know if they got the message before a scheduled communications blackout occurred. The landing site, Kirtland Air Force Base in Albuquerque, has no sign of the shuttle. At 16:26 into the flight, Generoo tries contacting the astronauts again, and jubilantly gets a response.

In a hospital, Belt watches Generoo's press conference on the landing, then throws himself out a window, killing himself to keep the Martian from escaping. Mulder, later reading about Belt's death in the paper, tells Scully something must have possessed Belt in space. Scully replies that doctors diagnosed severe dementia. Mulder concludes Belt had sent the documents anonymously to Generoo—his human self fighting his alien other.

Ed Lauter	Lt. Col. Marcus Aurelius Belt
Susanna Thompson	Michelle Generoo
Tom McBeath	Scientist
Terry David Mulligan	Mission Controller
French Tickner	Preacher
Norma Wick	(TV) Reporter
Alf Humphreys	2nd Controller
David Cameron	Young Scientist
Tyronne L'Hirondelle	Data Bank Scientist
Paul Des Roches	Paramedic

68

X-actitude: Time until liftoff when Scully and Mulder are first seen at Houston Space Center: 10:45:27 (hours/minutes/seconds).

Time until liftoff when they reach Belt's office: 10:39:39.

X-otica: "Space" is perhaps the series' dullest, least suspenseful episode, with highly unclear motivations from the Martian—which Generoo *and* Scully see, yet dismiss, even though Generoo crashed her car because of it!

"It's not my favorite episode, and I think our least successful," Carter has said.

1.10 "FALLEN ANGEL"   November 19, 1993
Writers: Howard Gordon & Alex Gansa
Director: Larry Shaw

TOWNSEND, WISCONSIN, 12:57 A.M., DAY 1: Radio interference prevents Deputy Sheriff Wright from reporting a fire off County Road D-7. Shortly afterward he dies screaming, enveloped by flashing lights.

U.S. SPACE SURVEILLANCE CENTER, CHEYENNE MOUNTAIN, COLORADO: A lieutenant and a female radar operator, Chief Koretz, inform Commander Calvin Henderson an unidentified object broke into the radar grid off the Connecticut coast going north-by-northwest, "went crazy" in unearthly trajectories, and impacted west of Lake Michigan at over 800 mph. Henderson orders them to report only a meteor, and the radar findings as "instrument malfunction." Away from them, he phones to announce "Code Indigo Echo Delta Niner—I have a confirmed fallen angel in sector 87. Mobilize Operation Falcon immediately."

BUDGET-REST MOTEL, TOWNSEND, 12:57 A.M., DAY 1: [N] Mulder watches a female reporter on Highway 38 say the government is vague about the "toxic cargo" forcing the evacuation of 12,000 residents. Mulder flashes back to Deep Throat telling him about Operation Falcon beginning at 0100, headed by air force "reclamations" expert Henderson; Mulder has twenty-four hours before the area is "sanitized." A half hour before nightfall, at Falcon field headquarters, Henderson chastises a late-arriving lieutenant (not the one from Cheyenne Mountain). Mulder, unseen, drops from underneath the lieutenant's truck chassis and hides.

At the site, Mulder snaps photos of soldiers, firefighters with foam extinguishers, and strange objects until he's rifle-butted unconscious. When he awakens, Henderson berates him for violating a government quarantine; the film's been destroyed. Mulder's pushed into a brig alongside that of hapless UFO–conspiracy theorist Max Fenig, of NICAP. Fenig's gone by dawn, when Scully arrives saying Section Chief McGrath wants to close the X-Files and fire Mulder. Scully concedes there are no railroad tracks on which "toxic cargo" could've derailed [N]—it was actually a Libyan jet with a nuclear warhead. We see a hovering, light-bending being flash through the woods.

69

The agents find Fenig in Mulder's (ransacked) room. Fenig has followed Mulder's career through his public-record travel expenses, saw Mulder's picture in a trade magazine, and even read Mulder's pseudonymous *Omni* article about the Gulf Breeze Sightings. Fenig takes them to his camper-trailer—a UFO–sighting mobile headquarters, with serious surveillance electronics. Scully notices prescription drugs, among them the anti-convulsant Dilantin and the schizophrenia-treatment drug Mellaril.

MILL ROAD HIGH SCHOOL EVACUATION CENTER, 6:27 P.M., DAY 2: Scully and Mulder ask Mrs. Wright about her husband. The widow with a small child says the government won't release Wright's body, and threatened to withhold his pension if she talked. At U.S. Microwave Substation B21, there's screeching static of a 200K megahertz signal, and thermography spots something moving seven mph on the northeast side. Beta Team, led by the Falcon lieutenant, arrives to search and destroy. Another man, Jackson, behind the lieutenant, sees nothing—till the alien attacks.

COUNTY HOSPITAL, TOWNSEND, 11:42 P.M.: ER physician Dr. Oppenheim says he saw Wright and three firefighters all DOA with "fifth- and sixth-degree burns" over 90 percent of their bodies [N]. The government whisked them away before autopsies could be done. Suddenly, soldiers bang in with severely burned comrades. Mulder tells Henderson hunting the alien only forces it to defend itself. Henderson throws Mulder out, but Oppenheim insists they need medical doctor Scully. Afterward, as Mulder helps Fenig to bed after finding him having an epileptic seizure, Mulder notices a V-shaped scar behind Fenig's left ear. Later, Mulder shows Scully alien-abductee photos of two women with the same scar as Fenig.

Back at Cheyenne Mountain, Koretz announces unidentified "flash traffic" from a much larger craft—or, as the lieutenant corrects her, "Meteor." Whitmarsh Air Force Base says the "meteor" is hovering over Townsend. At Fenig's camper, Fenig's ears bleed, and he vanishes in a flash. Scully and Mulder, with less than an hour before their flight, find Fenig missing, and blood on his pillow. His radio scanner crackles about a "target" on the waterfront, and Henderson saying "move on target."

LAKE MICHIGAN WATERFRONT, DOCK 7: Henderson tells his men Fenig's not a civilian and to take him with extreme caution. Mulder and Scully arrive to find soldiers burned to death. They follow the sound of Fenig's cry into a warehouse. Scully's arrested, plastique explosives are applied to the building, and Alpha Team reports *three* moving forms in the building. Inside, after a flash of light throws Mulder across the room, he sees Fenig floating like a rag doll. Then another bright flash—only Mulder remains when the soldiers blow down the door. Mulder tells Henderson, "He's gone. They got to him first."

Facing charges of insubordination and misconduct, Mulder loses patience during an OPR hearing as officials deem his evidence "irrelevant," and claim Fenig's body was found two hours later in a cargo container. Later McGrath demands of Deep Throat why someone countermanded the Committee's decision. Deep Throat says having Mulder active is "less dangerous . . . than having him be exposed to the wrong people." And he remarks about what Mulder knows, and "what he *thinks* he knows."

Jerry Hardin	Deep Throat
Frederick Coffin	Section Chief Joseph McGrath (first name not given in episode)
Marshall Bell	Commander Calvin Henderson
Scott Bellis	Max Fenig
Brent Stait	Corp. Taylor (unnamed in episode)
Alvin Sanders	Deputy Sheriff J. Wright (first initial not given in episode)
Sheila Paterson	Gina Watkins (unnamed in episode)
Tony Pantages	Lt. Fraser (unnamed in episode)
Freda Perry	Mrs. Wright
Michael Rogers	Lt. Griffin (unnamed in episode)
William McDonald	Dr. Oppenheim
Jane MacDougall	Laura Dalton (unnamed in episode)
Kimberly Unger	(Chief) Karen Koretz (first name not given in episode)

X-actitude: Mulder's *Omni* psuedonym: M. F. Luder, an anagram of "F. Mulder"

70

TV station with news report: Channel 5

Agents' rental-car license plate: RAH-615

Deputy Wright's sheriff department cruiser plate: 29406

Location of fire near County Road D-7: two miles west of the Canyon Ridge intersection

UFO groups Fenig mentions: MUFON, CUFOS, and "that new group," CSICOP; NICAP stands for National Investigative Committee of Aerial Phenomena.

Where Fenig is arrested: 100 yards past Falcon roadblock

Mellaril prescription filled at: All-Nighter Pharmacy

Headline of Scully's newspaper: TOXIC CLEAN-UP A SUCCESS

Radar points of the UFO's path:

Connecticut coastline where it "tripped the fence": 2317

Lake Michigan area where it dropped off the screen: 2418

Max's high-tech spy electronics include: Wolf's Ear 200 listening, from "CIA supplier" Wolf Industries.

Condition of soldiers in ER: All died but two, who are in critical condition on their way to the burn unit Johns Hopkins.

X-otica: The deadly creature's appearance and actions indicate that this episode involves a *real* extraterrestrial, and not an Earth-made spacecraft (*a la* episode 1.02, "Deep Throat") or alien-human hybrid (*a la* Dr. Secare of episode 1.24, "The Erlenmeyer Flask").

The Gulf Breeze incidents Mulder wrote of refer to sightings claimed around that small Pensacola, FL, suburb from November 1987 to May 1988, primarily by real estate developer Ed Walters who had photos, some scientific endorsement, and much credible evidence to back up his story. Later, a young man revealed he'd helped Walters fake it all. But for a while, Gulf Breeze became a UFOlogist's mecca.

Inspiration Alert: The image of a wavily visible/invisible alien is a direct takeoff from *Predator* (1987).

1.11 "EVE"   December 10, 1993

Writers: Kenneth Biller & Chris Brancato

Director: Fred Gerber

GREENWICH, CONNECTICUT: A couple jogging find eight-year-old Teena Simmons sitting dazedly in her front yard, and her dad, Joel, dead. The FBI autopsy report says Joel's death was by hypovolemia—he'd lost over 75 percent of his blood. Teena claims no memory of what's occurred, and any physical evidence was washed away by rain. The ME found traces of digitalis, a heart stimulant made from the plant of the same name (a.k.a. foxglove), which can be used as a paralytic drug. Mulder notes the wounds and blood-removal resemble those of "alien" cattle mutilation.

FAIRFIELD COUNTY SOCIAL SERVICES HOSTEL, GREENWICH: Teena tells the agents of red lightning yesterday, and of "men from the clouds." The agents learn of an identical murder in Marin County, outside San Francisco: Doug Reardon died of hypovolemia at 2:30 P.M. PST—the same time as Simmons. Daughter Cindy, returning tomorrow from Sacramento with her mother, has also said she remembers nothing.

Later that night Teena is abducted from the hostel. Mulder and Scully still in California, discover eight-year-old Cindy looks exactly like Teena. When the agents show her mom a photo of Teena, mom states Cindy is her only child. She and her husband tried for six years to get pregnant, finally choosing in vitro fertilization at the Luther Stapes Center for Reproductive Medicine in San Francisco.

Because Teena was kidnapped, Mulder and the San Francisco bureau stake out Cindy. Scully meets with a Dr. Katz at the Stapes Center, who says Mrs. Simmons came nine years ago, treated by Dr. Sally Kendrick, a resident who earned a Yale medical degree after completing her doctorate in bio-genetics. But the center believed Kendrick was conducting eugenics experiments, fired her, and asked for a federal investigation—but the Department of Health wouldn't investigate.

At their hotel, Scully gives Mulder the information, but he rushes her out after a phone call of only clicks—a signal to meet Deep Throat. He tells Mulder about the classified "Litchfield" experiments: In the 1950s, the U.S. heard the Russians were using crude eugenics to try to develop a super-soldier. The U.S. followed suit, at a compound in Litchfield, Connecticut. Boys were codenamed Adam, girls Eve. Deep Throat arranges for the agents to see the grown-up Eve 6.

The straitjacketed woman looks exactly like Kendrick. She says the only remaining, suicide-prone Eves are her, Eve 7 (who escaped as a child), and Eve 8 (who escaped ten years later). Each Eve has fifty-six (rather than the normal forty-six) chromosomes, having extra pairs of chromosomes number 4, 5, 12, 16, and 22—which, she says, produced additional genes, heightening strength, intelligence, and psychosis. Mulder believes Kendrick cloned herself to produce Cindy and Teena, and that Kendrick (Eve 7), perhaps with Eve 8, killed the girls' parents in order to raise the girls themselves.

During their stakeout, Scully and Mulder can't prevent Cindy from being kidnapped by a grown-up Eve, who escapes to Point Reyes National Seashore. Identifying herself as Kendrick, she introduces the girls to each other. She'd always kept watch on them, she says, while also searching for the remaining Eve; the girls' recent "activity" forced her hand. She'd hoped to correct the Litchfield flaws, saying the Eves developed homicidal tendencies at age twenty. Yet she herself was raised by a Litchfield genetic engineer in a good environment with medication. Then she begins shaking: The girls had slipped four ounces of home-grown digitalis extract into her soda. Police and FBI burst in, the motel manager having alerted them about a woman fitting Kendrick's description. But Kendrick is dead, and the girls say this lady and another wanted them all to take poison.

Scully and Mulder, driving the girls to social services, pull into a truck-stop diner—where Cindy spikes the agents' diet sodas. But when Mulder returns to the counter to fetch his keys, he notices a green liquid there—poison. He warns Scully, and the girls escape amid the tractor-trailers. When Mulder corners them, their screams bring help from an apparent trucker (who's actually a hunter, per the end-credits). The girls evidently escape in a school bus—but when the agents' car follows it, the girls come out of hiding to be caught by the clever Mulder. The girls, labeled Eves 9 and 10, are eventually sent to Whiting. When Eve 8 visits, dressed as Kendrick, they give each other a chilling look of mutual knowledge.

Jerry Hardin	Deep Throat
Harriet Harris	Dr. Sally Kendrick/Eves 6 and 8
Erika Krievins	Cindy Reardon
Sabrina Krievins	Teena Simmons
George Touliatos	Dr. Katz
Tasha Simms	Ellen Reardon (first name not given in episode)
Janet Hodgkinson	Waitress
David Kirby	Ted Watkins (jogger; unnamed in episode)
Tina Gilbertson	Donna Watkins (jogger; unnamed in episode)
Christine Upright-Letain	Ms. Wells (social worker; unnamed in episode)
Gordon Tipple	Detective
Garry Davey	Hunter
Joe Maffei	1st Guard
Maria Herrera	2nd Guard
Robert Lewis	Officer

73

X-actitude: Teena was born in the San Rafael (CA) General Hospital. Her mother, Claudia, died of ovarian cancer two years ago, leaving no other family.

What Teena watches on TV: both an *Eek the Cat* cartoon, and a news report (President Clinton signing a crime bill)

Eve 6: confined since 1983 at the Whiting Institute for the Criminally Insane, Cell Block 2. Her IQ: 265

Kendrick's room at the Point Reyes motel: no. 2

X-otica: Point Reyes National Seashore is an actual locale, forty miles north of San Francisco.

A theater heavy-weight, Harriet Harris, a.k.a Harriet Sansom Harris, plays the recurring role of Bebe Glaser on *Frasier*.

1.12 "FIRE" December 17, 1993
Writer: Chris Carter
Director: Larry Shaw

X-File case no.: 11214893

BOSHAM, ENGLAND, 70 MILES SOUTHWEST OF LONDON: As he gets into his chauffeured car, a distinguished older man spontaneously combusts in front of his wife and others, as gardener Cecil L'Ively glares evily.

WASHINGTON, D.C.: At the Hoover Building garage, Mulder and Scully find a mysterious audiotape in an FBI car. A female British voice tells them Parliament member Reggie Ellicott was killed six months ago when a similar cassette triggered a car explosion. The agents are apparently sitting on a bomb, but then Mulder's door suddenly opens to reveal beautiful Scotland Yard Inspector Phoebe Green, a practical-joking acquaintance from Mulder's Oxford days. Though having broken his heart more than ten years before, she kisses him heartily now, as Scully looks away.

Phoebe explains someone is burning up Parliament members, then sending love letters to their wives. One MP, Sir Malcolm, had barely escaped a garage fire. Sir Malcolm and family, she says, are now in Cape Cod, Massachusetts, on vacation, and Mulder runs the information by the arson guys as a professional courtesy. An Agent Beatty suggests the cause is rocket fuel, which burns almost completely. Mulder suggests pyrokinesis. At Sir Malcolm's vacation cottage, a caretaker, Bob, is applying argotypoline rocket-propulsion class-3 liquid to a windowpane. And then "Bob"—the gardener from England—makes a cigarette light by itself. Outside, a dog scratches at the makeshift grave of the real caretaker.

In his office, Mulder tells Scully that Phoebe is playing mind-games with him, since she knows he has a phobia about fire. Meantime, at a Boston bar, Bob uses his finger to light a cigarette for a Miss Kotchik. She thinks it's just a charming magic trick—until he sets his arm and the whole bar afire. At Boston Mercy Hospital, Kotchik describes the events to Scully and Mulder (who's pulled a newswire report of this suspicious fire). At Cape Cod, Bob poisons the MP's chauffeur in order to report him ill and to take his place tonight driving the family to a Boston party in Sir Malcolm's honor. He also shows a "magic" fire trick to the MP's children, Michael and Jimmie.

Phoebe agrees with Mulder that the arsonist may be telekinetic; she also mentions with a sly smile she's taken a hotel room in Boston. At 5:15 P.M., Mulder arrives at the Venable Plaza Hotel, suitcase in hand. When Scully calls to say she wants to fly up with some data on a possible suspect, he suggests she not: "I anticipate having my hands full." Phoebe and Mulder work undercover waiting for the arsonist. When the arsonist doesn't show, she invites Mulder to dance. Scully appears, but hangs back—then interrupts them when a monitor shows a fire on the fourteenth floor, where the MP's children are. Mulder races upstairs, but the fire panics him and he has to be rescued by firefighters; Bob himself "saves" the kids.

Scully tells Mulder she ran an Interpol check on the victims' domestic help. The only duplicated name: Cecil L'Ively, a gardener for two of the victims. Searching further, she found him listed as having died in a London tenement fire in 1971—*and* having died with a group of kids in a British Satanic-cult sacrifice in 1963. His name also turned up at a Boston immigration office list of recent visas. Scully gets a fax of the composite sketch of the bar arsonist—whom she recognizes as the "hero," Bob. Mulder races to the Cape Cod house, where he barges in on the married MP nuzzling on the stairs with Phoebe.

When Scully arrives, they find the real driver bound up in the bathroom. Suddenly, the house catches fire. The agents hustle everyone out except the missing children. Mulder hears them screaming behind a door which he (somehow with his elbow) breaks down. Bob sets a hallway on fire, and when Scully tells him to freeze, he dares her to shoot and risk an explosion. But Phoebe splashes him with an accelerant, and he catches on fire himself. Badly wounded, he laughs that he cannot be killed this way.

At Boston Mercy, where Bob/Cecil is in a hyperbaric chamber with "fifth- and sixth-degree burns" [N] and a temperature of 109°F, specialists find phenomenally rapid regeneration of his fundamental, basal cell tissue. He'll recover in as little as a month—at which point he'll be tried for the murder of the caretaker.

75

Amanda Pays	Inspector Phoebe Green
Mark Sheppard	Bob the Caretaker/Cecil L'Ively
Dan Lett	Sir Malcolm Marsden (last name per several print sources; not given in episode)
Laurie Paton	Mrs. Marsden
Duncan Fraser	Beatty
Phil Hayes	Driver no. 1
Keegan Macintosh	Michael
Lynda Boyd	Woman in Bar (Miss Kotchik)
Christopher Gray	Jimmie
Alan Robertson	Grey-Haired man

X-**actitude:**   Kotchik's hospital room: 28E

Site of Phoebe and Mulder's "youthful indiscretion": Sir Arthur Conan Doyle's tombstone

Site of Satanic-cult sacrifice: Tottingham Woods, near Bath, England

X-**otica:**   An earlier draft of the script included Scully's psychological profile of serial arsonists: Though they may be academically retarded, with below-average intelligence, their crimes are often well-planned; in some cases, they refer to their targeted buildings as "the bride" or "the girlfriend" and the setting of the fire, "the wedding." A new voiceover replaced this with Scully suggesting that the bar arsonist is an immigrant, and that she's checking recent immigration data.

According to Carter, Duchovny, in one of the fire scenes, suffered a burn bad enough that "David still has a scar on one of his hands."

Brit beauty Amanda Pays, a former model, became the thinking teen's heartthrob as the lovely and brainy Theora Jones on *Max Headroom* and as Tina McGee on *The Flash*. She married actor Corbin Bernsen, her second husband, in 1988.

In-joke: Minus the "Sir," Malcolm Marsden is the name of *The X-Files*'s hairstylist.

1.13 "BEYOND THE SEA"   January 7, 1994
Writers: Glen Morgan & James Wong
Director: David Nutter

Scully, at home, finishes a Christmastime dinner with her parents, Maggie and William (whose name isn't given in this episode, but in 2.08, "One Breath"). Scully salutes her dad with a heartfelt "Good sailing, Ahab," and he hugs her and replies, "Good night, Starbuck." Later, at 1:47 A.M., Scully's half asleep on her couch and awakens to see her dad across the room. His moving lips make no sound as he eerily mouths the Lord's prayer, and his rigid eyes aren't quite right. Then the phone rings, and dad disappears— while mom, on the phone, sobs that he suffered a coronary an hour ago, and died.

JACKSON UNIVERSITY, RALEIGH, NORTH CAROLINA: Nineteen-year-olds Elizabeth (Liz) Hawley and James (Jim) Summers are necking in a car until a "cop" lures Jim out and hits him.

FBI HEADQUARTERS: Scully returns to work after her father's death, a concerned Mulder asks, "How are you, Dana?" She repeats her name to herself, realizing it's the first time Mulder's used it.

Mulder apprises her of the Jackson U. couple, kidnapped two days ago. A year earlier on that day, two students were kidnapped at Duke University. In North Carolina, serial killer Luther Lee Boggs, scheduled to be executed in a week, will trade information about the kidnapping in exchange for his sentence being commuted to life imprisonment. Boggs also claims to be able to channel spirits and demons. Mulder, whose psychological profile helped to capture Boggs, thinks it's a scam.

Scully attends her father's noon ashes-scattering ceremony, where the song "Beyond the Sea" plays. She tells her mom that as a naval captain,

Dad was entitled to burial at Arlington. Scully, knowing her dad would've preferred she pursue her medical career, wonders if he was proud of her.

CENTRAL PRISON, RALEIGH: As Boggs "channels" a Jack Nicholson–like voice, Mulder hands him a piece of blue cloth from an evidence bag. Boggs, touching it, says Jim is in a condemned-warehouse cellar, tied up in packing twine, being whipped with a wire hanger. He mentions "an angel of stone" and a waterfall without water. Mulder replies he tore the cloth off his New York Knicks T-shirt. Yet as Mulder and Scully leave, Boggs starts singing "Beyond the Sea." When Scully looks back, she sees her father in Boggs's place—a grief-induced hallucination? Then she sees Boggs again, and he calls her "Starbuck."

Shaken, she drives back to her hotel and sees a neon sign for the Hotel Niagara, and across the street is an "angel of stone" statue. Nearby is a condemned warehouse. Deciding to investigate, she finds a lit candle, a wire hanger, and a bracelet Hawley's family identifies as Liz's. Mulder suggests Boggs set it all up, but Scully confesses she believes Boggs can contact the dead, and convinces Mulder that if last year's murders are the model, the kidnapped couple has only three days left.

Boggs, their only lead, apparently channels one of the teens, who describes a small, thin male in his late twenties. He mentions a boathouse close to nearby Lake Jordan, and warns Mulder to avoid "the white cross." At the lake, the agents and police find Liz alive. Mulder approaches a suspicious boat, and is downed by a single gunshot. Scully sees two white dock timbers forming a cross.

Liz ID's a mug shot of Luther Jackson Henry, twenty-eight. Scully discovers that in three days, it's the seventh anniversary of a car accident in which Henry's girlfriend was killed and his mother decapitated. A detective tells her the Durham, North Carolina, police believe Henry was Boggs's partner in Boggs's last five murders.

Scully—in perhaps the most mesmerizing, slow-build dramatic crescendo in the series—warns Boggs that if he and Henry orchestrated all this to kill Mulder, she will personally execute him. Yet Boggs, looking momentarily like Mulder, assures her she believes and then apparently channels *her*, remembering a night at age fourteen when she snuck a cigarette. Boggs then begins apparently channeling her dad, but the Nicholson-like voice interrupts, demanding a deal. The warden refuses.

Mulder, recovering in intensive care, warns Scully that Boggs wants to make her his last victim. Scully lies to Boggs, claiming the warden agreed. Tearfully thanking her, Boggs channels a vision of the abandoned Blue Devil Brewery, near Morrisville, North Carolina. Scully, disappointed, starts to tell Boggs that if he really *were* psychic—and he finishes her thought: "I'd have known you lied. (pause) I know you tried." And he warns her, "Don't follow Henry to the Devil."

77

At the brewery, Henry raises an ax over Jim, as Scully and police burst in. Scully shoots his arm, then as she chases him, Henry falls to his death near the Blue Devil logo. Scully later tells Boggs that if all this *had* been orchestrated, Henry would've avoided the bridge—Boggs saved her and Jim's lives. He says he'll channel her father tonight, at the execution. Yet at midnight, Scully's not there.

She's in Mulder's hospital room, trying to convince him—and herself—of Boggs's fakery. Mulder asks why, after all she's seen, she still doesn't believe. "I'm afraid. I'm afraid to believe." And she's realized what her father would have said. "He was, after all, my father. . . ."

Brad Dourif	Luther Lee Boggs
Don Davis	Captain William Scully
Sheila Larken	Margaret (Maggie) Scully
Lawrence King	Lucas (Jackson) Henry
Fred Henderson	Agent Thomas (unnamed in episode)
Don Mackay	Warden Joseph Cash (unnamed in episode)
Lisa Vultaggio	Liz Hawley
Chad Willett	Jim Summers
Kathrynn Chisholm	Nurse
Randy Lee	Paramedic
Len Rose	ER Doctor

X-actitude: The X-File Scully looks up (unrelated to the Boggs case) is "Visionary Encounters w/The Dead," file X167512; the front cover is stamped with blurry initials, apparently "WC."

Mulder's medical status: Blood pressure 67 on palpitation; he's received two units of O-negative.

Tattoos on Boggs's hands: KISS and KILL

Boggs's murders include: Strangling family members over Thanksgiving dinner

Prop newspaper Mulder uses to trick Boggs: *The Carolinian*

X-otica: The song "Beyond the Sea" sung by Bobby Darin—played at the memorial ceremony and "channeled" by Boggs—spent eleven weeks on the *Billboard* Top 40 in 1960.

The character names "Luther Lee Boggs" and "Lucas Henry" evoke that of the real-life serial killer Henry Lee Lucas. The KISS and KILL tattoos on Boggs's hands likewise evoke the famous LOVE and HATE tattoos on Robert Mitchum's in *Night of the Hunter* (1955), though cowriter Glen Morgan attributed the specific words "kiss" and "kill" to lyrics in a song by the band X.

Huntington, WV, native Brad Dourif received an Oscar nomination and a Golden Globe Award as the doomed Billy Bibbitt in *One Flew Over the Cuckoo's Nest*. Among his many credits, he's the voice of the reincarnated killer Chucky in the *Child's Play* films. Don (a.k.a. Don S.) Davis, is best known as Maj. Briggs on *Twin Peaks*.

Brooklynite Sheila Larken, beginning her recurring role as Scully's mother, is the wife of *X-Files* coexecutive producer R. W. Goodwin. She costarred as attorney Deborah Sullivan in *The Storefront Lawyers/Men at Law*, and was a prolific TV actress before semi-retiring in the 1980s to earn a master's degree in social work.

1.14 "GENDERBENDER"   January 21, 1994
Writers: Larry Barber & Paul Barber
Director: Rob Bowman

GERMANTOWN, MARYLAND: At a dance club, a plain-looking woman lustily whispers in a man's ear. In a motel, they have spectacular sex—after which the man chokes and painfully dies, and the woman morphs into a man. A police detective later tells Scully a security camera showed a man and a woman entered the thirtieth-floor room at 10:13 P.M. But only a man left at midnight—with no trace of the woman.

Mulder informs Scully of five similar deaths, four in the past six weeks: two women, three men, all dead of coronaries, all with 100 times the natural level of pheromones—chemicals secreted by animals as sexual attractants. The first death involved a thirty-two-year-old United Auto Workers organizer in Steveston, Massachusetts, the home of the Kindred, who make pottery using a white clay Mulder found in scratches on the new victim.

STEVESTON, MASSACHUSETTS: Shopkeepers show Scully and Mulder photos of 1930s Kindred. When the agents spot a horse-drawn carriage at a feed store, Mulder goes inside while Scully speaks with Brother Andrew—a plain-looking man whose mesmerizing handshake leaves a Scully a bit breathless.

The agents drive up a rough road toward the Kindred settlement as far as possible. With about a mile left to hike, the two get lost, and a group of Kindred surround them. Brother Oakley and Sister Abby have them hand over their guns. At a communal dinner Mulder and Scully ask the Kindred to try identifying the suspects in the video. Brother Wilton angrily denounces these outsiders. As Abby admonishes Wilton, Brother Aaron begins choking to death. Scully rushes to help, but Abby has the man whisked away. At a dance club, a young man asks a teased-hair blonde to dance. She declines—until he rubs her hand as Andrew did Scully's.

Wilton directs Scully and Mulder to the path to their car. Out of earshot, the agents wonder why they saw no Kindred children—and Mulder swears he saw some of these faces in the 1930s photos. Doubling back, they find the community gathered in a barn, amid a ritual in which the congregants march Aaron into a cellar. Mulder sneaks below himself. Scully is surprised by Andrew, who promises information. In his room, he tells her the killer is his best friend, Brother Martin, who'd found some discarded men's magazines on Route 44. Having gotten a taste of the outside world, he'd left.

79

Mulder sees Aaron's body being slathered with white clay and placed into a cave opening. Wilton and another man talk about Scully being with Andrew, and Mulder being missing. After they go, Mulder sees Aaron's corpse beginning to morph into a female. Andrew tells Scully the Kindred are "different"; he demonstrates his mesmerizing touch, and kisses her to her helpless acquiescence. Mulder (somehow) finds the right room, breaks in, and pulls her away. A Kindred mob waits outside, but lets the agents through—then pours into Andrew's building. Scully, vomiting, doesn't knows what happened.

At a club, the female Marty mesmerizes a man named Michael. Soon they're going at it in a car, until a cop breaks them up. Marty gets out, and when the cop's distracted by Michael's painful groaning, she decks him and morphs into a man as Michael watches in astonishment. Later, in the hospital, he admits to the agents what he saw. Scully theorizes the killer is simply a transvestite.

Another agent informs Mulder and Scully a credit card from the previous victim was used at the Hotel Catherine, eight blocks away. There, Marty is telling someone about the temptations of the flesh. Marty conks Scully, then beats up Mulder and escapes. Scully chases Marty into an alley, where he surrenders, and Kindred suddenly appear. They engulf Marty, and ignore the armed Scully, whom Andrew calmly slugs when Mulder inadvertently distracts her. Then the Kindred disappear.

The agents and two carloads of sheriffs invade the Kindred compound at daybreak, but the group is gone, and the cellar entrance covered in concrete. One officer finds something in a hay field—a crane shot reveals a large, unnaturally round, flattened imprint . . . that which a spaceship might or might not have left.

Brent Hinkley	Brother Andrew
Michele Goodger	Sister Abby
Kate Twa	Female Marty
Peter Stebbings	Male Marty
Nicholas Lea	Michael (note: "Michel" in closed-captioning and some print sources)
Mitchell Kosterman	Detective Horton (last name not given in episode)
Paul Batten	Brother Wilton
Doug Abrahams	2nd (FBI) Agent
Aundrea MacDonald	Pretty Woman
John R. Taylor	Husband (in mom-and-pop store)
Grai Carrington	Tall Man (the Germantown victim)
Tony Morelli	Cop
Lesley Ewen	1st (FBI) Agent
David Thomson	Brother Oakley

X-actitude: Agents' rental-car license plate: 4O2-J7A
One of the horses outside the feed store: Alice

Sites of the previous "genderbender" murders: Steveston and Boston, MA; Hartford, CT; Philadelphia, PA; Washington, D.C.

Hotel Catherine address: 771 Catherine St.

X-otica: The Kindreds' chant, its words unspecified in the script, was written by producer Paul Rabwin.

Germantown is a real-life suburb of Washington, D.C.

The fictional Steveston, MA, was picturesque Steveston Village, in the Vancouver suburb of Richmond. It was used again, to portray fictional Kenwood, TN, in episode 1.18, "Miracle Man."

The Germantown, MD police detective played by Mitchell Kosterman evidently got a job in New York City: Identified as "Horton" in the end-credits (though not episode dialog), he shows up again in 2.04 "Sleepless"—still played by Kosterman, but now as Lt. Horton of the NYPD.

1.15 "LAZARUS"   February 4, 1994
Writers: Alex Gansa & Howard Gordon
Director: David Nutter

MARYLAND MARINE BANK, 5:55 P.M.: Scully and Jack Willis of the Washington bureau's Violent Crimes section investigate a robbery tip. Outside are latter-day Bonnie and Clyde Warren James Dupre and Lula Phillips. Dupre bursts in, unloading a pump-action shotgun at Willis before Scully downs Dupre with three shots. After much defibrillation, Willis survives. Lying unseen, the dead Dupre reacts to the final two jolts.

TWO DAYS LATER, BETHESDA NAVAL HOSPITAL, 12:51 A.M.: Willis leaves—first cutting off three of Dupre's fingers to get at his wedding ring. The next morning Scully tells Mulder that Willis, who's been obsessed with the case for a year, left his prints on a pair of surgical shears; she figures he's suffering post-traumatic stress. Meantime, "Willis" breaks into Dupre's house looking for Lula—and finds Dupre's tattoo appearing on him.

Analysis shows Dupre's mutilator was left-handed. Willis was right-handed, but Dupre himself was a lefty. Mulder finds Willis's EKG readings odd: a long flatline followed by two different heartbeat patterns. Scully attributes it to equipment malfunction or electrical overload, but Mulder believes Dupre returned in Willis's body. At the University of Maryland biology department, a Dr. Varnes tells the agents that in near-death experiences, the tremendous energy-release can cause profound personality changes. Scully knows Willis's personality well—he was one of her Academy instructors, and her boyfriend for almost a year.

DESMOND ARMS RESIDENCE HOTEL: "Willis" rousts Lula's brother Tommy. When the TV news says an anonymous tip brought the FBI to the bank, "Willis" believes Tommy sold them out, and shoots him dead with a .45. Scully and an Agent Bruskin later investigate as a cleaned-up "Willis" arrives, recognizing Scully as the one who shot him. Mulder later notices "Willis" at the FBI firing range working on recertification—shooting left-handed. "Willis" also signs a birthday card for Scully—two months early. Scully still thinks it's stress.

"Willis" takes a hotline call from a reward-minded landlord, Multrevich, in Boyle Heights, who thinks he rented a room to Lula two days ago. As Scully handcuffs Lula, "Willis" makes Scully cuff *herself*. At Lula's home afterward, "Willis" convinces Lula he's Dupre.

MULDER'S APARTMENT: Mulder and fellow agent Bruskin haven't heard from Scully for twelve hours. "Willis" calls Mulder's cel phone and says Scully's with him. Scully tries to convince "Willis"—and herself—that he really *is* a traumatized Willis. And she wonders aloud about the soda he's been drinking because Willis is diabetic.

Mulder tells the agents searching for Scully that the Catonsville, Maryland, police have reported a drugstore broken into for syringes and insulin. Scully wants to administer "Willis"'s insulin—but Lula won't let her. She sneers it was *she* who set up Dupre. She phones the FBI's tactical room, demanding $1 million ransom for Scully, by tomorrow. The FBI trace the call, but find it's Scully's own cel-phone number. A tape of the call reveals the sound of a small plane taking off, which convinces police to canvass the three square miles around Washington County Regional Airport.

At the Dupre house, a canvassing cop, posing as a door-to-door Bible salesperson, identifies the weakening, diabetic "Willis." Lula, thinking Willis/Dupre's dead, contemptuously drops her wedding ring on him. But he's playing possum, and snags her gun. In a line of sight encompassing both Lula and a handcuffed Scully, Willis/Dupre pleads to one or both, "I love you. Don't you know? You're why I came back." Willis/Dupre sees a deathly light and, insisting "There's nothing to be afraid of," shoots Lula. As the feds burst in, Willis/Dupre dies of diabetes complications.

Sometime later, Mulder retrieves Willis's personal effects from the morgue, and gives Scully a watch inscribed "HAPPY 35th Love D"—a gift Scully had given him three years ago. Since Jack was an only child and his parents died while he was in college, she'll give his effects to a boy in Parklawn to whom Jack was a Big Brother. The watch stopped at 6:47—the moment Jack went into cardiac arrest.

Christopher Allport	Agent Jack Willis
Cec Verrell	Lula Phillips
Jackson Davies	Agent Bruskin
Jason Schombing	Warren James Dupre
Callum Keith Rennie	Tommy (Phillips)
Jay Brazeau	Professor Varnes
Lisa Bunting	1st Doctor

82

Peter Kelamis   O'Dell (unidentified in episode; possibly either
       the snide tactical-room agent or the FBI audio
       technician)
Brenda Crichlow   (TV) Reporter
Mark Saunders   2nd Doctor
Alexander Boynton   Clean-Cut Man
Russell Hamilton   Officer Daniels

The official Fox *X-Files* website erroneously lists the character Lula
Phillips as Lula Velasquez—possibly the name in an early script draft.

X-actitude: Willis's and Scully's joint birthday: Feb. 23; Willis born 1957
    Willis's address: 51 Stanhope St.
    Dupre's birthplace: Klamath Falls, OR
    Patient whose clothes are stolen: Mr. Goldbaum, Room 28
    Filter the audio technician uses: "an extra Z14," to isolate sounds above
a half-decibel
    Tommy Phillips's landlord/building manager: Cosmo
    Multrevich apartment: no. 202; Lula's: no. 207
    Catonsville drugstore location: Old Stone Road at Madison
    First three agents to whom Bruskin gives canvass-grid assignments: Steinberg, Calder, Westin

X-otica   Cowriter Howard Gordon has said the original story conception involved Dupre inhabiting Mulder. Fox "balked at the idea of Mulder experiencing directly, first-hand, a supernatural event like that. And I think that was a wise decision, although at the time we were angry and up in arms."

    Mulder for the first time calls Scully by the truncated familiarity, "Scull."

1.16 "YOUNG AT HEART"   February 11, 1994
Writers: Scott Kaufer and Chris Carter
Director: Michael Lange

TASHLOO FEDERAL CORRECTIONAL FACILITY, PENNSYLVANIA, 1989: Wheelchair-bound prisoner Joe Crandall hears screaming from the infirmary. When he asks Dr. Joe Ridley what he's doing to Johnny Barnett on the operating table, Ridley insists Barnett is dead.

WASHINGTON, D.C., PRESENT DAY: At a jewelery-store crime scene, Mulder's old agent-friend, Reggie Purdue shows him a note: "Fox can't guard chicken coop." It's the MO of John Barnett, whom Mulder recalls from his first FBI case. Barnett was involved in multiple bank robberies and seven murders. During Barnett's capture, an agent died, Mulder says remorsefully, "because I screwed up." While Barnett supposedly died in prison four years ago, evidence indicates the note was written by Barnett.

83

A videotape of Barnett's capture shows that Mulder hesitated in firing upon the armed Barnett. That allowed Barnett to kill both his hostage and agent Steve Wallenberg before Mulder shot Barnett. Later, Mulder finds a note on his car—"A hunted Fox eventually dies".

FBI HEADQUARTERS: Purdue tries convincing Mulder the note is not from Barnett. When Purdue reminisces how the FBI had once had big plans for Mulder, Mulder wonders aloud whether the Bureau is playing a mind-game. While a computer technician helps assess what Barnett might look like today, Mulder flashes back to Barnett's trial. Scully arrives, saying that though Barnett's listed cause of death was heart attack, he'd gone to the infirmary with a hand ailment and no mention of coronary problems.

Later at Tashloo, Crandall tells Mulder and Scully about the night he confronted Ridley. Then at FBI headquarters, Mulder gets a taunting call from someone claiming to be Barnett. Mulder later calls Purdue, who as he speaks is strangled to death by someone who leaves a note on the body—"Funeral for Fox's friends—then for Fox".

84

Scully discovers that Ridley's medical license was revoked in 1979 for research malpractice and misuse of a government grant. A scientist at the National Institute of Health in Bethesda, Maryland, recalls that Ridley did secret, unauthorized human experimentation on children suffering from progeria, which causes rapid aging. Mulder suspects Ridley managed to reverse Barnett's aging process. Ridley, later, shows up at Scully's home.

After Mulder arrives, Ridley—who says he's dying—tells them that Barnett is the sole survivor of his research. He'd altered Barnett's treatment to grow him a new hand—albeit a humanoid salamander hand, since Ridley was using reptile regenerative-cell morphegins. Then "certain sponsors" appeared—including the U.S. government.

Later, Deep Throat admits to Mulder the government knew Barnett was alive. Indeed, they're now negotiating to buy the research Barnett stole from Ridley. At 7:20 A.M., Scully hears an intruder retrieving her phone messages; later, the FBI discovers a Barnett fingerprint. Barnett phones Mulder at his office to taunt him about killing his friends; Mulder deduces Barnett will stalk Scully at her friend's cello recital tonight, which he would have learned of through the phone messages.

JANIE TAYLOR MEMORIAL RECITAL HALL, WASHINGTON D.C.: FBI agents convene before the show. Barnett is there incognito as a piano tuner. He shoots Scully in the lobby, then takes Scully's friend hostage announcing the government needs him alive, so he could just shoot the woman if he wanted to. But Mulder kills Barnett with a single shot. Scully luckily wore a bullet-proof vest. At an operating room, three specialists try to save Barnett; the Cigarette-Smoking Man from the first episode, whom Mulder says is "probably CIA," unsuccessfully tries to get Barnett to talk before he dies.

Jerry Hardin	Deep Throat
Dick Anthony Williams	Agent Reggie Purdue
Alan Boyce	Young John Irvin Barnett
Christine Estabrook	Agent Henderson
Graham Jarvis	NIH Doctor
Robin Mossley	Dr. Joe Ridley
Merrilyn Gann	Prosecuting Attorney
Gordon Tipple	Joe Crandall
William B. Davis	CIA Agent
Courtney Arciaga	Young Child (with progeria)
David Petersen	Older (John Irvin) Barnett
Robin Douglas	Computer Tekkie

The official Fox *X-Files* website neglects to list front-credit guest actors Dick Anthony Williams and Christine Estabrook.

Note: The character played by William B. Davis has not been specifically linked with the CIA; this is Mulder's supposition, despite the end-credit listing for "CIA Agent." In subsequent end-credits, the character is identified as "Smoking Man," and is referred to in print and elsewhere as both that and "Cigarette-Smoking Man." In episode 2.08, "One Breath" Mulder (with Skinner repeating it) offhandedly refers to him as "Cancer Man." Incidentally, since he's inaudible from the other side of a plate-glass window here, Smoking Man doesn't yet have his first line of dialogue in the series; that comes in episode 1.21, "Tooms."

85

X-actitude: Barnett death-certificate data: John Irvin Barnett, cardiac arrest, died Sept. 16, 1989

Barnett's will: executed six months after his death; left his possessions to Crandall; specified cremation

Barnett's accent: New Hampshire

Henderson note analysis: fresh ink, indicating written within last forty-eight hours; ballpoint; right-handed writer sitting down

Location where Barnett hid Ridley's aging-reversal research: Locker 935 of some nondescript bus or railroad station, or airport

X-otica: When Scully writes her report at home, she does so by gauzy lamp and candlelight—evidence of a secret romantic?

"Young at Heart" began as freelance script by Carter-acquaintance Scott Kaufer, the former editor of *California* magazine and former head of Warner Bros. comedy development. Carter's rewrite added, among other things, Barnett's regenerative salamander hand.

Inspiration Alert: The notion of using reptilian cells to regrow missing limbs was used in the comic book *The Amazing Spiderman* #6 (1963), as the origin of an amputee scientist who became the two-armed beast, The Lizard.

1.17 "EBE"   February 18, 1994
Writers: Glen Morgan & James Wong
Director: William Graham

THE SKIES OF IRAQ, 37TH PARALLEL, PRESENT DAY: An Iraqi fighter pilot, fearing he's under attack, shoots down a UFO. At a NATO Surveillance Station in Hakkari, Turkey, near the border, two NATO soldiers are jolted by the nearby crash and arrange for retrieval.

ROUTE 100, REAGAN, TENNESSEE, 12:20 A.M. CST: Tractor-trailer driver Ranheim hears three CBers bewilderingly reporting UFOs. Suddenly, the electricity goes out; Ranheim, investigating, sees his cargo doors slam open, seemingly by themselves. He fires his gun at something in the bushes and witnesses an apparent spacecraft overhead.

The next day, Scully attributes the sightings to explanations such as lightning and swamp gas, which doesn't account, Mulder notes, for a radiation level five-times-normal. Ranheim, being held at the Lexington, Tennessee, police station on a weapons-firing charge, keeps changing his story about what he saw. They let Ranheim go but won't let the agents examine the truck. At a car-rental agency, where a woman borrows Scully's pen, Mulder says he suspects it wasn't an alien vessel but a secret military aircraft.

Back in D.C., Mulder takes Scully to the cluttered office of "an extreme government watchdog group." These three conspiracy theorists—Byers, Langly, and Frohike—publish a magazine, *The Lone Gunman* (and, per episode 2.08, "One Breath," refer to themselves as "The Lone Gunmen"). Byers tears a magnetic strip out from inside a twenty-dollar bill of Scully's, saying this is how the covert government-within-the-government tracks money carried through airport metal detectors. Scully responds it's an anticounterfeiting measure. They haven't heard of recent Persian Gulf UFO sightings. Scully later tells Mulder the three are paranoid, but then finds surveillance electronics inside her pen.

At the Jefferson Memorial, Deep Throat hands Mulder a folder marked "Top Secret" containing an intercepted Iraqi transmission which was addressed to the CO of something called the Majestic Project. Scully reports the truck and driver both were bogus: The manifest gave 108 auto-parts cartons totaling 3,100 pounds, but three weigh stations each gave the cargo's weight as 5,100 pounds. And Ranheim—real name Frank Druce—had been in the Persian Gulf War as a Special Operations Black Beret; he was in Mosul, northern Iraq, four days before when the Iraqis shot down a UFO. The U.S. Army recovered wreckage and possibly bodies—now being transported via Druce's unmarked truck, currently headed west toward Colorado.

When Mulder returns home he meets Deep Throat, who hands him a photo he says was taken by an officer at Fort Benning, Georgia, where seventeen

UFOs were spotted in one hour. Mulder theorizes the truck was a decoy, but Scully says the photo is fake, convincing Mulder to have it analyzed. "The truth is out there," she says, "but so are lies." At FBI headquarters, the next day, Mulder's confirmed the photo's fake. [N] At an aquarium, he confronts Deep Throat—who asserts his life's in danger whenever he and Mulder speak, and that there are "truths that people are just not ready to know. . . . The world's reaction to such knowledge would be far too dangerous." But Mulder is unswayed. Later Scully and Mulder are both followed to the airport. They lose their pursuers, and Scully arrives at Dulles Airport and buys round-trip tickets to Chicago. She also uses untraceable cash to buy a ticket to Los Angeles with a stop in Las Vegas. Mulder drives separately to the Baltimore Airport.

LAS VEGAS, MCCARRAN AIRPORT, 11:30 A.M. PST: Scully and Mulder compare notes of weigh-station calls they made on (allegedly) untraceable airplane phones. The truck is headed northwest on I-90, toward Seattle, and they decide to stake out the truck. Hours later, Mulder and Scully encounter a freak storm, and find the truck stalled and the driver gone. Inside they find a hidden room, suggesting that an EBE (Extraterrestrial Biological Entity) was there. Mulder phones the Center for UFO Studies in Chicago, and the UFO groups MUFON and NICAP, who report UFO activity along what Mulder knows to be the truck's route. And last night, there were seven reported sightings in Mattawa, Washington—100 miles away.

87

In Mattawa, the agents find UFO buffs saying spacecraft have been hovering near a power plant—from which Mulder and Scully see Druce exiting. Mulder phones the Lone Gunmen, offering Langly an EBE photo in exchange for computer-hacked IDs. A printer soon chugs out false-name "Level 5" security passes for the "Northwest Facility, Mattawa, WA."

The agents attempt Level 6 access, but a military guard stops them. Mulder bolts down some stairs, chased by rifle-toting soldiers. He finds a lab with an odd, empty chamber, and Deep Throat, who waves away the soldiers and tells Mulder the EBE is dead. He explains that in an "ultrasecret conference" after Roswell, the U.S., the U.S.S.R., the People's Republic of China, the U.K., France, and both East and West Germany agreed to exterminate any EBEs. Deep Throat confesses he's one of three men to have done so: When he was with the CIA in Vietnam, the Marines shot down a UFO over Hanoi. Deep Throat personally shot the creature—and the memory has haunted him since. Deep Throat sets the agents free, asserting that through them, "The truth will be known."

Jerry Hardin	Deep Throat
Allan Lysell	Chief Rivers
Peter LaCroix	Ranheim (a.k.a. Frank Druce; surname spelling per closed captioning)
Bruce Harwood	Byers

Dean Haglund   Langly
Tom Braidwood   Frohike

The fighter pilot, the base radar operator, and the NATO soldier, who all have lines, are uncredited.

***X*-actitude:**   Scully's coffee: Nondairy creamer, no sugar

Title (partially obscured) of the folder Deep Throat hands Mulder: "Response to Request for Information on Contact and Other Related . . ."

Mulder's method of contacting Deep Throat: Shining a blue light out his apartment window, then waiting for his phone to ring and clicks to be heard on the receiver.

Some sights where Mulder has investigated multiple-witness UFO sightings: Chesapeake Bay, Lake Okobogee, Nevada's Area 51 Iraqi pilot designation/position: Patrol no. 6, on bearing 340

NATO surveillance-station designation: Southern Crescent

NATO base designation: Red Crescent

Trucker's radio station: WSM 650, broadcasting music from the Grand Ole Opry; program sponsored by Goody's Headache Powder

CBers UFO sightings: male saw something cigar-shaped with red and green lights; female saw three in Chester County; second male saw six state trooper vehicles chasing strange lights down Route 22.

In-joke: The agents' false IDs: Mulder is Tom Braidwood (PIN 7593) and Scully is Val Stefoff (PIN 5311). Tom Braidwood is the series' first assistant director and an occasional Lone Gunman; Vladimir Stefoff is a frequent second assistant director on the show.

***X*-otica:**   Lexington, TN is a real place through which the north-south Route 22 does pass; there's no Reagan, TN, though. Interstate 90 does run east-west through Washington state, but the only other one it intersects outside Seattle is I-82, about eighty miles away.

Inspiration alert: Mulder's desperate search through his apartment for an electronic bug recalls a similar scene climaxing Francis Ford Coppola's *The Conversation* (1974) starring Gene Hackman as an equally manipulated surveillance expert.

***X*-act Location:**   Subbing for the secret UFO facility was Powertech Labs, Inc., a B.C. Hydro subsidiary, in Surrey, B.C., about 17 miles south of downtown Vancouver.

88

1.18 "MIRACLE MAN"   March 18, 1994
Writers: Howard Gordon & Chris Carter
Director: Michael Lange

At a fire, Rev. Calvin Hartley leads his young adopted son, Samuel, to a body bag, where faith-healing Samuel evidently brings the man inside to life. Years later, Tennessee FBI have sent Mulder a videotape of the Hartleys at a Kenwood, Tennessee, revival meeting. Samuel attempted to heal a woman with a malignant spine tumor, but she died twenty minutes later, not from cancer. Kenwood County Sheriff Maurice Daniels considers the Hartleys's "Miracle Ministry" a hoax, and is enraged over the woman's death.

Mulder and Scully attend a Ministry meeting in Kenwood along with Daniels, whose wife is unwell. Samuel isn't there; Hartley tells the agents he doesn't know where Samuel is, as ominous aide Leonard Vance whisks Hartley off. Daniels, who notes Samuel's been missing since Tuesday (March 1), says the coroner is a Ministry member, so no autopsies were done on anyone who died after Samuel's "healing." Later that night, as the agents and police try to exhume a Carol Wallace, Vance and others stage a threatening vigil.

Daniels finds Samuel at a downtown pool hall and arrests him on suspicion of murder. The teen says God has taken away his powers as penance for his pride. He then stuns Mulder by saying the agent's in pain from a sister who went away when quite young, with strangers and a bright light involved. At a bail hearing, the next day, Samuel wishes to remain jailed. The judge sets $100,000 bail, whereupon the courtroom fills with locust. Scully dismisses it as typical farmland infestation.

89

Scott Bairstow costarred in the unsold
ABC pilot *Country Estates*, written by Howard Gordon
and Alex Gansa, who specifically called him in to play Samuel.

Mulder shows Scully reports from the county hospital showing spontaneous remission from cancer, regenerated nerve growth, etc., and theorizes that if a body is an electromagnetic system, Samuel may be able to manipulate its energy. Vance invites the agents to see Hartley at home, where Hartley says Daniels's bitterness toward him is so intense, that despite Samuel's efficacy, he won't even bring in his severely arthritic wife. Mulder sees a little girl outside the window, reminding him of his abducted sister, Samantha. When he looks for her, she's gone; a guy polishing a car says he saw no one.

At the revival meeting, Vance gives a soft drink in a cup to wheelchair-bound multiple sclerotic Margaret Hohman, and places her in the front row. We learn the disfigured Vance is the fire victim Samuel had allegedly raised from the dead. Mulder thinks he sees the girl again, but loses her in the crowd. When Samuel lays hands on Margaret, she gasps and dies despite the quick-acting Scully's efforts. Scully later tells Margaret's dad this is the third such suspicious death, and despite his trepidation, convinces him to allow an autopsy.

Scully's autopsy report reveals lesions on the lungs and throughout the cardiovascular and pulmonary systems. Scully theorizes cellular hypoxia caused by arsenic or by sodium or potassium cyanide. Mulder, having seen no opportunity for Samuel to have poisoned Margaret, rushes to the jail—ostensibly to reassure Samuel, but also to see what Samuel can tell him about Samantha. Samuel can't or won't say anything, and after Mulder leaves, a deputy brings in two thugs who beat Samuel to death.

The next morning, Deputy Dennis Tyson gives Daniels the awful news. At the jail, Daniels tells an infuriated Mulder that Samuel had picked a fight with two rowdies booked on DUI. Hartley arrives accusing Daniels of a fatal vendetta; Mulder and Scully check the courthouse for clues. They find locust and a trail of food from the roof into the ventilation system. Since biological supply houses sell locust to farms and universities, the agents believe the "plague" was deliberate.

That night, a ghostly Samuel asks why Vance betrayed him after he'd saved his life. The anguished, disfigured Vance declares he hates Samuel for this mockery of living. Downstairs, Daniels and the agents arrive to arrest Vance, having linked him to a Knoxville, Tennessee, pesticide-company order for cyanogen bromide, a cyanide derivative; he'd evidently poisoned some of the soft drinks at the meetings. They find Vance dying of cyanide poisoning, deliriously saying Samuel was here and forgave him.

In the light of day, Scully's report says Vance tried to destroy faith in the Ministry, and his conscience led to his suicide. But Samuel's body turns up missing; no-nonsense nurse Beatrice Salinger says she and others saw Samuel walk out by himself. As the agents leave town, Scully hopes Hartley didn't arrange a body-snatching—while Deputy Tyson brings Daniels in for questioning about Samuel's death.

R. D. Call	Sheriff Maurice Daniels
Scott Bairstow	Samuel Hartley
George Gerdes	Reverend Calvin Hartley
Dennis Lipscomb	Leonard Vance
Walter Marsh	Judge
Campbell Lane	Hohman's Father
Chilton Crane	Margaret Hohman
Howard Storey	Fire Chief
Iris Quinn Bernard	Lillian Daniels (first name not given in episode)
Lisa Ann Beley	Beatrice Salinger
Alex Doduk	Young Samuel
Roger Haskett	Deputy Tyson

Samuel's female defense attorney, the prosecuting attorney, the man polishing the car and the little girl are all uncredited.

The official Fox *X-Files* website neglects to list front-credit actor R. D. Call.

91

X-actitude: Woman victim on Tennessee FBI videotape: Lucy Jelly
   Miracle Ministry marquee slogan: "Come as you are. . . . Leave as you always wanted to be."
   Rev. Hartley's license plate: B HEALD
   Margaret Hohman: Female Caucasian, 107 pounds
   Cellular hypoxia: a lack of oxygen to the cells

1.19 "SHAPES"   April 1, 1994
Writer: Marilyn Osborn
Director: David Nutter

TWO MEDICINE RANCH, BROWNING, MONTANA: Jim Parker and his grown son Lyle find a slaughtered steer in their corral—the fourth this month. Lyle is suddenly savaged by some creature, yet after Jim shoots the beast dead, all they find is a young Native American, Joe Goodensnake, of the Trego tribe. Parker had sued the tribe over grazing rights and a border dispute. The next day, Scully and Mulder meet with the free-on-bail Parker and his attorney. Outside, Mulder finds what looks like a recently shed snakeskin—in the shape of a human wrist and hand.

While looking for Sheriff Charlie Tskany at the reservation, the agents find Goodensnake's sister, Gwen, who accuses her tribesmen of being scared of a "stupid Indian legend." The bitter Tskany arrives to escort the agents to his office, where Joe's body is laid. Mulder notices Joe has fangs not seen

Werewolf? There wolf: Ty Miller as the lycanthropic Lyle.

on his dental records; Scully attributes them to calcium phosphate salts that can gather with age. But Mulder also notes Lyle's chest had animal scars similar to those on Joe. He wants an autopsy, but Tskany says desecration of the body angers the Spirit, and the body will be cremated tonight on a pyre. Scully says Tskany can't destroy evidence, but the sheriff has to live and work here, and won't buck his neighbors' beliefs.

Later, watching as the pyre is prepared, Mulder tells Scully about the first X-File, which involved similar lycanthropic deaths near here. Scully retorts that in the rare insanity called lyncanthropy, a person merely *believes* he or she can turn into a wolf. Lyle comes to give his respects at the pyre, but Gwen demands he leave. Shortly afterward, at the ranch, Jim is slashed to death by some lupine yet humanoid creature.

The next morning, Scully suggests it might be retaliation. Tskany's already put an APB out on the missing Gwen. Lyle also can't be found. The agents find a tuft of fur near another piece of shed skin, as well as a caged cougar and Lyle—naked and unconscious. Scully takes him to the Crowe Medical Clinic, where Lyle says he'd gotten drunk on bourbon and passed out. Scully tells him his father's dead and confesses she'd lost her father recently, too.

Tskany takes Mulder to the home of old man Ish, who recounts the 1946 deaths. The Tregoes, he says, realized a man named Richard Watkins had been attacked by what the Algonquian Indians called the Manitou, an evil spirit that can turn men into beasts. When Ish was sixteen, returning from fishing in the Cut Bank Creek, he walked by Watkins's house and saw the man turn beastlike. Watkins was killed soon afterward, but the curse passed through bloodlines to his son and, eventually, to Joe Goodensnake. If that's the case, Gwen might also bear the curse. She happens to be just outside, trying to steal Ish's pickup. When Tskany arrests her, the terrified woman says she'd gone to the Parker ranch "to mess up the kid" and saw "it" kill Jim Parker.

Mulder calls the clinic, but a Dr. Josephs there has already released Lyle to Scully's care. The doctor volunteers that Lyle's blood showed traces of Jim's blood type, which could only have gotten there through ingestion. As evening falls, Scully drives Lyle back to the ranch. There the power is off, and a woozy Lyle excuses himself for the bathroom.

Seven miles away, Tskany and Mulder race with police lights flashing, unable to reach Scully by cel phone because of the mountains. Scully, fearing Lyle is growing sicker, starts picking the bathroom lock, seemingly oblivious to the growling inside. A furry arm smashes through the door. Mulder arrives to find claw marks across a wall, and fires his gun at two shadowy figures. Scully is upstairs and okay. Venturing with flashlights through the dark, they're attacked by a growling something; before Mulder can fire again, Tskany blasts it with a pump-action shotgun. It's Lyle, dead. Scully believes it was the mountain lion that had attacked her, but Tskany points out it's still in its cage. The next day as the agents leave, Ish predicts he'll see Mulder again, in about eight years.

93

Ty Miller	Lyle Parker
Michael Horse	Sheriff Tskany
Donnelly Rhodes	Jim Parker
Jimmy Herman	Ish
Renae Morriseau	Gwen Goodensnake
Dwight McFee	(lawyer) David Gates
Paul McLean	Dr. Josephs

X-actitude: Native Americans guarding Joe's body at Tskany's office: Bill and Tom

The file on the first X-File: personally initiated by J. Edgar Hoover, 1946.

There had been murders in and around the northwest—seven of them here in Browning—in which victims were shredded and eaten. Police that year cornered and shot an animal in a cabin in Glacier National Park—but the "animal" proved to be a man named Richard Watkins. Coincidentally, perhaps, the murders stopped, and Hoover locked away the files for this inexplicable case. However, they were updated when similar murders occurred in 1954, '59, '64, '78, and now.

***X*-otica:** Ty Miller costarred on *The Young Riders*. Michael Horse was a regular on *Twin Peaks*. Winnipeg-born Donnelly Rhodes had a prominent stint on *Soap* before starring in the Canadian hit series *Danger Bay*; among his countless other TV roles was the recurring part of Tony Danza's dad on *Taxi*.

1.20 "DARKNESS FALLS"   April 15, 1994
Writer: Chris Carter
Director: Joe Napolitano

OLYMPIC NATIONAL FOREST, NORTHWEST WASHINGTON: A group of terrified loggers, led by one Bob Perkins, are being killed by something mysterious. One logger, Dyer, says they should split up and run; Perkins ultimately goes along. In running, Dyer breaks his ankle and Perkins carries him until a swarm of green iridescent "fireflies" engulfs them.

FBI HEADQUARTERS: Mulder shows Scully a slide of the thirty missing loggers, and says radical eco-activists Doug Spinney and Steven Teague were in the area a week before. Two Federal Forest Service officials investigated, but never returned. In 1934, a Works Project Administration (WPA) crew in the same area also vanished. At Olympic, Mulder and Scully meet up with Forest Service ranger Larry Moore, and Schiff-Immergut Lumber security chief Steve Humphreys. During the four-hour drive to the logging camp, their truck gets two flat tires from eco-saboteur spikes in the road, so they start hiking.

The cabin's been abruptly abandoned, with the radio destroyed and vehicles sabotaged; they're stranded and incommunicado. Exploring, they find an odd-looking cocoon and inside, a mummified man. Humphreys, working to fix a small power generator, surprises eco-saboteur Spinney inside the cabin. Spinney warns they all have to leave before darkness falls, and tells of a swarm that devoured his colleague, Teague. He also tells the agents the loggers were illegally cutting marked, protected, old-growth trees; Humphreys denies knowledge of this, and accuses Spinney of manufacturing both the cocoon and the swarm story.

The next morning, they examine a fallen marked tree at least 500 to 600 years old, with a highly unusual growth ring. Moore analyzes a core sample containing microscopic parasites which shouldn't be there—this is dead wood, and the sample came from too deep for wood borers. Moore suggests they're wood mites; Spinney suggests they were dormant for hundreds of years and woke up hungry. Humphrey, meantime, has hiked to the truck to radio for help, but found the radio dead. That night, while trying to get it running, he's attacked and killed by the swarm, coming through the air vents.

At the cabin, Spinney deduces that light keeps the swarm away. Mulder theorizes that the old tree's odd rings resulted from a season of unusual

94

natural activity, like volcanic eruption. He notes Mount St. Helens released radiation that produced amoeba mutations at nearby Spirit Lake. Scully rejoins that unlike insects, amoeba are single-celled and easily mutated. Mulder then suggests the swarm may come from an "extinct" larvae. Maybe millions-of-years-old insect eggs were deposited by volcano into the ground, and came up through the roots to lay dormant.

The next morning, Mulder finds Spinney preparing to leave with precious gasoline and a battery. Spinney says he is going to hike to his colleagues and their jeep, two valleys over, then come rescue them tomorrow. Mulder lets him go [N], and then, having partly fixed the cabin's radio, sends one-way distress calls. Scully loses her temper at Mulder's not consulting them. Now, with no way to hike through the woods before dark, she's convinced they'll die once the generator runs out.

That night, with only one lightbulb working, the agents and Moore stay awake. Some of the iridescent insects seep in under the walls and cover the three, but the light keeps them from swarming. The generator sputters and runs out of gas, just as the sun rises. Now, desperate, they take a tire from one of the sabotaged trucks with the idea of at least replacing one of the two flat tires on the Forest Service truck. But then Spinney, keeping his word, arrives in a covered Jeep; his friends hadn't made it, he says. Taking the agents and Moore down the mountain, in sudden, stormy darkness, Spinney's jeep ironically gets a spike-punctured tire itself. And Spinney, caught outside in the glare of the headlight, is engulfed and killed by the swarm [N], which then enters the Jeep through the air vents.

95

A helicopter and three white vans arrive during full daylight, and men in protective gear find a cocoon-filled Jeep. The agents and Moore are rushed to the High Containment Facility in Winthrop, Washington, where scientists find large concentrations of luciferine, an enzyme found in fireflies and other bioluminescent insects. One scientist, wearing an anticontamination clean suit, tells Mulder the government will use pesticides and controlled burning to end the swarm, which, he assures the skeptical Mulder, will keep it from migrating.

Jason Beghe	Larry Moore
Tom O'Rourke	Steve Humphreys
Titus Welliver	Doug Spinney
Ken Tremblett	Dyer
Barry Greene	(Bob) Perkins
David Hay	Clean Suited Man

X-actitude: The eco-radicals' nickname for Federal Forest Service officers: Freddies

X-otica: The old-growth forest is in reality West Vancouver's Lighthouse Park. There is no Winthrop, WA.

1.21 "TOOMS"   April 22, 1994

Writers: Glen Morgan & James Wong

Director: David Nutter

DRUID HILL SANITARIUM, BALTIMORE, MARYLAND: Dr. Aaron Monte checks in on his patient, Eugene Victor Tooms, on the eve of his commitment review. (See Episode 1.03, "Squeeze.")

FBI HEADQUARTERS: Scully meets her newly seen superior, Assistant Director Walter S. Skinner. As the Cigarette-Smoking Man watches, Skinner demands more conclusive reports and orthodox procedures; their high conviction/case-solution rate of 75 percent doesn't impress him.

Back at the hearing, Dr. Pamela Karetzsky testifies Tooms has no physiological dysfunction. A psychology expert says Tooms's attack on Scully was simply wrongful frustration due to losing his job and being falsely arrested by the FBI. Mulder grows agitated as Judge Kann dismisses his mutation theory, despite his showing that Tooms's fingerprints were at seven of nineteen crime scenes since 1903. She says Tooms doesn't look 100 years old. Tooms is released providing he remain under Monte's care, regain his job, and reside at a halfway house with Susan and Arlan Green.

LYNNE ACRES RETIREMENT HOME: Scully meets with former investigating detective Frank Briggs. He recalls a jar of evidence he'd found at Powhattan Mill's Ruxton Chemical Plant when it was under construction in 1963; perhaps something else at the site could implicate Tooms. Having no luck with ground-penetrating radar, he follows a hunch and finds skeletal remains.

Tooms, back on the job in his Baltimore animal regulation van, stalks a businessman. When Mulder searches the van, Tooms is already gone, having slipped down a maintenance hole in the street. Tooms squeezes through a barred window of a house. Mulder notices blood on a windowsill and tells the owner he suspects an intruder inside. But Tooms has retreated.

At the Smithsonian Institute's Forensic Anthropology Lab, a professor, examining the bones Briggs and Scully found, discovers that the skull matches the photo of a missing person suspected of being a 1933 victim. But it's not enough to convict Tooms. Scully worries about Mulder, on stakeout alone for three days, since he can't request help without alerting higher-ups who want to quash the X-Files. She volunteers to take over surveillance in her own car. Mulder drives off—with Tooms in his trunk.

On his couch, Mulder is asleep as Tooms enters through a vent, but rather than kill Mulder, simply scratches his own face until he bleeds. [N] At a hospital the next day, a detective tells a doctor that police found Tooms unconscious in the street, beaten and kicked in the jaw. Tooms says Mulder did it. While police speak to Mulder at his apartment, they find an athletic shoe matching the jaw print. As they haul Mulder in for questioning, Mulder notices a screw from the vent underfoot.

At Skinner's office, as Smoking Man watches, Mulder notes forensic evidence showed the shoe wasn't worn. Tooms had tried to frame him. Scully lies that Mulder was with her on surveillance when Tooms was admitted to the hospital. Skinner, expresses admiration for Mulder's talents, and tells him if stress is making him or *other* agents behave inappropriately, to take a vacation. And with a glance toward Smoking Man, Skinner orders Mulder to stay away from Tooms, or *all* of his Congressional contacts together won't be enough to save his job.

With Tooms's dental records, Scully and the Smithsonian ID the gnaw marks as Tooms's. At Tooms's halfway house, Arlan is just leaving when Monte arrives. Mulder and Scully arrive shortly afterward to find the doctor's corpse. The agents go to 66 Exeter Street, where they'd last found Tooms, but the building's been torn down; a shopping mall now occupies the site. In the closed, darkened department store, Mulder crawls through a narrow utility passageway beneath the floor, its entrance at the foot of an escalator. He pushes through a vent into a cavelike area, where the animalistic Tooms attacks. Mulder escapes and activates the escalator, killing Tooms in the mechanism.

97

Skinner, later, reading Scully's unorthodox report, asks if Smoking Man believes it. He knowingly replies, "Of course I do."

Doug Hutchison	Eugene Victor Tooms
Paul Ben Victor	Dr. Aaron Monte
Mitch Pileggi	Assistant Director Walter S. Skinner
Henry Beckman	Detective Frank Briggs
Tim Webber	Detective Talbot (evidently the radar operator; unnamed in episode)
Jan D'Arcy	Judge Kann
Jerry Wasserman	Doctor Plith (unnamed in episode)
Frank C. Turner	Doctor Collins (unnamed in episode)
Gillian Carfra	Christine Ranford (bald man's wife; unnamed in episode)
Pat Bermel	Frank Ranford (bald man; unnamed in episode)
Mikal Dughi	Dr. (Pamela) Karetzky
Glynis Davies	Nelson (Tooms's attorney; unnamed in episode)
Steve Adams	Myers (State's Attorney; unnamed in episode)
Catherine Lough	Dr. Richmond (Tooms's medical doctor; unnamed in episode)
William B. Davis	Smoking Man
Andre Daniels	Arlan Green

The official Fox *X-files* website misspells lead guest-star Doug Hutchison's name as "Hutchinson."

X-actitude: License plate on Mulder's car: Maryland KMH 2N5. Since the FBI's cars would presumably have Washington, D.C., plates, and since Mulder probably wouldn't have requisitioned one and risked alerting the higher-ups about his stakeout, this is very likely Mulder's own car, indicating he lives in Maryland. Or perhaps he borrowed this car to help lessen the chance of his being recognized, or rented one in Maryland for the same reason.

The two cells adjoining Tooms's are those of: L. Robbie Maier and Scott Schalin.

In-joke: Rob Maier is *The X-Files*'s construction coordinator.

Judges flanking Judge Kann: Hirsch and Sullivan

License on Tooms's Baltimore animal regulation van: NUB 9P3

Bald businessman's sweatshort logo: University of Maryland

Mulder's expert-witness credentials: three years with the FBI's Behavioral Science Unit, profiling serial killers.

X-File case no. X129202 includes a file titled "Field Office Criminal Investigative and Administrative File"; inside is a Metropolitan Police Department arrest report with Tooms's mug shot (3985-60) and fingerprints. Date and time of arrest: July 23, 1993. Place: 107 E. Cordova. Division reporting: Homicide. Age: 30.

X-otica: *Inspiration Alert:* Tooms's framing of Mulder for assault was a plot device used by killer Scorpio against *Dirty Harry* in that 1971 film.

1.22 "BORN AGAIN"   April 29, 1994
Writers: Howard Gordon & Alex Gansa
Director: Jerrold Freedman

X-File case no.: X40271

BUFFALO, NEW YORK, 14TH PRECINCT HOUSE: Detective Lazard finds eight-year-old Michelle Bishop outside, and asks Detective Rudy Barbala to question her. When Lazard leaves, Barbala mysteriously crashes backward through a window to his death. Later that day, Lazard asks Mulder and Scully onto the case since her brother, a Baltimore cop, had told her about their expertise with the unusual.

At the Bishops' Orchard Park home, the agents and computer sketch artist Harry try to get a description of a second man Michelle claims was in the room. When the monitor flashes and the moustache Harry's drawn is suddenly smaller, they attribute it to a software glitch. Mrs. Bishop says she'd arrived home to find sitter Mrs. Dougherty locked in the basement, and called the police. She adds Michelle never smiles; she sees and hears invisible things; would scream when Mrs. Bishop's ex-husband Jim tried teaching her to swim; and is oddly adept at origami. BRYLIN PSYCHIATRIC HOSPITAL, BUFFALO: Dr. Sheila Braun, whom Michelle sees twice a week, suspects Michelle fabricated the man in the sketch, and notes Michelle dismembers and disfigures baby dolls. Braun throws Mulder out when he asks about psychic abilities.

Lazard matches Michelle's sketch with Officer Charlie Morris, who'd worked Narcotics out of the 27th until his line-of-duty death nine years ago. Morris died in a reputed Chinatown gangland hit, with his right eye gouged and his left arm severed by chainsaw—the same disfigurements as Michelle's dolls.

The next day Detective Tony Fiore won't talk about his former partner's death, but Fiore suspects the heroin-peddling Triad gang Woo Shing Wu. At Buffalo Mutual Life later, Fiore meets with a Leon Felder, insisting they go to their safe-deposit box and get their $2 million-plus. But Felder says they'd promised to wait ten years—even if they're the last two left. That night, Felder steps off a city bus, and his scarf lifts and entangles itself in the bus's rear doors. The bus driver tries to stop, but the accelerator depresses without his help. Felder dies, as Michelle looks on from inside the bus.

Michelle and mom are taken to the safe house the police keep reserved at the Sheraton hotel. Mulder learns Felder was Barbala's old partner. Scully and Mulder examine files on them, and discover Fiore lied when he denied knowing Barbala. A page is missing from Morris's homicide file; the log sheet says Fiore had checked it out that afternoon. At the Fiore home, early next morning, Anita, Fiore's wife, says Fiore never came home last night. Mulder notices origami animals, which Anita says was the work of her first husband—Charlie Morris. Outside, Mulder tells Scully Michelle was conceived around the time Morris died.

As Michelle undergoes regression-hypnotherapy, she tells a Dr. Spitz she's twenty-four years old, then starts screaming, "They're killing me!" Scully concedes there's some extremely coincidental connection to Morris, but where does that leave them? Harry tries to clean up the image-noise from the regression videotape. Lazard's tracked down Morris's pathologist, Dr. Yamaguchi, now retired in Palm Beach. He's faxed the missing autopsy page, which reveals there was fluid in Morris's respiratory tract—he'd drowned before being mutilated. With no evidence of flesh submersion except for his head, he was likely drowned in a bathtub or toilet. Scully notices a marked bradycardia, indicating raised plasma sodium level: He was killed in sea-water?

Fiore arrives home, telling Anita to pack. They don't notice Michelle peeking in. At the FBI office, Harry has isolated the anomalous video signals leaving the blurry image of a squat, hunched man. Mulder recognizes it as the plastic deep-sea diver in the Fiore's fish tank, the last image Morris must have seen before he died. Scully and Mulder race to the Fiores's, where Michelle sends a flying poker toward Fiore. Scully frees Anita from the bedroom and brings her downstairs, where Fiore confesses he knew what they did to Charlie. Anita begs Charlie/Michelle to stop. Then the fish tank explodes, the lights come up, and it's over.

99

The field report (dated April 19, 1994) says Fiore pleaded guilty yesterday in Federal Court to first-degree murder after the fact, grand larceny, and obstructing justice. Barbala's and Felder's deaths have been ruled accidental. No charges were brought against Michelle.

Brian Markinson	Tony Fiore
Mimi Lieber	Anita Fiore
Maggie Wheeler	Detective Sharon Lazard (first name not given in episode)
Dey Young	Judy Bishop (first name not given in episode)
Andrea Libman	Michelle Bishop
P. Lynn Johnson	Dr. Sheila Braun
Leslie Carlson	Dr. Spitz
Richard Sali	Felder
Dwight Koss	Detective (Rudy) Barbala
Peter Lapres	Harry Linhart (last name not given in episode)

X-actitude: Case number assigned to Barbala's death: 51412-38

Fiore's badge number: 247

Felder's bus route and bus number: 245 Downtown; bus 4437

Drug that Dr. Braun has Michelle on: thorazine

Felder and Fiore's safe-deposit bank: Citibank

14th Precinct Captain: Gershom

Scully's autopsy on Barbala: Began 11 hours, 45 minutes postmortem; she found a raised lesion seven centimeters below the sternum, and deep necrosis inconsistent with the cause of death as pronounced by a Dr. Gilder. There's evidence of localized electrocution.

Time and date Fiore checked out Morris homicide file: 3/29/94, 2:00–2:15 P.M.

Where Charlie Morris learned origami: In Japan, where he was born to a military father stationed there.

How Harry isolated the video signals: Mapped the frequency of the interference, placed the coefficient for sine on one monitor, for cosine on another, then, using an algorithm program, removed those frequencies from the main monitor. Oh.

X-otica: Duchovny said he "detested" this episode. While it's indeed more of a straightforward police procedural than most, it has an intensely eerie buildup, highlighted by the too-wise deadpan of Michelle and the sudden, chilling realization of what that hunched computer-image is.

Maggie Wheeler (formerly billed as Maggie Jakobson) costarred in *These Friends of Mine*, the first version of the Ellen DeGeneres' sitcom *Ellen*; she plays the recurring role of Chandler's sometime-girlfriend on *Friends*. Her film credits include a lead role in *New Year's Day* opposite then-boyfriend David Duchovny.

1.23 "ROLAND"

May 6, 1994

Writer: Chris Ruppenthal
Director: David Nutter

Mahan Propulsion Laboratory of the Washington Institute of Technology, Colson, Washington: An abrasive Dr. Keats helps a retarded janitor, Roland fuller, get through a locked electronic door. Inside, Keats and the business-suited Dr. Frank Nollette argue with the Scottish-accented Dr. Ron Surnow over some experimental jet engine loudly revving toward their goal of breaking Mach 15. Surnow, arguing the engine is about blow up and ruin four years of work, shuts it down. The other two angrily leave. When Surnow enters the wind tunnel to check something, Roland closes the tunnel door, and—before going on to do complex mathematical equations on a chalkboard—turns on the engine, sucking Surnow to a grisly death.

The next day Scully and Mulder discuss this top-secret Icarus Project, the next generation of jet engines. Surnow is the second on the team to die within six months. The agents speak with Keats, who discovered what was left of Surnow, and Nollette, who confirms that team-member Dr. Arthur Grable had died in a car accident in November.

Heritage Halfway House Director Mrs. Stodie brings Mulder and Scully to Roland as he does some recreational project with retarded housemate Tracy, whom he likes romantically. Roland's an idiot savant, yet when they ask about his fondness for numbers, he gets agitated and has what we later learn is a premonition. Mulder takes a paper Roland's been writing on. A graphologist says that while a fourth person wrote on the chalkboard, it wasn't Roland.

At Mahan that night, Keats is working late. Roland dunks Keats's head in liquid nitrogen and then shatters it. The next day at an almost comically gruesome crime scene, where the chalk-figure outline includes dozens of little *x*'s, Mulder sees Keats closed his computer file at 12:31 A.M., on April 25, 1994, after which someone else logged on to Arthur Grable's file. Mulder uses 15626 (from Roland's paper) as the computer password. The agents learn Grable got Roland the janitor job, and that the two were both born in Seattle on July 15, 1952—Grable of rich parents, Roland of parents whose identities have been sealed by the court. Roland has been at Heritage since age three.

Roland has a premonition—or an order?—about killing Tracy after she asks him who this "Arthur" is that he sometimes mentions. But Roland barricades himself, not wanting to hurt her. Nollette, in his office, tells the agents he and Grable attended the medical school Harvey Mudd. He reveals that Grable has had his head preserved at the university's Avalon Foundation cryogenics facility. There, Dr. Larry Barrington shows the agents around.

Grable's medical records list Roland as a possible organ-tissue donor. Scully and Mulder, now thinking them twins, have a computer technician manipulate Arthur's picture to lose the glasses, beard, and some weight, and they see a face matching Roland's. When they go to speak with Roland, however, he gets upset and runs away.

Mulder believes Grable isn't dead, but in a rarefied state of consciousness; he further believes psychic abilities can exist between family members, particularly twins. Nollette, having eavesdropped on the agents by security camera, sneaks into the cryogenics lab and surreptitiously raises Grable's temperature. Scully finds the birth certificate listing Arthur and Roland Grable, born at Puget Presbyterian to Mr. and Mrs. Lewis Grable; Arthur is the older by four minutes. Dr. Barrington calls, saying Grable's capsule has been tampered with; Mulder suspects Nollette.

At the computer, Roland/Arthur finally accomplishes the project's goal: The engine revs to Mach 15.13. Nollette arrives and addresses Arthur, who in turn exclaims, "You took my work!" Nollette responds that Arthur died before he could publish it, so it wouldn't have done him any good anyway. Nollette pulls a gun, but Roland/Arthur knocks him out and places him in the wind tunnel. Scully and Mulder arrive, and at Scully's desperate urging, Roland (so it seems) stops the machine before Nollette's killed. Roland will be held for psychiatric evaluation, and may or may not be charged with a crime—while at Grable's capsule, the temperature reading hits 150°F, followed by a long, ominous beep.

Zeljko Ivanek	Roland Fuller
Micole Mercurio	Mrs. Stodie
Kerry Sandomirsky	Tracy
James Sloyan	Dr. Frank Nollette
Garry Davey	Dr. Keats
Matthew Walker	(Dr. Ron) Surnow
Dave Hurtubise	(Dr. Larry) Barrington
Sue Mathew	(Agent) Lisa Dole (graphologist; unnamed in episode)

The female video-technician agent and a male police detective at the Keats murder scene are both uncredited.

X-actitude: Roland's IQ: "barely 70," according to Scully
   Roland's electronic-door code number: 315
   Number of stars Roland says is on Scully's blouse: 147
   Mahan Propulsion Laboratory building number: 214
   Office number of wind-tunnel lab: MP-7001
   Heritage Halfway House address: 591 Broadway, Colson, WA
   Grable's cryogenic capsule: no. 18
   Journal in which Nollette mentions he was published: *Nature*

Earliest file in directory: NODERUN.EXE, last used 03-01-93, 05:00

X-otica: Zeljko Ivanek, born in the town of Lujubljana of the former Yugoslavia, was educated at Yale and the London Academy of Music and Dramatic Art. His films include *The Sender*, *Mass Appeal,* and *School Ties*, though not, as the Lowry book asserts, *Agnes of God.*

1.24 "THE ERLENMEYER FLASK"   May 13, 1994
Writer: Chris Carter
Director: R. W. Goodwin

The opening credo this episode: "Trust No One." This is the first episode with a different credo than "The Truth Is Out There."

ARDIS, MARYLAND: A police cruiser chases a car westbound to the waterfront. The fugitive runs from the car, and after two cops beat him with nightsticks and another fires a taser, he leaps into the harbor, leaving a trail of green blood.

EARLY MORNING, MAY 8: Mulder is awakened by a call from Deep Throat, telling him to watch Channel 8. On a newscast, Ardis Police Capt. Roy Lacerio talks about the manhunt. Mulder videotapes it, and later prints out a frame-grab, while he and Scully try to guess what Deep Throat wants.

THE HARBOR, NEARLY EIGHTEEN HOURS LATER: The body still hasn't been recovered. At the impound, the agents learn the car was rented at Gaithersburg, Maryland, yet from the TV-news frame, Mulder sees the impounded car is not the one on TV, which had a caduceus medical symbol. After checking plates, concentrating on doctors, Mulder visits Dr. Terrence Allen Berube at the Emgen Corporation in Gaithersburg. He claims he didn't realize his car was stolen since his housekeeper uses it.

That night, Deep Throat approaches Mulder and reassures him, "Trust me. You've never been closer." At Berube's lab, a man with crew cut demands to know if the fugitive, Dr. William Secare, has contacted him; then he kills Berube. At the harbor, Secare rises from the water to escape.

Mulder doubts the official ruling that Berube committed suicide. At Emgen, he finds a liquid-filled flask labeled Purity Control; Scully takes it to the Georgetown University Microbiology Department for analysis. By 6:30 P.M., Georgetown scientist Dr. Carpenter tells Scully she thinks the liquid is a bacteria specimen, though bacteria unlike any she's ever seen. Mulder breaks into Berube's house looking for clues and finds a phone number, traced to Zeus Storage. While Mulder waits for a call back from Danny at the FBI, Secare phones, and, assuming it's Berube, asks for help but collapses before he can give an address. Outside Berube's, Crew-Cut Man in a surveillance van monitors the call.

At the public phone where Secare collapsed, EMS workers try to save him. But when they attempt to do a thoractomy, Secare's body releases a gas that disables the medics. He again escapes. Scully calls Mulder's car phone to report that the lab found bacteria that contained chloroplasts: plant cells, [N] which Scully believes is for gene therapy. Mulder enters Berube's storage warehouse, Zeus, to find five people each suspended in a watery tank. Carpenter shows Scully a sequence of genes from the bacteria sample: DNA has only four nucleotides, yet these show a fifth and a sixth. What the flask contains "exists nowhere in nature," says Carpenter. Outside Zeus, Mulder is chased by three men, but he escapes.

Mulder brings Scully to Zeus—but everything's gone. Mulder deduces Berube was conducting human experiments with extraterrestrial viruses. Deep Throat says that has been going on for years. They've had the tissue, if not the technology, since 1947, Deep Throat claims, adding, "Roswell was a smokescreen. We've had half a dozen better salvage ops." This was the site of the first human-alien hybrids, using six terminally ill volunteers— including Berube's friend Secare. All six began recovering, and Secare gained superhuman strength and the ability to breathe underwater. Yet the government only wanted feasible technology, not survivors who posed a threat of exposure or toxicity. Berube was killed, and now the "clean-up" is moving so quickly, soon the only evidence will be Secare himself.

Scully learns Carpenter and her family all perished in an auto accident, and her evidence is gone. Mulder finds Secare hiding at Berube's home, as does a gas-masked Crew-Cut Man, who'd followed Mulder and now beats him and kills Secare.

Deep Throat surprises Scully outside the missing Mulder's apartment. Mulder won't be killed since he's "too high-profile," but they'll need something to trade for him. Deep Throat conspires to get Scully into the High-Containment Facility at Fort Marlene, Maryland, where original alien tissue is kept. On the seventh floor, a guard asks for the password; guessing, she says "Purity Control." Scully logs in, and opens a cabinet marked "P.C." to find a liquid nitrogen barrel containing an apparent alien the size of a human fetus. [N]

Scully meets Deep Throat on a deserted bridge later that night. She doesn't turn over the apparent alien fetus until he heatedly convinces her how ruthless the covert community can be: They once had schoolchildren injected with experimental organisms under the pretense of vaccinations. Crew-Cut Man arrives and after taking the box containing the fetus from Deep Throat, shoots him through the heart while a battered Mulder is thrown from their van. The killers roar away; Deep Throat dies, gurgling to Scully, "Trust no one."

WASHINGTON, D.C., THIRTEEN DAYS LATER: Mulder phones Scully that the X-Files unit is being closed, and they're being reassigned. Skinner claimed word had come from the top of the executive branch. Cigarette-Smoking Man nonchalantly puts the alien—or alien-human?—deep in the Pentagon basement.

Jerry Hardin	Deep Throat
Lindsey Ginter	Crew-Cut Man
Anne DeSalvo	Dr. Carpenter
Simon Webb	Dr. Secare
Ken Kramer	Dr. Berube
Jim Leard	Captain Roy Lacerio
Phillip MacKenzie	Medic
William B. Davis	Cigarette-Smoking Man
Jaylene Hamilton	(WDT *Newscan*) Reporter
Mike Mitchell	First Uniformed Cop
John Payne	Guard (at Fort Marlene)

The official Fox *X-Files* website erroneously lists the character Dr. Carpenter as Dr. Simon.

X-actitude: Police cruiser: Unit 50

Channel 8 call letters and news logo: WDF *Newscan*

Dr. Berube background: Harvard Medical School, 1974; address and phone 2650 W. 1st St., Ardis, M.D. 149376 [*sic*]; (301) 555-1517; his Silver Sierra's partial license plate: 3AYF____.

Zeus Storage: 1616 Pandora St., somewhere in Maryland, probably Gaithersburg or one of the many nearby towns; phone number 301-555-2804; room used for cloning lab: no. 1056.

Last names of some of Mulder's neighbors (per their mailboxes): Glaniceanu; Pao/Hu; Dommann

X-otica: This episode was nominated for an Edgar Award for Best Episode and Television Series by the Mystery Writers of America.

The disabling fumes emitted from Secare are based on two similar, widely reported incidents—at California's Riverside General Hospital on Feb. 19, 1994, and at Bakersfield, CA's, Mercy Hospital a week later—in which sickening, ammonia-like fumes rose from two patients' needle-punctures, causing exposed people to collapse from the toxin.

The waterfront of fictional Ardis, MD, is in reality Versatile Shipyards of North Vancouver.

Earthy beauty Anne DeSalvo, one TV's most familiar faces, had memorable recurring roles on *Wiseguy* and *Taxi*.

2.01 "LITTLE GREEN MEN"   September 16, 1994

Writers: Glen Morgan & James Wong
Director: David Nutter

Mulder, narrating over spacescapes, describes the NASA Voyager probes and the High-Resolution Microwave Survey, both seeking alien contact.

ARECIBO IONOSPHERIC OBSERVATORY, PUERTO RICO: At the shuttered observatory electronic equipment mysteriously springs to life.

WASHINGTON, D.C., OUTSIDE THE LONGSTREET MOTEL: Mulder has been assigned to dull electronic surveillance of white-collar criminals. Scully's back at the Academy, teaching autopsy. When Mulder returns to his desk (now on some main floor with other agents), he picks up a downturned photo of his sister—a signal to meet Scully at the Watergate Hotel and Office Complex, in a deserted staff parking lot. Mulder tells her he'd "attended" Deep Throat's funeral, using eight-power binoculars from 1,000 feet away. And he's begun to believe all the "little green men" he's thought he's seen are merely in his mind.

NOVEMBER 27, 1973, CHILMARK, MASSACHUSETTS, 6:53 P.M. (FLASHBACK): Over TV news of Rose Mary Woods's partial Nixon-tape erasure, a young Mulder plays Stratego with kid sister Samantha; he's planning to watch *The Magician* at nine. Suddenly, the house shakes, and amid eerie lights stands a thin silhouetted figure. Fox breaks open a locked gun box, but then seems paralyzed as Samantha floats away. Mulder wakes up and finds a messenger at his door to take him to Senator Matheson. The visionary senator urges Mulder to investigate Arecibo, and says he'll try to hold off for twenty-four hours the Blue Beret UFO Retrieval Team which is authorized to use terminal force.

FBI HEADQUARTERS, THE NEXT DAY: Skinner and the Cigarette-Smoking Man discover that Mulder is gone. Mulder, in Puerto Rico, has hitched a ride to the Arecibo gate, from where he hikes to the control room. Mulder finds a terrified Jorge Concepcion in the lavatory at Arecibo, jabbering in Spanish about what sounds like alien contact. Scully, seeking clues at Mulder's apartment, unsuccessfully tries the passwords "Spooky" and "Samantha" on his computer before succeeding with "Trustno1" and printing a list of numbers. Another agent, staking-out the place, demands to know why she's here. Just feeding the fish, she assures, pocketing the list.

U.S. NAVAL OBSERVATORY: A scientist tells Scully the numbers are a record of space signals thirty times stronger than galactic-background noise, and on the "21-centimeter" frequency satellites aren't allowed to use. He gives Scully a list of SETI (Search for Extraterrestrial Intelligence) research locales. Scully finds Mulder on a (Thursday) July 7 flight passenger list from Wash-

Deja vu: The light of other days.

ington to San Juan with a stop in Miami. (He'd used the pseudonym George E. Hale, founder of the landmark Palomar Observatory.)

Meanwhile Mulder finds a signal recorded at 6:30 A.M. Tuesday (July 5) showing an intelligence pattern. Jorge, fearful of a sudden noise, runs into the storm outside, and dies of fright. Scully suspects she's being tailed by a touristy couple at the Miami International Airport. She phones a message [N] to Mulder's answering machine: "CA 519, 705, 950." She slips away, but the so-called tourists "know" she's taking Caribbean Air flight 519, leaving at 7:05 for St. Croix. Yet at 6:30, Scully buys a ticket to San Juan.

ARECIBO, 10:30 P.M.: As Mulder tape-records medical observations of Jorge's corpse, the room shakes, printouts spew, and he hears a distorted repetition of his own tape recording—as a familiar bright light panics him. His gun doesn't work, and he sees that same silhouette as on the day Samantha disappeared. When Scully finds him later, Mulder excitedly tells her he finally has proof of aliens, in the form of the tapes and printouts. But outside, the Blue Beret are arriving. The agents barely escape Scully's car as the Blue Beret fire. Mulder's salvages only one tape-reel.

Later, Skinner tells Mulder that leaving his surveillance post "has four-bagger all over it . . . censure, transfer, suspension, probation." Smoking Man watches. Mulder tells Skinner he'll accept his discipline, but also notes he had enough wiretap evidence after three days to nail the suspects on forty counts of bank fraud—yet Skinner kept him there needlessly *and* someone illegally wiretapped his phone. Skinner, acknowledging all this, throws Smoking Man out and while he won't censure Mulder, he *will* keep him on electronic surveillance. Later, Mulder find his entire Arecibo reel blank. Scully thinks a power surge during the storm may have erased it. And Mulder, back on surveillance, listens long into the night.

Mitch Pileggi	Assistant Director Walter S. Skinner
Mike Gomez	Jorge Concepcion
Raymond J. Barry	Senator Richard Matheson
William B. Davis	Smoking Man
Les Carlson	Dr. Troisky (unnamed in episode)
Marcus Turner	Young Mulder
Vennessa Morley	Young Samantha
Fulvio Cecere	Aide (to Sen. Matheson)
Deryl Hayes	Agent Morris (unnamed in episode)
Dwight McFee	(Blue Beret) Commander
Lisa Ann Beley	Student (FBI cadet)
Gary Hetherington	Lewin (agent staking-out Mulder's apartment; unnamed in episode)
Bob Wilde	Rand

The official Fox *X-Files* website erroneously gives the alien contact site as Mexico.

Faithful partner Scully risks her career to help Mulder at the SETI.

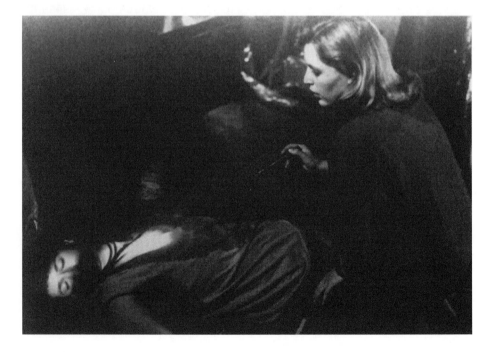

X-actitude: The airline manifest includes the names of prominent X-Philes Paulette Alves, Sylvia Bartle, T. C. Carstensen, and Pat Gonzales, and of *X-Files* novelist Charles Grant.

Longstreet Motel wiretap no.: 5A21147

Mulder's basketball shirt in flashback: KING 30

Smoking Man's brand of cigarettes: In Skinner's office, he picks up a pack of what looks like Marlboro—the fictional Morley, which as seen in episode 2.08, "One Breath," is packaged to look like Marlboro.

X-otica: Chris Carter and writers Morgan and Wong originally wanted to send Mulder on-location to Moscow, Russia. When the logistics proved impractical, they settled for faux Puerto Rico.

The Fox website's capsule synopsis lists the young Mulder as age twelve and Samantha as age eight but Mulder was just shy of twelve. The flashback itself contradicts Mulder's previous description of Samantha's abduction, but that can be chalked up to the vagaries of time and memory.

Jorge's Spanish dialogue, paraphrased in translation: He'd gone to investigate some strange lights in the sky, when men like animals grabbed him and put him here.

The Arecibo observatory, affiliated with Cornell University's National Astronomy and Ionosphere Center, is a real and operating research facility, with the world's largest radio-telescope.

Raymond J. Barry, a member of Willem Dafoe's celebrated Wooster Group theater ensemble, had major roles in *Dead Man Walking* and *Born on the Fourth of July*, and starred in *Headless Body in Topless Bar*. He appeared in Gillian Anderson's unreleased pre-*X-Files* film *The Turning*.

2.02 "THE HOST"   September 23, 1994

Writer: Chris Carter

Director: Daniel Sackheim

A RUSSIAN FREIGHTER, TWO MILES OFF THE NEW JERSEY COAST: As crewman Dmitri tries to fix the ship's backed-up toilets, he is violently pulled into the septic system and washes up dead, with one side eaten away, in the sewers of Newark, New Jersey.

After being relieved of his surveillance work, Mulder flies from National Airport in Washington, D.C., to Newark, where his contact is Detective Norman. Mulder, uniformed officer Kenny, and others descend into the sewer to find the unidentified body. Later, back in D.C., Mulder angrily demands to meet with Skinner about this simple—and smelly—local homicide. Skinner is outraged that Mulder regards this assignment as punishment.

That night, Mulder tells Scully he's thinking of leaving the Bureau. Scully suggests he request a transfer to the Behavioral Science Unit at the FBI

Academy in Quantico, Virginia, but Mulder says the FBI doesn't want them working together and their partnership is his only reason to stay. As Scully performs the victim's autopsy she finds a tattoo of indecipherable markings, and a slug-like creature emerging from the liver.

In Newark, two sewer workers are fixing a hole in a screen when one of them, Craig, is pulled under. The other man saves him, but later, at the Middlesex County Hospital in Sayreville, Mulder observes as Craig complains of a bad taste in his mouth. Craig suspects he was grabbed by a python—except that his wound has four points. Mulder gets an odd, anonymous call in which a voice tells him he has "a friend at the FBI," and hangs up. At the FBI Academy lab, Scully shows Mulder the turbellaria, a.k.a. fluke or flat-worm, she found. Its scolex (sucker with four spikes) matches the wound on Craig's back. That night, Craig gorily coughs up a flatworm, which disappears down the bathtub drain.

NEWARK COUNTY SEWAGE PROCESSING PLANT: Foreman Ray explains the system to Mulder. An old-timer, Charlie, hears splashing in a sewer reservoir, and when he backflushes the system, the three men all look inside a clear examination tube at what appears to be a hairless, mottled human with a sucker mouth.

SCULLY'S LAB: Someone slips a supermarket tabloid under the door, with an article about a Russian ship's similar sewage death. Scully now realizes the tattoo is of Russian Cyrillic letters, and eventually IDs the John Doe.

MIDDLESEX COUNTY PSYCHIATRIC HOSPITAL: Mulder and Scully observe the sewer-creature. Skinner told the local prosecutor the Justice Department wants to institutionalize the suspect for psychiatric evaluation. Mulder argues it's not a man but a monster; Skinner retorts, "Well, what do you want me to do with it, put it in a zoo?" Then Skinner says Craig was found dead—a possibly preventable tragedy that prompts Skinner to mutter, "This should have been an X-File." Not looking Mulder in the eye, he tells him, "We all take our orders from someone. . . ."

That night EMS workers load the creature into a U.S. Marshal's van [N]. When the marshal later notices the flukeman missing, he radios for backup and parks outside the Lake Betty campsite/recreation area. The creature kills the marshal (having evidently hidden beneath the stretcher) and slithers down a campsite toilet. Early the next morning the toilet is drained into a truck—with something momentarily clogging the vacuum tube. At the murder scene, Mulder gets another call from the mysterious voice, saying this case is imperative if the X-Files are to be revived. Mulder, learning dogs have tracked a scent to the toilet, traces the tank-cleaning truck to the Newark plant.

At the plant Ray tells Mulder if the creature's here, filters and screens should trap it. Scully calls, saying the liver fluke was an incubatory larvae—meaning the hermaphrodite creature is trying to multiply. Ray, investigating an ancient storm-overflow part of the sewer, is pulled under. Mulder rescues him, and pins the flukeman beneath a sewer gate. Back in Washington, Scully says larvae analysis indicates reproductive and physiological "cross-traiting," resulting in a quasi-vertebrate human. She says the creature came here from a decommissioned Russian freighter hauling salvage from the Chernobyl meltdown; it was born in a "primordial soup of radioactive sewage." And inexplicably, somewhere, we see a flukeman opening its eyes.

Mitch Pileggi	Assistant Director Walter S. Skinner
Darin Morgan	Flukeman
Matthew Bennett	First Workman (Craig)
Freddy Andreiuci	Detective Norman
Don MacKay	Charlie
Marc Bauer	Agent Brisentine (unnamed in episode)
Gabrielle Rose	Dr. Zenzols (unnamed in episode)
Ron Sauve	Foreman (Ray)
Dmitri Boudrine	Russian Engineer
Raoul Ganee	Dmitri
William MacDonald	Federal Marshal
Uncredited:	
Steven Williams	Telephone Caller

111

***X*-actitude:** The initial Newark victim: John Doe no. 101356, case no. DP112148

U.S. Marshal's van: no. 4940

Agent taking over Mulder's surveillance: Bozoff

Septic-tank service at Lake Betty: A & A Anderson Tank Cleaning Service, phone number 277-1628

***X*-otica:** Darin Morgan, younger brother of producer Glen Morgan, later became an *X-Files* writer and story editor. The "Flukeman" suit unfortunately dissolved in water, he recalls, so special-effects makeup artist Toby Lindala "had to rebuild everything from scratch each day, so it was just an ordeal." The sulfurous-smelling mask allowed no breathing through the nose, "so I didn't eat, because you had to eat and breathe at the same time."

In the scene where Mulder first sees the flukeman, the shots of the creature and of Mulder's reaction were filmed separately. "I knew it was a big worm, but I hadn't seen it," Duchovny says. "So, not wanting to overplay it, I kinda went like, 'Mmm-hmmm.' And then later on, here's this *six-foot intestinal worm*!" So there in the combined shot, "There's me going, 'Uh-huh. It's a six-foot worm. With human features. Uh-huh. Hmmmm, well, what do you think of that? . . . Hey, it's another one of those goddamned six-foot intestinal worms!'" he says, laughing.

Substituting for Newark's sewer facility was Canada's Iona Island Sewage Treatment Plant, where the poor and doubtless pungent *X-Filers* spent twelve hours filming on a hot July day.

2.03 "BLOOD"   September 30, 1994

Teleplay: Glen Morgan & James Wong
Story: Darin Morgan
Director: David Nutter

FRANKLIN, PENNSYLVANIA POSTAL CENTER: Worker Ed Funsch gets a paper cut. Then after his supervisor regretfully lays him off for budget reasons, Ed sees an electronic readout KILL, then KILL 'EM and KILL 'EM ALL. In an elevator at the town's Civic Center, a claustrophobic businessman, Taber, sees a digital readout NO AIR, then CAN'T BREATHE and KILL 'EM ALL.

Later Venango County Sheriff Spencer tells Mulder (here on a routine Behavioral Science assignment not related to the X-Files) that Taber murdered four people before being killed by a security guard. The town's had only three murders in over two hundred years, yet in six months, there've been twenty-two committed by seven different people. No drug or alcohol traces account for it. Funsch, at a Commercial Trust ATM, sees a mother tending to her little girl's nosebleed; then the ATM reads TAKE HIS GUN (referring to a security guard) and KILL 'EM ALL. Instead, he runs.

Residue on Taber's fingers, of an unidentified, nontoxic chemical compound found in plants, lead Mulder to suspect a chemical cause. The only consistent clue is the destruction of electronic devices. That night a mechanic tells a young, pretty Mrs. McRoberts her car needs expensive repair. She sees the word LIAR in the diagnostic computer, then HE'S A LIAR and HE'LL RAPE YOU, followed by HE'LL KILL YOU and KILL HIM FIRST. She hits him with a wrench, then stabs him to death with an oil-can spout. By 7:35 A.M., a repair order at the scene has prompted Spencer and Mulder to see McRoberts. Her microwave-oven readout tells her, HE KNOWS and KILL 'EM BOTH. Berserk, she stabs Mulder until Spencer shoots her dead. At the Academy, Scully's autopsy on McRoberts reveals anomalies the coroner missed: Adrenaline levels 200 times normal, and a high concentration of an undetermined chemical compound, similar to that found on Taber's fingers. Scully suspects it reacts with adrenaline to produce a substance similar to the hallucinogen LSD.

At a department store, Funsch job-hunts. He sees a blood-drive table, then violent TV images of Waco, the L.A. riots, etc., and the words BEHIND YOU (referring to the gun department), followed by DO IT. Jogging, Mulder notices a yard-care truck tossing insects onto a lawn. Curious, he takes one to the Lone Gunmen who say it's a Eurasian cluster fly. Mulder asks if the Gunmen are familiar with the chemical compound LSDM. Byers recognizes it as the toxic pesticide lysergic dimethrin, an unreleased synthetic botanical insecticide that, acting as a pheromone, triggers a fear response in a pest.

That night or the early morning, in Franklin, Mulder uses infrared goggles to stake out a field. He's suddenly sprayed by a crop-dusting helicopter. Later, at Franklin Community Hospital, county supervisor Larry Winter insists no "stealth" helicopter is spraying experimental pesticides, but with pressure changes his story: Irradiated flies didn't work, crop failures would ruin lives, and this chemical was proven safe to him—though he won't say by whom. Scully, having flown in, says exposure to LSDM *doesn't* cause violent behavior—Mulder is proof. But Mulder suggests LSDM heightens the fear response of individuals with phobias; he suspects the readout messages were real but subliminal.

Winter agrees to stop the spraying and to test the blood of all those exposed but only if the explanation for the tests not be linked to LSDM. With astonishing immediacy, a door-to-door "cholesterol-test drive" is launched. By mid-morning a canvasser reaches Funsch, who's afraid to let the person in. On TV, he sees the word BLOOD and destroys the TV set. After closing his gun case, he sees BLOOD on a calculator, and KILL in his digital watch. The agents learn that twenty-five people, including Funsch, went untested.

At Funsch's deserted home, Scully and Mulder deduce Funsch is phobic about blood, and that he's headed to shoot up the hospital. But Funsch, on a bus, sees the readouts THEY'RE WAITING and GET OFF. When the bus arrives at the hospital, the driver says the man they're looking for got off at Franklin Community College—where there's a blood fair.

There Funsch, seeing the readout UP, climbs to the top of a clock tower and begins a sniper assault. Mulder, fighting his own fear of heights, eventually disarms him; Funsch is taken to the hospital. Mulder, finally pausing to take a breath, sits and makes a cel-phone call to Scully and in the readout sees the words, ALL DONE and BYE BYE.

113

William Sanderson	Ed Funsch
John Cygan	Sheriff Spencer
Kimberly Ashlyn Gere	Mrs. McRoberts
George Touliatos	County Supervisor Larry Winter
Bruce Harwood	Byers
Dean Haglund	Langly
Tom Braidwood	Frohike
Gerry Rosseau	Mechanic
Andre Daniels	Harry (Funsch's boss; unnamed in episode; last name McNally per print sources)
William MacKenzie	Bus Driver
Diana Stevan	Mrs. Adams

David Fredericks	Security Guard
Kathleen Duborg	Mother
John Harris	Taber
B. J. Harrison	Clerk

The official Fox *X-Files* website erroneously gives the locale as Virginia, and truncates the name of actress Kimberly Ashlyn Gere to Ashlyn Gere. It also neglects to list front-credit guest-actor George Touliatos.

X-actitude: The facts on Funsch: Age fifty-two. High school diploma. No driver's license. Former navy radio operator. Wife died ten years ago; no other family or kids.

Taber: forty-two-year-old real-estate agent

X-otica: Funsch's clock-tower sniping recalls Charles Whitman's real-life Texas Tower massacre of Aug. 4, 1966, at the University of Texas. Using a high-powered rifle, Whitman killed thirteen people and wounded thirty-four.

The University of British Columbia, with its clock tower, filled-in for Franklin Community College. *X*-guest Don Davis (Capt. William Scully) taught acting at UBC before becoming an actor full time.

Memphis-born William Sanderson is best known as Vermont backwoodsman Larry on *Newhart*, and as the tragic Dr. Sebastian in *Blade Runner* (1982).

Kimberly Ashlyn Gere is the adult-video star known under the *nom de porn* Ashlyn Gere—winner of the adult-film industry's FOXE 1991 Fan Favorite, 1992 Vixen of the Year, and 1993 Best Female Performer awards. As Kim McKamy, she's appeared in non-X horror and exploitation films, and as Kimberly Patton played the recurring role of Feliciti OH 519 on the Morgan-Wong series *Space: Above and Beyond*.

2.04 "SLEEPLESS"   October 7, 1994

Writer: Howard Gordon
Director: Rob Bowman

MANHATTAN, 11:23 P.M.: Dr. Saul Grissom finds a fire outside his apartment door and calls 911. An African-American man, Preacher, leaves the high-rise, and smiles enigmatically. Firefighter Lt. Regan finds no fire in the sixth-floor hallway—nor in Grissom's apartment, where Grissom is seen dead near a spent fire extinguisher.

Mulder finds an audiocassette tucked into his morning newspaper; circled is "Prominent Doctor Dies—Pioneer in Sleep Disorders." Rookie agent Alex Krycek brings Mulder a file on this "302" assignment—with him as partner, since Krycek had opened the file two hours before Mulder. Scully, teaching autopsy at the Academy, gets a call from "George Hale" (Mulder's sometime pseudonym, used in "Little Green Men"). Mulder's at National

Airport (minus Krycek), catching a shuttle to New York's LaGuardia Airport and he'll have a body for her to examine by 5 P.M.

GRISSOM SLEEP DISORDER CENTER, STAMFORD, CONNECTICUT: A doctor describes experimental modification of brain-wave patterns by electrical stimulation to theoretically alter dreams. Later, Mulder introduces Krycek to Scully, who says Grissom died not of the reported heart attack, but of intense heat with no external burns, as if his body simply believed it was burning.

In a run-down Brooklyn apartment, Preacher finds old acquaintance Henry Willig watching a home-shopping channel. Willig's suddenly gunned down by a vision of bloodied Vietnamese. Mulder and Krycek later find an odd scar on Willig, and learn he was with the Marines in Vietnam in 1970; Grissom was also with the Marines, though at Parris Island, South Carolina, from 1968–71, while Willig was in Special Forces and Recon Squad J-7—one of two survivors out of thirteen, the other being Cpl. Augustus D. Cole. Cole was discharged from the V.A. Medical Center in North Orange, New Jersey, two days ago.

The mysterious man who called Mulder in episode 2.02, "The Host," meets Mulder and hands him data from a secret military project: Grissom was experimenting to get the ideal soldier psyche by ending the need for sleep, since wakefulness dulls fear and heightens aggression. Cole hasn't slept in twenty-four years. The man tells Mulder there's a third living squad-member, Salvatore Matola, reported killed in action.

Someone matching Cole's description robbed a drugstore and is holed up in a motel. After a shootout with the SWAT team, Cole—a.k.a. Preacher—escapes. Mulder later tells Scully he believes years without sleep have allowed Cole to produce telepathic imagery.

THE 2 JAYS CAFE, ROSLYN, LONG ISLAND: Matola tells Mulder and Krycek that J-7 had gone AWOL, making up their own missions, killing civilians, finally wiping out a school full of three hundred children outside Phu Bai. No charges were ever brought against them. He says Dr. Francis Girardi (now a Harvard neurosurgery professor) did the brain-stem surgeries the experiment required. The twenty-fourth anniversary of the Phu Bai killings was two days ago. Scully phones to say Girardi is coming to Grissom's funeral in New York, arriving at a Bronx train station at 7:30. She'll get his photo to the security desk there. Mulder and Krycek reach the station just after the train arrives. Cole is there, too. Cole shoots Girardi and then Mulder—or does he? Krycek rouses Mulder on the platform, saying he was waving his gun around, and that Girardi never showed.

At the station's Metropolitan Transit Authority office, Mulder has police check out security videos. A cop shows Mulder that a car parked in a restricted area at 19:38:37 isn't there at 19:43:19. This somehow leads the agents to Track 17, where Cole holds Girardi hostage. Girardi is shot by a

115

J-7 firing squad. Mulder and Krycek find him severely wounded. Mulder goes after Cole and implores Cole to seek justice by giving testimony. Krycek kills Cole when Cole raises his gun. In the car immediately afterward, Mulder finds his files missing. Scully, at headquarters later, says her office and computer were broken into. Mulder tells Scully of a new covert source.

Elsewhere, Krycek meets with a shadow cabinet of three silhouetted figures, including the Cigarette-Smoking Man. No one knows how Mulder got the files. Krycek reports Scully is a bigger problem than anticipated. Says Cigarette-Smoking Man, "Every problem has a solution."

Mitch Pileggi	Assistant Director Walter S. Skinner
Nicholas Lea	"Agent Alex Krycek"
Jonathan Gries	Salvatore Matola
Steven Williams	Mr. X (undesignated in episode)
Tony Todd	Corporal Augustus D. "Preacher" Cole
Don Thompson	Henry Willig
David Adams	Dr. (Francis) Girardi
Michael Puttonen	Dr. Pilsson (at V.A. hospital)
Anna Hagan	Dr. Charyn (at sleep-disorder center; unnamed in episode)
William B. Davis	Cigarette-Smoking Man
Mitch Kosterman	Detective (Lt.) Horton
Paul Bittante	Team Leader
Claude DeMartino	Dr. Grissom

The actor who plays firefighter Lt. Regan is uncredited.

As subsequent events on the series strongly suggest, "Alex Krycek" is almost certainly a pseudonym. As a shadow-government plant—and assassin, *a la* the identity-free Crew-Cut Man—he certainly wouldn't have given the FBI his real name. Additionally, neither Smoking Man nor other shadow-government operatives have referred to him as "Krycek."

X-actitude: Dr. Grissom's address, 700 East 56th St., no. 606, New York, NY, would put his building smack dab in the East River!

Number of confirmed J-7 kills: 4,100

Cole's medical background: Treated by Dr. Pilsson at North Orange, NJ, V.A. hospital since admittance twelve years ago; discharged with Pilsson's evidently forged or acquired signature. There is no North Orange, NJ.

Scully's report, based on the secret documents Mulder faxed her, describes an experimental neurological procedure to induce a permanent waking state. It included brain-stem surgery, explaining Willig's scar. The antidepressants Cole stole from the drugstore are consistent with drugs given to maintain high blood-levels of serotonin, produced by the body during sleep.

X-otica: "Mr. X actually began as Ms. X," remembered coexecutive producer James Wong. Indeed, he's confirmed, an actress was even cast and filmed for this episode.

Though the surveillance tape that Mulder is transcribing has the epithet "stupid bitch" in the final shooting script, it was changed to "stupid bimbo" by airdate.

This episode features two knockout visuals by director Rob Bowman and his crew: An eerie shot of Scully's face, the top half in shadow while her round glasses shine like blue spotlights; and a beautifully vertiginous transition shot from a computer screen to the V.A. hospital, with pivoting angles and a sweeping, backward-moving camera.

This episode netted Stephen Mark one of this season's two Emmy nominations for Editing, Single-Camera Production.

2.05 "DUANE BARRY"   October 14, 1994
Writer-Director: Chris Carter
Part 1 of a 2-part episode

PULASKI, VIRGINIA, JUNE 3, 1986: At a large, gloomy home, a man wakes and yells, encompassed by a flash of light and the appearance of humanoid figures. A dog barks at a spaceship hovering overhead. Memory? Or dream? Years later, guards take the man, Duane Barry, through a psychiatric hospital to meet with a Dr. Hakkie; "Duane Barry" (who refers to himself in the third person) swears he isn't crazy, and that his abductors are coming back. He steals a guard's gun and takes Hakkie hostage.

WASHINGTON, D.C., AUGUST 7, 1994: Krycek, locating Mulder doing laps in a pool, says four people are being held hostage in an office building in downtown Richmond, Virginia, by someone claiming to be an alien-abductee. Police and FBI have set up a command post across from a storefront travel agency. The negotiation commander, FBI Agent Lucy Kazdin, says Barry wants safe passage for himself and Hakkie to the site of his alleged abduction; unfortunately he can't quite remember where that is, so he'd stopped at this travel agency. Kazdin had requested Mulder since she'd heard he knows UFO jargon and could talk the perp's language; she had no idea Mulder really believes this stuff and now decides to reevaluate his progress every three hours to determine whether to storm the place.

When Mulder phones, Barry retorts that he knows the routine, and recites the words written on the command center's chalkboard—"Honesty, containment, conciliation"—and teases he forgets the last one, "resolution." Barry's a former FBI agent let go in 1982, and institutionalized for a decade. Mulder demands Barry's patient records in order to understand him better. But Kazdin doesn't want to risk "psychoanalyzing" the guy for fear it'll set him off. Krycek asks Kazdin what he can do to help; she sends him for coffee.

Mulder phones Scully, who's following the events on the news, to have her look up Barry's FBI background and his abduction experience. That night at the travel agency, the lights and electricity go screwy and a panicked Barry fires five shots, inadvertently hitting hostage Bob Morris. He asks the police for a doctor. Mulder, volunteering to impersonate an EMS medic, gets equipped with an inner-ear receiver, and a microphone on top of his hidden flak jacket; he goes in with trained medic Agent Janus. If possible, they're to get Barry near the front door so that one of three snipers can kill him. Inside, Mulder asks Barry if "they" were just here, and if time had just stopped. The insightful questions makes Barry remember/imagine his abduction, and he exchanges Bob for Mulder—who's desperate to speak to an abductee firsthand.

As a hole is drilled for covert video, Scully phones to tell Krycek that Barry is dangerously delusional. She later arrives to tell the negotiators in person that Barry has a rare psychosis resulting from being shot in the line of duty in 1982: The bullet effectively destroyed the moral center of his brain, as in a (real-life) nineteenth-century case. Inside, Barry tells Mulder the government cooperates with the aliens, but "wouldn't dare let the truth out." Mulder convinces him to let the women go; then, as Barry gets enraged at Mulder's wondering if he'd made any of this up, Mulder says Barry forgot to lock the front door. When Barry goes to do so, he's shot.

RICHMOND'S JEFFERSON MEMORIAL HOSPITAL, EVIDENTLY THE NEXT DAY: Kazdin tells Mulder that Barry's critical but stable, and that his FBI career had been exemplary until he'd gotten shot with his own gun during a drug raid and

The brilliant Steve Railsback (left), in a scene from his critically acclaimed starring feature, *The Stunt Man.*

left for dead in the woods. Then she lays the bombshell: X-rays showed pieces of metal in Barry's gums, sinus cavity, and abdomen, and tiny drill holes in his left and right rear molars—all as Barry had claimed. A dentist told her the drill-work couldn't have been done with available technology. Scully, later, says Barry might have shrapnel from his Vietnam duty. But that doesn't address the gum and sinus metal which an FBI ballistics expert says contain finely tooled or etched markings. Later, at a supermarket, Scully exposes a piece of it to a cash-register scanner, which goes crazy.

At the hospital, Barry's jolted awake by white light and the images of aliens. The posted cop outside doesn't notice and Barry clubs him with a fire extinguisher and escapes. Scully leaves a message on Mulder's machine about the scanner experience that just happened, and saying Barry's metal shard has numbers on it "almost as if somebody was using it to catalog him." Suddenly Barry breaks in and kidnaps Scully, as she screams on the phone for help.

Steve Railsback	Duane Barry
Nicholas Lea	"Agent Alex Krycek"
C. C. H. Pounder	Agent Lucy Kazdin
Stephen E. Miller	Tactical Commander
Frank C. Turner	Dr. Hakkie
Fred Henderson	Agent Rich
Barbara Pollard	Gwen (blond hostage)
Sarah Strange	Kimberly (brunette hostage)
Robert Lewis	Officer
Michael Dobson	Marksman #2
Tosca Baggoo	(Supermarket) Clerk
Tim Dixon	Bob (Morris)
Prince Maryland	Agent Janus
John Sampson	Marksman #1

The animal performer is uncredited.

X-actitude: Name of travel agency: Travel Time

Barry's gun: 9mm Smith & Wesson handgun with one nine-round magazine

Kazdin's coffee: grande 2 percent cappuccino with vanilla

Scully's supermarket bill: $11.14; she pays by check, aisle 1

Size of entire magnified square showing part of etched shard: 10 microns

Barry's heart monitor: Life Force 9; his pulse is 80

Receiver in Mulder's ear: IntraAudio Mid-Aural Implant Receiver model JD-111471

The aliens, per Barry: Unspeaking, they can read minds; Mulder says abductees call this telepathy a "mindscan."

***X*-otica:** Ah, the infamous red Speedo swimsuit scene! "Oh, that was completely gratuitous," Duchovny says, hardly seeming unpleased at how that suit's become a female-fan icon.

This episode netted director of photography John S. Bartley a nomination for Outstanding Achievement Award for Episodic Television, by the American Society of Cinematographers. The Lowry book erroneously claims it was an Emmy nomination. "Duane Barry" also marks Chris Carter's well-done directorial debut.

The silhouetted aliens in Barry's dream/recollection were played by several costumed kids ages six to ten.

Pulaski is a real town waaaaay off in rural southwest Virginia, at the foot of the Appalachian Mountains.

The electrifying Steve Railsback made his biggest splashes as Charles Manson in the acclaimed *Helter Skelter* (1976 TV-movie), and as the title character of *The Stunt Man* (1980). "He's the person I wanted, the only person I ever thought of for the role," Carter says. "He really became the part, and I think also that the levels of your actors rise to that."

Carol Christine Hilaria Pounder, born in Georgetown, British Guyana, and educated at convent school in Sussex, England, played the recurring role of Dr. Angela Hicks on *ER*, and a head nurse on *Birdland*. In film, she starred in the arthouse hit *Bagdad Cafe*.

In-joke: With Gillian Anderson pregnant, Scully's supermarket props reportedly include pickles and ice cream; only the latter is evident onscreen.

2.06 "ASCENSION"   October 21, 1994
Writer: Paul Brown
Director: Michael Lange

Part 2 of a 2-part episode

Opening credo: "Deny Everything."

WASHINGTON, D.C., 11:23 P.M.: Mulder hears Scully's desperate message. At the police-filled crime scene, he speaks with Scully's mother, Margaret. By 11:40, Mulder's finished checking around. FBI HEADQUARTERS, 8:03 A.M.: Skinner meets with Mulder, Krycek, a silver-haired male agent, and a woman agent. Cigarette-Smoking Man observes. Skinner says Mulder's "too close" to the case, and has Krycek escort him home.

ROUTE 229, RIXEYVILLE, VIRGINIA, 11:23 A.M.: Barry kills a cop who's pulled over his speeding car (stolen from Scully, who's in the trunk). By mid-afternoon, the FBI has the police-car video of the scene. Mulder has a video technician enhance the image—revealing Scully (visible when Barry opens the trunk to check on her). At 4:03 P.M., Mulder hears a tape of Barry describing his abduction site with words like "a mountain" and "ascending to the stars," and realizes Route 229 leads to the Blue Ridge Parkway. The Yellow Pages display a tram ride, Skyland Mountain, with the motto: Ascend to the stars. Krycek, waiting in a car downstairs, phones Smoking Man to say he'll hold off Mulder "until they locate her."

Route 211, Warrenton, Virginia, 5:43 p.m.: Krycek and Mulder, not alerting Skinner, are on the road to Skyland. There the tram-operator says that forty-five minutes ago, he'd sent the man they're looking for up the back road, since the tram's had its cable refitted and is still untested. Mulder forces the operator to send him up anyway. Watching Mulder via video, Krycek knocks the tram-operator unconscious, moments before Mulder reaches the summit. He makes a cel call saying he'll leave Mulder hanging "till you advise."

Mulder, getting no radio response, goes through a hatch to the roof. Seeing this, Krycek turns the tram back on, intending to kill Mulder and have it appear accidental. Mulder goes hand over hand on the cable until he reaches ground. He finds Scully's empty car, with her gold-cross necklace in the trunk. A helicopter appears, and Mulder hears Barry howling that the aliens took Scully instead. Search-and-rescue operations are underway that evening, explaining the helicopter (though not who called for it and when).

At the summit, Mulder questions Barry, who says the black-suited men outside the office know all about Scully's abduction but when Mulder turns to see them, they're gone. Mulder, losing it, starts to choke Barry, then walks away to calm down. He returns to find Krycek with Barry, claiming Barry was gagging. Skinner arrives, to see Barry collapse and die—from Mulder's choking? Or did Krycek poison him? Later, at the Academy, a pathologist shows Mulder evidence of asphyxiation—but she won't send toxicological results unless he goes through military channels. Quantico, she explains, is under military jurisdiction, and she claims there "wasn't an FBI pathologist available this morning."

Krycek meets Smoking Man in the garage at FBI headquarters to ask how he should write the field report. Smoking Man instructs him to write the truth—Krycek's earned Mulder's trust, and now must preserve it. Krycek pointedly wonders if Mulder's such a threat, why not eliminate him? Not policy, says Smoking Man. "It's not?" asks Krycek, smirking. "After what you had me do?" Smoking Man coolly says killing Mulder risks "turning one man's religion into a crusade." As for Scully, he says, "We've taken care of that"—and implies Krycek better not overstep his bounds. Skinner later holds a meeting that includes Mulder, the silver-haired man, and the female agent seen before, plus an African-American man (who is not Mr. X). Krycek backs up Mulder's testimony; Skinner orders both take polygraph tests at OPC.

Duchovny, doing his own stuntwork atop a real-life tram car.

122

The next morning, outside the office of Senator Richard Matheson, 11:45 A.M., Mr. X informs Mulder the senator can't help him anymore: "They have something on everyone, Mr. Mulder." He suggests the government wouldn't have killed Barry unless it had something to hide regarding Scully. Afterward, Mulder notices cigarette butts in the car Krycek was driving, even though Krycek doesn't smoke. Mulder later gives Skinner a document accusing Krycek of impeding his investigation, and of possibly murdering both a suspect and the vanished tram operator (the first mention of the latter's death). Skinner calls for Krycek, and with a look as if events have taken a turn even this company man can't accept, he tells Mulder he can protect him only to a certain point. When they learn Krycek has disappeared, Skinner declares he's reopening the X-Files. Outside later, a hopeful Margaret hands Mulder back Dana's necklace—he can give it to her when he finds her.

Steve Railsback	Duane Barry
Nicholas Lea	"Agent Alex Krycek"
Mitch Pileggi	Assistant Director Walter S. Skinner
Sheila Larken	Margaret (Maggie) Scully
Steven Williams	Mr. X (undesignated in episode)
Meredith Bain Woodward	Dr. Ruth Slaughter (pathologist; unnamed in episode)
William B. Davis	Smoking Man
Michael David Simms	FBI Agent
Peter LaCroix	Dwight (tram operator; unnamed in episode)
Steve Makaj	Patrolman
Peter Lapres	Video Technician
Bobby L. Stewart	Deputy

Within the episode itself, the mysterious contact played by Steven Williams is still not called "Mr. X" in dialog. By episode 2.08, however, when Mulder tapes an "X" on his window in order to contact him, we can infer this is how Mulder himself designates the man.

X-actitude: Barry's sweatshirt: University of Maryland
  Song on car radio: "Red Right Hand" by Nick Dave and the Bad Seeds
  Barry's official cause of death: hypoxemia secondary to asphyxiation
  The exterior of Mulder's apartment house is shown here as a white clapboard row house with dark shutters.

X-otica: Duchovny, dangling from the suspended tram, did his own stunt-work, and by all accounts, at an actual location above actual ground. Two Vancouver-area ski sites were used for these and related scenes: Grouse Mountain and Seymour Mountain.

Scully's apartment number remains 35, but Barry's break-in makes particularly clear she's in a ground-floor and not third-floor apartment.

The OPR is referred to this episode as the Office of Professional Conduct.

123

2.07 "3"   November 4, 1994
Writers: Chris Ruppenthal, Glen Morgan, & James Wong
Director: David Nutter

X-File case no.: X256933VW Trinity Killers

LOS ANGELES, THE HOLLYWOOD HILLS, 12:41 A.M.: In the midst of sex, a married, well-to-do Garrett Lorre is attacked by his lover, a shadowy woman he'd met at a party, and by a man with a syringe. Mulder in his darkened X-Files office, flips a swimsuit calendar from May to the present November. He files his latest X-File—"Scully, Dana"—and puts Scully's glasses and badge in an evidence bag.

LOS ANGELES: Mulder's been alerted to the vampire-like killing by news reports—he's waited three months for this MO to reappear. He impresses the crime-scene commander with his knowledge of the killers, whose pattern indicates they'll murder twice more by week's end.

On a wall inside, "John 52:54" is written in the victim's blood [N]; Mulder recites the biblical chapter and verse about eating flesh and drinking blood for eternal life, and says the killers extract blood and store it. The cop wants to pair Mulder with a Detective Gwynn, but Mulder demurs. Phoning blood banks to check on recent hires, Mulder learns the Hollywood Blood Bank has a new night watchman, "Frank." Mulder gets into the closed offices [N] and arrests a man slurping blood.

POLICE INTERROGATION ROOM 4: "Frank" tells Mulder he's "The Son," and he's with "The Father" and "The Unholy Spirit." He believes drinking blood prolongs life, and that only the other two can kill him. Mulder, by now convinced the man's no real vampire, hopes exposure to the soon-to-rise sun will frighten him into giving up the others. Yet after Mulder leaves, the sunlight burns the Son to death. A doctor suggests Gunther's disease: congenital erythropoietic porphyria. Mulder muses that the disease probably led to the creation of vampire myths in Middle-Ages Asia, but only causes lesions and blisters.

They decipher an inkstamp on the Son's hand: "Club Tepes." There Mulder meets Kristen, who practically confesses to the murders. She take a syringe, pokes her finger, and offers Mulder her blood. When he turns her down, she leaves. With the Father watching, Mulder follows as Kristen takes a man she's picked up to a nearby closed restaurant, Ra. After the man beats up "Peeping Tom" Mulder, the Father and the shadowy woman kill the man.

Later, Gwynn says the murder matches the killers' MO. Forensic dentist Dr. Jacobs finds human bite marks from three different people. Mulder, having found Kristen's prints at the scene, pulls her license on the DMV computer and sees she lived in the two cities where these "Trinity" murders last occurred.

Mulder and the police search her Malibu Canyon home. Gwynn finds veterinary hypos, and a piece of a snakebite kit that was used to extract blood. Mulder finds blood-filled bread in an oven but keeps it to himself and tells the cops she's skipped and won't return. Yet she does, at 2:15 A.M.—greeted by Mulder, who knows European legends about blood-baked bread as vampire protection. As she speaks with the weary and vulnerable Mulder, the kinky Kristen tells him she met John—"The Son"—in Chicago; he beat her, and in tasting each other's blood they got into "blood sports." One night John returned with two others and it all became "unnatural." They've since followed her around the country. Soon, with Mulder shirtless and shaving, they lustily kiss—while the Son, undead, watches.

Early the next morning, John accosts Kristen in the hallway. He tells her he loves her and wants to atone for all eternity for beating her. He tells her to kill Mulder and drink the blood of his spirit—that of a believer. Brandishing a knife, she approaches Mulder in the bedroom, but instead stabs the hiding Father. The Son attacks Mulder in the hall, but Mulder binds him with electrical cord. In the garage, the female Unholy Spirit attacks Mulder, but Kristen guns the car to knock her down. As the vampiress tells Mulder something in Romanian, Kristen backs up and impales her on a wooden peg.

Kristen tricks Mulder away from the house, which she douses with gasoline. Having tasted the blood of a believer, she tells John she'll now complete the ritual by taking a human life—her own. She'll become one of them

With Perry Reeves, Duchovny's real-life girlfriend at the time.

and thus, can kill them in the fire. Firefighters later find four sets of ashes and bones, as a shattered Mulder stares at Scully's cross.

Justina Vail	The Unholy Spirit
Perrey Reeves	Kristen Kilar
Frank Military	John/The Son
Tom McBeath	Detective Gwynn
Malcolm Stewart	Commander Carver (uniformed cop; unnamed in episode)
Frank Ferrucci	Detective Nettles (glasses-wearing detective; unnamed in episode)
Ken Kramer	Dr. Browning (unnamed in episode)
Roger Allford	Garrett Lorre
Richard Yee	David Yung (Ra victim; unnamed in episode)
Brad Lorre	Fireman
Gustavo Moreno	(the) Father
John Tierney	Dr. Jacobs
David Livingstone	Guard (at blood bank)
Also, per Lowry (uncredited onscreen):	
Guyle Frazier	Officer

The official Fox *X-Files* website erroneously leaves Chris Ruppenthal off the writing credits. Both it and the Lowry book erroneously list the character of Detective Gwynn as Detective Munson. Lowry spells the character name "Lore," though the closed-captioning spells it "Lorre."

X-actitude: In addition to the X-File Trinity Killers case number, this episode also reveals an X-File labeled "Scully, Dana: Bureau File no. 73317"; the unexplained number no. 650657 is in the lower-right corner.

The previous six victims:

In Memphis, TN: James Ellis, Linda Sun, and a Jesuit theologian.

In Portland, OR: a priest, the only son in a family of six children, and the owner of a New Age bookstore, "The Holy Spirit."

Club Tepes address: 8115 Hollywood Blvd., Los Angeles, CA

Ra address: 8428 Melrose Ave., Los Angeles, CA

Kristen Kilar background: 1533 Malibu Canyon Road, Malibu, CA 91607 Height 5 feet 8 inches, weight 100 pounds. Previous addresses: 164 Valley View Drive, Portland, OR 97223; 4057 Sweetgum Lane, Memphis, TN 88151.

X-otica: This was the only episode that Anderson missed due to her pregnancy.

Kristin's luxurious house, in real life, is that of hockey star Pavel Bure of the Vancouver Canucks.

Perrey Reeves was, at the time, the actress-girlfriend of David Duchovny; they later broke up, after a couple of years. How was it for Duchovny, acting with his significant other? "The bad part," he says, "is that in acting you're more honest and more vulnerable and more in the moment than you are in life. And the people that you live with in your life are used to seeing you defensive and uptight, as you normally are." When a previous girlfriend saw how gentlemanly he could be in *Red Shoe Diaries*, he explains, "She said: 'Now I know you can be really nice and sweet. Now I want to see you do it.'"

Morgan and Wong, on a tight deadline when a hole opened up in the schedule, rewrote a script by former *Quantum Leap* producer Chris Ruppenthal; the major retained points were the blood-baked bread, three vampires, and the Club Tapes.

126

2.08 "ONE BREATH"   November 11, 1994
Writers: Glen Morgan & James Wong
Director: R. W. Goodwin

Scully's mom, Margaret, reminisces with Mulder about tomboy Dana using a BB-gun given as a birthday present from her two brothers. Then a young man brings out a gravestone:

DANA KATHERINE SCULLY
1964–1994
LOVING DAUGHTER & FRIEND
"The Spirit is the Truth"   1 John 5:07

Later, however, Mulder's barges into intensive care at Northeast George-town Medical Center, Washington, D.C., where Scully lies unconscious, on a respirator, her mother at bedside. When Mulder heatedly demands answers from a Dr. Daly, two security guards throw him out. Later, Daly tells Mulder and Margaret that Scully is in critical condition and in a coma. Daly claims no one knows how Scully arrived or was admitted or administered to, and, after every possible test, they still also don't know what's wrong. Moreover, Scully has a living will, specifying ending life-support once her Glasgow Out-come Scale reaches a certain level.

At Scully's bedside, Mulder meets Scully's New Agey sister, Melissa. On some other plane, Scully sits passively in a rowboat tied to shore, where Mulder and Melissa wait. Back home, Mulder tries to contact Mr. X, but there's no response. At the hospital, a somber Frohike notices something odd on Scully's chart—abnormal protein chains in her blood, with an animo-acid sequence in an unknown combination. Byers had uploaded [N] Scully's file to "the newest Lone Gunman," genius hacker "The Thinker," who says these protein chains are byproducts of branched DNA. It might be an "ID card," or the result of grafting a human to something nonhuman. This DNA branch is now inactive with a poisonous waste product, compromising Scully's immune system.

At the spiritual lake, a Nurse Owens beckons; we see her again, at the hospital, ministering to Scully. As a Nurse Wilkins takes blood, a man in an overcoat surreptitiously watches. Scully flatlines, causing a medical scram-ble during which someone swipes Scully's blood sample. Mulder chases the Overcoat Man to an underground parking garage where Mr. X puts a gun to Mulder's head, ordering him to stop. He says Mulder won't get *him* killed like his predecessor—"You're *my* tool, you understand?" Mulder escapes and grapples with the Overcoat Man. Mr. X breaks the man's arm, and demanding of Mulder, "You want to see what it takes to find the truth?" he executes the man. Out on the spiritual lake, the rowboat line snaps.

Later, Cigarette-Smoking Man subtly threatens Skinner about the trou-blesome Mulder. Mulder, called in about the hospital incident, denies and obfuscates, accusing "Cancer Man" as "the one responsible for what hap-pened to Scully."

In an ethereal room, Scully lies on a table, listening as her ghostly father confirms his love and pride. In the hospital cafeteria, a woman chattily tells Mulder and Melissa someone left a pack of Morleys in the cigarette machine; too bad it's not her brand. Mulder, his antennae up, retrieves it to find an address inside.

At a shabby hotel, he bursts into Cigarette-Smoking Man's room. Cigarette-Smoking Man won't be threatened: "I've watched presidents die," he sneers. Mulder demands, "Why her and not me?" "I like you," Cigarette-Smoking

Man scornfully answers. "I like her, too. That's why she was returned to you." Talking Mulder down, the Cigarette-Smoking Man says, "I'm in the game because I believe what I'm doing is right. If people were to know of the things I know, it would all fall apart." He adds that if Mulder kills him, Mulder will never know the "truth."

FBI HEADQUARTERS: Mulder resigns. Skinner drops by Mulder's office, which he notes used to be a copier room. Mulder confesses, "I hate what I've become." Skinner sorrowfully relates how as a marine in Vietnam, he'd killed a ten-year-old boy who'd entered his camp covered with grenades; later, he'd had a near-death, out-of-body experience. Now, "I'm afraid to look any further beyond that experience. You—you're not." Mulder, still quitting, carries an armload of files through the FBI garage—where he's startled by Mr. X, who tells him to wait for men who will search his apartment for Scully's file at 8:17 P.M., offering Mulder ready-made revenge.

MULDER'S APARTMENT, 7:30 P.M.: Melissa's come to tell him Scully's weakening. He says he can't go; they argue and she leaves. Yet Mulder, with a change of heart, is at Scully's bedside by 8:17. When he returns, his apartment is ransacked. Mulder, breaking down, cries.

128

Scully, row your boat ashore, hallelujah.

In intensive care, Nurse Wilkins notices Scully's eyelids fluttering. Some-one phones Mulder, who rushes to the private room to which Scully's been transferred. In good spirits, she remembers nothing after her kidnapping by Duane Barry. A relieved and grateful Mulder hands her back her cross. Later, Scully asks Nurse Wilkins for Nurse Owens, who'd kept speaking to her and encouraging her during her coma but Wilkins says she's worked there ten years, and there's never been any Nurse Owens.

Sheila Larken	Margaret (Maggie) Scully
Melinda McGraw	Melissa Scully
Mitch Pileggi	Assistant Director Walter S. Skinner
Steven Williams	Mr. X
William B. Davis	Cigarette-Smoking Man
Don Davis	Captain William Scully
Jay Brazeau	Dr. Daly
Nicola Cavendish	Nurse (G.) Owens
Lorena Gale	Nurse Williams
Bruce Harwood	Byers
Dean Haglund	Langly
Tom Braidwood	Frohike
Ryan Michael	Overcoat Man
Tegan Moss	Young Dana Scully

Scully awakens, after her abduction by . . . aliens? Alien-human hybrids? The government? Melinda McGraw is at far right.

The brothers in Scully's flashback are uncredited.

The naming here of one of Scully's brothers—Bill, Jr.—marks the first time her father's name, William, can be inferred. He had not been named in his previous appearance,

X-actitude: Scully's chart: Dated 01/03/94 [N], lab no. 0476

Cigarette-Smoking Man's hotel: 900 W. Georgia St.

Mulder's waking-up gift to Scully: The videotape *Superstars of the Super Bowls*

The skinny on Skinner: Enlisted in marine corps at eighteen. Served in Vietnam; when his entire patrol was killed by enemy fire, and he'd already been placed in a body bag, a corpsman noticed he was barely alive; two weeks later, he awoke in a Saigon hospital.

X-otica: The episode title refers to William Scully's soliloquy to Dana, where he compares the length of a lifetime to "one breath, one heartbeat."

For this episode, director of photography John S. Bartley was Emmy-nominated in the category of Cinematography for a Series. The Lowry book erroneously cites this nomination as for episode 2.05, "Duane Barry."

The character name "The Thinker" was inspired by the America Online *nom de plume* "DuhThinker," used by the highly knowledgeable online X-Phile Yung Jun Kim.

Melinda McGraw had met then-boyfriend Nicholas Lea on the Vancouver-filmed series *The Commish*, where she played Chief of Detectives Cyd Madison for two seasons, and Lea played Officer Ricky Caruso. Future *X-Files* producers Glen Morgan and James Wong had helmed that show, and wrote the part of Melissa with McGraw in mind.

"Melissa was someone who had to understand Scully and yet be different, to challenge Mulder's actions," Morgan says. "Who better than a mother or a sister? Considering where Mulder was at that time, we thought it would be interesting to see Mulder's reaction to a believer of 'positive' ideas." The producers gave some thought to what would have been an unlikely romance between Mulder and Melissa, but backed off.

William B. Davis recalls how his Cigarette-Smoking Man lines in the hotel-room confrontation "went through two or three stages. There was an earlier one that was in some ways more interesting, or at least more textured. Mulder would knock the cigarette away and say, 'Those things are slow suicide,' and my line was 'That's the point.' I know why they changed the scene, because it really wasn't right for the intensity with which David would be coming into the scene. He wasn't ready to have a chat with me about who I am. So I think they did the right thing."

2.09 "FIREWALKER"   November 18, 1994
Writer: Howard Gordon
Director: David Nutter

MOUNT AVALON, WASHINGTON, VOLCANO RESEARCH TEAM DATA ROOM: Dr. Adam Pierce, watching the video feed of the otherwise disabled volcanic-exploration robot "Firewalker," sees chief seismologist Erikson dead, and a shadow moving in the 130°F temperature where nothing should exist [N].

FBI HEADQUARTERS: Pierce tells Mulder and Scully he left the project six weeks ago after disagreements with visionary volcanologist Daniel Trepkos. Mulder worries about Scully going back into the field so soon after her abduction ordeal.

Back in Mt. Avalon, the agents enter the heavily damaged project office while Pierce inspects the satellite dishes and other outdoor equipment. Inside the darkened office, Mulder subdues an attacker, robotics engineer Jason Ludwig, who nervously claims he'd thought Mulder was Trepkos, whom he says has gone mad. Ludwig introduces systems analyst Peter Tanaka and university student Jesse O'Neil.

In the woods, Pierce is garroted to his death by a soot-covered Trepkos. Later, Tanaka finds the body, and brings it to the office. Mulder discovers references in Trepkos's work to an unknown subterranean organism. Scully argues that volcanic heat and toxic gases make that impossible. Mulder suggests that this might be a silicon-based life-form, and wants to search for physical evidence.

Jesse tells Scully that Trepkos became paranoid and stopped taking his medication. She'd been there eight months and wants desperately to go home. Tanaka coughs, collapses, and turns feverish. Mulder and Ludwig carry him out on a stretcher while Scully radios for medevac, but Tanaka bolts for the woods, where a tentacle bursts through his throat. Scully analyzes it as a fungus of probably unknown genus; she believes a spore grew inside Tanaka and eventually outgrew its host. Mulder notes that Tanaka's lungs contained sand—silicon dioxide, the theoretical waste product of silicon-based life-form. They need to find the means of transmission before they risk exposing the outside world. Mulder radios Search and Rescue to Notify the FBI office in Spokane, and to have the CDC set up an evacuation unit on high alert.

Mulder, with the insistent Ludwig as guide, searches in the volcano for Trepkos. Trepkos kills Ludwig with a flare gun and sets him ablaze as Ludwig's throat begins to pulse. Topside, Scully has made seven unsuccessful attempts at culturing the spore, using temperatures ranging from human basal to volcanic, and nutrients of human tissue, blood, saliva, and even sulfur. She believes that unless ingested immediately upon release,

131

the spore dies. Inside the volcano, Trepkos—saying he realizes now that "the Earth holds some truths best left buried"—tells Mulder that the robot Fire-walker brought back a porous, obsidian rock Erikson pulverized for analysis. Trepkos then hermited himself in his lab for three days, until he heard screaming: The team-members had been exposed to the spore, which grew in each until it *became* them. Trepkos destroyed his notes, and killed Pierce to prevent contagion. Mulder realizes that with Jesse exposed, Scully may soon be as well.

Indeed, with Jesse's throat about to burst—and with no other potential hosts available—the spore-enthralled Jesse handcuffs Scully and herself together. Scully desperately manages to shove Jesse into a lockable room, putting a door between them. Jesse's throat bursts, and splatters the window with spores.

Mulder, arriving with Trepkos, calls for Search and Rescue but Army Bio-hazard answers. Mulder lies, stating that only he and Scully are there. Three days later, Mulder writes that they're in a month-long quarantine, undergoing Level 4 decontamination. The military confiscated all specimens and field notes, and sealed off access to Avalon. The robot was recovered, but too damaged to yield any data. While Trepkos and O'Neil are considered unaccounted for, we see Trepkos carry Jesse's body deep into the cave.

132

Anderson with Shawnee Smith in a posed promotional still. Is that an asparagus in your throat, or are you just glad to see me?

Bradley Whitford	Dr. Daniel Trepkos
Leland Orser	Jason Ludwig
Shawnee Smith	Jesse O'Neil
Tuck Milligan	Dr. Adam Pierce
David Lewis	Vosberg (opening-scene project-member; unnamed in episode)
David Kaye	(TV) Reporter (Eric)
Hiro Kanagawa	Peter Tanaka
Torren Rolfsen	Technician

The official Fox *X-Files* website neglects to list front-credit performers Leland Orser and Shawnee Smith.

X-actitude: Date of the events, per Mulder's report: Nov. 11–13, 1994

Volcano Research Team Data Room office number: 105

Cost of Firewalker project: Over $20 million

Real-life mountain range containing the fictional Mount Avalon: Cascade Mountains

Helicopter bringing the agents and Pierce from the Seattle airport: Cascade Search and Rescue, N-9747-P

Trepkos's medication: lithium carbonate

X-otica: The shooting script cited the inner-volcano temperature as 400° Celsius rather than 130° Fahrenheit. Good thing they changed it—the Celsius reading translates to nearly 752°F!

2.10 "RED MUSEUM"   December 9, 1994

Writer: Chris Carter

Director: Win Phelps

X-File case no.: XWC060361

DELTA GLEN, WISCONSIN: Beth Kane, the single mom of young Steve and sixteen-year-old Gary, undresses to shower as someone watches through a peephole. The next morning, two deputy sheriffs find Gary wandering in the road, wearing only underwear and with a red-marker notation on his back: HE IS ONE.

Sometime later, Sheriff Mazeroski drives Mulder and Scully to the Church of the Red Museum, which he suspects of cult-oriented activity. The Church occupies a ranch, where followers of California vegetarianism guru Richard Odin settled three years ago. At a mass, Mulder, hearing talk of second souls and the New Kingdom, says these are "walk-ins"—believers in soul transference, in which enlightened beings take control of one's body.

Gary remembers little except feeling a possibly animal spirit enter him. Later, as Mulder and Scully have dinner at Clay's BBQ, four teens including the sheriff's son Rick harass a Church-member until Mulder intervenes. The next morning, clad only in underwear, Rick's girlfriend Katie stumbles through the woods, hallucinating. On her back is written: SHE IS ONE.

Scully learns Katie's blood contained traces of an alkaloid, possibly an opiate derivative, plus the controlled substance scopolamine, which in quantities above 2mg changes from motion-sickness remedy to hallucinogenic anesthetic. Odin, a.k.a. Dr. Doug Herman, was booted from the AMA in 1986.

GRAHAM COUNTY SHERIFF'S STATION: While questioning Odin they learn of a Red Museum demonstration at Clay's BBQ. There an older man in a red pickup asks to show the FBI agents something.

At a pasture, the man points out two men injecting cattle with, he believes, BST (bovine somatropin)—a (real-life) genetically engineered growth hormone. One of them is the Peeping Tom, Gird Thomas. Later that night, local doctor, Jerrold Larson, is killed in a small plane crash. Investigating the wreck, Mazeroski and the agents find an empty chemical vial, a suitcase of money, and printouts of shipping orders listing credit-card numbers for families of the abducted teens.

At the pasture, Thomas leaves for the day. The Crew-Cut Man who assassinated Deep Throat kills the other man, who was Thomas's boss. The agents learn Gary and the other abducted teens had regularly gone to Dr. Larson for "vitamin shots." Mulder, noticing the peephole in the Kanes' bathroom, finds a videocamera along with tapes. That night, Thomas kidnaps Rick, who is found dead in the woods the next day, with HE IS ONE on his back. Crew-Cut Man, gun in hand, leaves the woods. The agents pass Crew-Cut Man's car turning onto the road, and Scully thinks she knows that face.

Thomas—the Kanes's peeping landlord—says he didn't murder Rick, but admits that he is the abductor. He wrote on their backs because Larson and "the tests" have made the kids "monsters." Larson conducted secret chemical experiments on them, and inoculated cattle with the same drug; after seven rapes in the small town, Larson had told Thomas's boss he felt responsible for the kids' behavior. Scully suddenly remembers where she's seen Crew-Cut Man before.

The residual substance left in the plane-crash vial had been treated with synthetic corticosteroids containing unidentified amino acids. Scully suspects it involves Purity Control, the project from which she'd taken the alien/alien-human hybrid (in episode 1.24, "The Erlenmeyer Flask"). Are they injecting kids with antibodies derived from alien DNA?

When Thomas's boss is found dead, Scully is convinced that Crew-Cut Man's responsible. Mulder has Mazeroski pack up every family on the credit-card list. Odin opens up the Church as their sanctuary. At J.A.S.D. Beef, where the injected cows are processed, Mulder finds Crew-Cut Man pouring

134

gasoline. Crew-Cut Man then locks Mulder in a meat locker. Just as Crew-Cut Man flicks his lighter, Scully, Mazeroski, and the deputies arrive and Mazeroski empties his gun into his son's killer.

Scully's report says the nameless man had no identity record, and his fingerprints weren't on file with either the FBI or the National System of Records. The inoculant was found to be an unstable, probably synthetic antibody of unknown origin, and after three weeks of study, the components couldn't be analyzed further. The inoculated kids and some of their families developed a flu-like illness but the Red Museum members remained healthy, leading Scully to theorize they were the experiment's unwitting control group.

Paul Sand	Gird Thomas
Steve Eastin	Sheriff Mazeroski
Mark Rolston	Richard Odin a.k.a. Dr. Doug Herman
Lindsey Ginter	Crew-Cut Man
Gillian Barber	Beth Kane
Bob Frazer	Gary Kane
Robert Clothier	Old Man (in red pickup)
Elisabeth Rosen	Katie
Crystal Verge	Woman Reading Words (at mass)
Cameron Labine	Rick Mazeroski
Tony Sampson	Brad (Rick's friend; unnamed in episode)
Gerry Nairn	1st Man
Brian McGugan	1st Officer

The actors playing the pilot, Dr. Larson, and Steve Kane are uncredited.

The official Fox *X-Files* website neglects to list front-credit actor Paul Sand.

X-actitude: Beth Kane's late husband: Jay, killed seven years ago in an accident with a machine at the meat-packing plant.

Crew-Cut Man's car: blue, with license-plate (partial) 9LW-9N___; in all likelihood, it's an assumed-name rental.

Number of shots the sheriff fires into Crew-Cut Man: Five. Since he kept pulling the empty gun's trigger, this means for some reason he didn't have a full six-bullet cartridge. Where'd the other bullet go?

Famous walk-ins, per Mulder: Abraham Lincoln, Mikhail Gorbachev, Nixon advisor Charles Colson.

Katie's small, mixed-breed dog: Pupperdog

Head of cattle at the Red Museum sanctuary ranch: 500

Scully's dinner at the barbecue restaurant: ribs

X-otica: Plans were afoot to make "Red Museum" cross over to an episode of CBS's *Picket Fences*, until CBS quashed that idea.

The sympathetically hangdog Paul Sand starred in the 1970s series *Paul Sand in Friends and Lovers* shortly after winning a Tony Award for Broadway's *Story Theatre*. Sand played Dr. Michael Ridley on *St. Elsewhere*, and has had recurring roles on several shows.

2.11 "EXCELSIUS DEI"   December 16, 1994
Writer: Paul Brown
Director: Stephen Surjik

Excelsis Dei Convalescent Home, Worcester, Massachusetts: Nurse Michelle Charters peremptorily shuts off the TV set of frisky Stan Phillips and Hal Arden, and sternly tells attendant Gung Bituen there's no TV after 9 P.M. Minutes later, in an empty room, Charters is raped by some invisible entity.

FBI HEADQUARTERS: Charters is suing the government because she can't get Social Security disability or workman's compensation, and so must return to work around her alleged rapist: Old Hal Arden, who in his five years there has continually harassed her.

At Excelsis Dei, Scully and Mulder question the seventy-four year old, who laughs at the allegation. A worried Stan watches, later warning Hal not to "ruin it" for all of them. Stan takes a mysterious pill, having found a secret stash; when he won't let Hal have one, Hal threatens to rat on him. Mrs. Dawson, the director of the home, insinuates to Scully that Charters has a history of frivolous claims.

Hal chokes to death, and Dr. John Grago, who provides medical attention at the home, tells the agents he'd been successfully treating Hal for eleven months with an experimental Alzheimer's drug called depranil—an enzyme inhibitor that increases the amount of acetylcholine in the brain. Stan ignores Gung's warning about taking too many of the special pills.

At 6:53 P.M., as the agents check out of their hotel, their investigation fruitless, Scully suggests high cholonergic activity could have caused a schizophrenia-like state in Hal; Mulder reminds her that attacker was supposedly invisible. Scully suggests environmental factors, like fungal contaminants that can cause delusional or violent behavior. When Mulder suggests Charters is faking, Scully retorts that the nurse's wounds needed thirteen stitches and the head blow resulted in a subdural hematoma.

Resident Leo Kreutzer asks Gung for more pills for himself and his friend Dorothy, but Gung politely refuses. Stan protests as his daughter, Mrs. Kelly, prepares to take him home; she tells the agents that Stan had needed twenty-four-hour attention when he came here three years ago. Stan bolts from attendant Tiernan, who chases the curiously fleet-footed oldster to the top floor. Some unseen force pushes Tiernan through the window, and pries his fingers off the edge despite Mulder's attempts to save him. Tiernan falls four stories and dies.

Mulder tells Grago that Stan's been present at two deaths in twenty-four hours. The wheelchair-bound Dorothy tells Scully and Dawson there are unseen people here; Dawson attributes this to senile dementia yet we see three ghostly old men in bathrobes huddled around Scully. They may be real or just in Dorothy's mind. Grago tells Mulder that Hal's autopsy revealed poisonous ibotenic acid; Scully says the trace amount wasn't necessarily fatal, but could've caused hallucinations.

Looking for Gung, Mulder breaks through a locked basement door to find a mushroom farm and attendant Upshaw's buried body. Gung admits it's his medicinal mushroom crop, but that he didn't kill Upshaw. These mushrooms have been used for centuries in his country, Malaysia; he'd wanted to help the poorly treated residents here. He claims the mushrooms allow contact with dead ancestors and this place is full of angry spirits taking revenge for their mistreatment. The agents try to confiscate the mushroom pills, but they're missing.

137

Mrs. Kelly sees her father taking a pill, then hears Dorothy shooing away ghosts. Both women see Leo being dragged across the floor by some invisible entity. Mulder rushes to Charters screaming in a bathroom, where the unseen forces lock them inside as it fills with water; Gung finds the water main stuck. As Scully runs to get help, Mrs. Kelly screams Stan is choking and needs doc Scully immediately; Scully tells Grago that Stan needs atropine, in case he, too, has been poisoned. Water pressure finally busts down the bathroom door as Scully, Mulder, Charters, and Mrs. Dawson are all engulfed by the water surge. After Grago administers atropine to Stan, Dorothy says the spirits have gone.

Scully's report says the Massachusetts Department of Health took over the home; they found traces of ibotenic acid in more than half the residents. Grago was replaced and his experiment stopped; most of his patients then had relapses of Alzheimer's. Gung was remanded to the INS for illegal-medication activity, and was to be deported. The government settled Charters's claims out of court.

Teryl Rothery	Nurse Michelle Charters
Sab Shimono	Gung Bituen
Frances Bay	Dorothy
Erick Christmas	Stan Phillips
David Fresco	Hal Arden
Shelia Moore	Mrs. Dawson
Jerry Wasserman	Dr. John Grago
Tasha Simms	Laura (Kelly; first name not given in episode)

Jon Cuthbert	Tiernan
Paul Jarrett	Upshaw
Ernie Prentice	Leo (Kreutzer)

The official Fox *X-Files* website neglects to list front-credit performer Frances Bay. The Lowry book omits nearly half the cast.

X-actitude: Mulder and Scully's hotel in Worcester: Hotel Hartley, rooms 206 and 210

Mrs. Kelly's husband: Jack

Upshaw's wage: $5.50 an hour

Recently deceased resident: Mrs. T. Richardson

Boxing match on TV: Mike Tyson vs. a contender named Danelle

Hour that Scully began researching Charters's case: 6 A.M.

Scully's stat request when Hal begins choking to death: 75mg of lidocaine, 1 amp of epinephrine, and a crash cart

X-otica: The corridor where the flood was shot is at the abandoned Riverview Mental Institution in nearby Coquitlam, B.C.

Title translation: Latin for "glory of God." The episode title is spelled differently from that of the home as seen on-screen

The closed captioning misspells "epinephrine" as "ampinephrine."

Eric Christmas is familiar as Sam Malone's parish priest, Father Barry, on *Cheers*, and the much more apoplectic priest in the cult-hit *Harold and Maude*. Frances Bay, who played the eerie Mrs. Tremond on *Twin Peaks*, seems destined to be forever known as the marble-rye-bread lady from two 1996 episodes of *Seinfeld*. Sacramento native Sab Shimono, recently seen as an elder in *Waterworld* (1995), came to prominence as traditionalist Mr. Saito in the movie and TV series *Gung Ho*.

2.12 "AUBREY"   January 6, 1995

Writer: Sara B. Charno

Director: Rob Bowman

POLICE HEADQUARTERS, AUBREY, MISSOURI: Detective B. J. Morrow tells married detective chief Lt. Brian Tillman she's pregnant. He instructs her to go to Motel Black at 8 P.M. to talk. There a painful vision leads her to a field down the road, where she digs up human remains and an FBI badge. FBI HEADQUARTERS: Scully later confirms the body is that of legendary agent Sam Cheney. Mulder says Cheney and partner Tim Ledbetter were investigating three serial murders in Aubrey in 1942.

At the crime scene, Scully and Mulder find discrepancies in Morrow's story; when Mulder starts asking her about premonitions, Tillman hustles her away. Scully performs an autopsy on Cheney. Mulder describes Cheney's last case, where three raped and murdered women had SISTER razored onto their chests; the killer was never found. Scully, using a digital scanner, tries to determine if there's a matching razor pattern here. Morrow comes in, has a vision upon seeing Cheney's skull, then gets sick. To a sympathetic Scully, she confirms her affair with Tillman and describes her nightmares. Morrow, to her own surprise, says Cheney's cuts spell BROTHER.

Tillman demands to know where they got these new crime-scene photos; Scully says they're from 1942. A shocked Tillman says three days ago, a young woman was found murdered with SISTER carved into her chest. An aide tells Tillman there's just been another such killing. At this latest crime scene, Morrow says the victim is a woman she's seen in a recurring dream. Later she tells the agents about it: A woman is hurt in an unfamiliar house; Morrow looks in a mirror and sees a man with intense eyes and a rash; she then sees a monument, which she now draws. Mulder recognizes it as the famous Trylon and Perisphere of the 1939 World's Fair.

That night, while looking at 1942 mug shots, Morrow sees the man from her nightmare. The suspect is Harry Cokely, living in Gainesville, Nebraska, since his release from McCallister Penitentiary on December 5, 1993. He was convicted in 1945 for the rape and attempted murder of Linda Thibedeaux—carving SISTER on her chest before she escaped. Scully suggests Morrow has cryptomnesia—consciously forgotten information—and maybe her cop father had discussed the case and the information remained in her subconscious. At Cokely's rundown house, the seventy-seven year old defiantly says he's served his time, and convincingly insists he was right there two nights ago.

Morrow awakens from a nightmare covered with blood and SISTER carved on her chest. She sees a young Cokely in the mirror and collapses experiencing visions—including one of the floorboard at her feet, which she then pulls up. Neighbors, hearing the commotion, call the police; Tillman arrives to take Morrow to the hospital. Mulder finds a sack of human remains beneath the floor.

At Memorial Hospital, Morrow swears Cokely attacked her. Tillman questions the old man, who denies everything. Scully tells Mulder that blood found under the nails of Roberta Johnson, the most recent victim, belonged to Cokely. The agents visit widow Linda Thibedeaux. She describes the 1940s rape that happened here on her stairwell landing and where Mulder notices a photo of her and her late husband Martin at the 1939 World's Fair. She admits to having Cokely's child and putting it up for adoption. Scully learns the floorboard remains were Tim Ledbetter's and that a razor with possible fingerprints was found beneath Morrow's house, which Cokely had rented in 1942. Danny from the FBI calls to say he's tracked down Thibedeaux's son: police officer Raymond Morrow—B. J.'s father.

Morrow attacks Mrs. Thibedeaux, stopping when SISTER mysteriously appears on both of their chests; later, Mulder and Scully find Mrs. Thibedeaux alive. Scully, noting the new murders began after Morrow had found herself pregnant, deduces Morrow will go after Tillman next; Mulder believes she'll go after Cokely, now that she knows the truth.

Cokely, at home watching TV, finds his respirator cut. Morrow attacks. Minutes later, after Mulder finds a moaning Cokely, Morrow bludgeons Mulder and puts a razor to his neck. Cokely dies just as Scully and Tillman burst in, and Morrow becomes herself again. Scully's report says tests on Morrow remain inconclusive—perhaps a mutator gene activated previously dormant genes. At the Shamrock Women's Prison Psychiatric Ward, a very pregnant Morrow is on suicide watch after an attempted self-abortion. The fetus shows no abnormality . . . yet. Tillman has petitioned to adopt the child.

Terry O'Quinn	Lieutenant Brian Tillman
Deborah Strang	Detective B. J. Morrow
Morgan Woodward	Harry Cokely
Joy Coghill	Linda Thibedeaux
Roby Driscoll	Detective Joe Darnell (unnamed in episode)
Peter Fleming	1st Officer
Sara Jane Redmond	Young Mom
Emanuel Hajek	Young Cokely

The official Fox *X-Files* website neglects to list front-credit performer Joy Coghill.

X-actitude: Cheney's last case: "The Slash Killer": three young women (Antonia Bradsean, Kathy Eberhardt, Laura Van Cleef), ages twenty-five to thirty, disabled with a blow to the head.

Police "Slash Killer" file: HOM, RAP 1942 Case 147815

Mug shot: State Police 958674, in Cimarron County Catalogue No. 4756 (for year) 1942

Thibedeaux's address: 238 North 54th St., Edmond, NB

Cokely's background: Only son in a family with five daughters. Lives in Terrence, NB (an hour from Aubrey, MO), in 1942.

Continuity error: Mulder's FBI friend, Danny, has the last name Bernstow in episode 1.04, "Conduit." But it's Vallodeo or Valodeo here per dialogue. (It doesn't appear in closed-captioning.) The Lowry book erroneously has it Valodella.

X-otica: All the towns mentioned in this episode are fictional.

Terry O'Quinn played the titular fiend of *The Stepfather* (1987) and *Stepfather 2* (1989). Morgan Woodard is best known for two outstanding performances on the original *Star Trek*: As a tragically maddened penal-colony second-in-command, in "Dagger of the Mind," and as the immortality-hungry captain of the starship *Exeter* in "The Omega Glory."

2.13 "IRRESISTIBLE"   January 13, 1995
Writer: Chris Carter
Director: David Nutter

MINNEAPOLIS, MINNESOTA: At a memorial chapel, a young woman eulogizes her friend Jennifer. That night, the funeral director finds his assistant, Donnie Pfaster, has cut off most of Jennifer's hair. Pfaster's fired. Scully and Mulder are at a Minneapolis cemetery with local FBI agent Moe Bocks and the mutilated corpse of Katharine Ann Terle. Mulder shoots down Bocks's assertion that aliens are involved, and suggests a search of the area will show backhoe tracks. Later, a woman named Marilyn interviews Pfaster for a delivery-person job at Ficicello Frozen Foods.

FBI MINNEAPOLIS OFFICE, NEXT DAY: Bocks tells Mulder and Scully they've found more desecrated bodies, bringing the total to three in the last two days. Two had their hair cut, the third had fingernails removed. To Mulder it suggests the work of an "escalating fetishist," who may resort to murder to obtain warm corpses. A queasy Scully writes a field report on necrophiles and examines mug shots of local offenders.

141

Pfaster picks up a streetwalker and takes her to his apartment; he runs a bath for her and asks that she shampoo. Marilyn calls to tell Pfaster he got the job and can start right away. The prostitute grows alarmed upon seeing a collection of funeral wreaths around Pfaster's bedroom. She screams and tries to get away, but he pursues her. Later that night, the three agents are at a muddy field waiting for a body to be identified. The MO matches that of the escalating fetishist; he took not only fingernails, but the fingers. A prostitute IDs the victim as one of her colleagues. The next morning, Pfaster introduces himself to a suburban housewife as the new deliveryperson, and creepily contemplates teenaged Lisa, one of the woman's three daughters.

COUNTY MORGUE: Three plainclothes men and a uniform cop appear with Scully for the streetwalker's autopsy. At a lineup, the identifying prostitute has no luck determining a suspect.

LOS CERRITOS ADULT EDUCATION, THAT NIGHT: After class, Pfaster approaches a pretty classmate to ask about their homework assignment. When he begins to menace her, she groin-kicks him and runs for help.

Scully dreams she's preparing to do an autopsy on herself; then, through the open eyes of her live self on the table, she sees the silhouette of a peering figure with pointed ears. At 11:21 P.M., Mulder phones to announce an arrest—it turns out to be just a businessman with an assault history, who's quickly ruled out. Arrested for his night-school assault, Pfaster is held in another cell. A creeped-out Scully tells Mulder she'd like to concentrate on the forensic evidence back in Washington. Pfaster is then released, but not before learning Scully's name.

FBI LATENT FINGERPRINT ANALYSIS LAB, WASHINGTON D.C.: Agent Busch awaits the prostitute's body for a bloodstain print. Scully, who plans to return to Minneapolis tonight, meets with social worker Karen F. Kosseff LCSW (whose first name and middle initial are revealed in 2.21, "The Calusari") at the Employee Assistance Program Office. Scully learns Busch lifted a print from the woman's nail polish. Busch also says someone from Minneapolis phoned for her; when Scully calls Mulder to say she's modeming the print, she discovers it was neither he nor Bocks.

Bocks (having evidently matched the print to Pfaster's local arrest record) leads a raid on Pfaster's home. They find evidence including a refrigerated finger. Meanwhile Pfaster awaits Scully at the airport, having learned from Busch she was flying in. Trailing her car, he rear-ends her and makes her crash.

BOCKS'S OFFICE: An agent reports they've found Scully's car; Mulder, at the scene, finds white paint stains and has Bocks send this evidence to Washington to determine the car's make and model.

In a deserted house, Pfaster runs a bath for the bound-and-gagged Scully, who momentarily imagines him as the apparently alien silhouette from her dream. Mulder and Bocks, having no luck with the paint sample, run a computer check on Pfaster's mother. They learn she wintered in Boca Raton, Florida until her death a year ago, and owned a late-model white sedan; they look to see if she had a Minneapolis residence.

At that residence, Scully momentarily escapes from Pfaster; he recaptures her just as Bocks and Mulder lead a raid. The bruised and scraped Scully insists she's fine—until she breaks down sobbing while Mulder comforts her. In voice-over, Mulder makes the final report.

142

Bruce Weitz	Agent Moe Bocks
Nick Chinlund	Donnie Addie Pfaster
Christine Willes	Karen F. Kossef
Deanna Milligan	Satin (murdered prostitute; unnamed in episode)
Robert Thurston	Toews (unnamed in episode)
Glynis Davies	Ellen (housewife; unnamed in episode)
Tim Progish	Mr. Fiebling (unnamed in episode)
Dwight McFee	Suspect
Denalda Williams	Marilyn
Maggie O'Hara	Young Woman (doing eulogy)
Kathleen Duborg	Prostitute
Mark Saunders	Agent Busch
Clara Hunter	Coed (adult-ed classmate)

Neither Lisa nor the female agent, who have speaking lines, are credited.

X-actitude: Donnie Addie Pfaster's background: Age twenty-eight. Grew up in the Twin Cities, went away for a few years, studied cosmetology, and returned to work as a funeral-home cosmetologist and attend night school to study comparative religions.

The book on Bocks: A paranormal buff; tells Mulder and Scully, "Anything slightly freakazoid, that's the drill, call Moe Bocks"—an eerie image of Mulder grown older and never having found The Truth. Friend at MUFON (Mutual UFO Network) who claims to know Mulder: Andy Schneider. Years on force: twenty-two.

Mulder's football tickets: a pair of forty-yard-line seats for the Minnesota Vikings vs. Washington Redskins game at the Hubert H. Humphrey Metrodome.

Scully's airport locales: Charles Lindbergh Terminal; Lariat Rent-a-Car

Necrophile mug shots—names and case numbers:

John (last name unreadable)	83610272
Wayne (last name unreadable)	49803212
Antonio (last name unreadable)	58801297
Vick Sepa	30227618

143

Results of paint analysis: Color is "ivory base," a two-step enamel used by three makers of late-model midsize cars—an estimated 60,000 of them in the Twin Cities metropolitan area.

Katherine Ann Terle's life dates: 1975–1995

Name of previous deliveryperson on Pfaster's route: Skip

X-otica: The original episode title was reportedly "Fascination."

LCSW stands for Licensed Certified Social Worker.

Bruce Weitz won a 1984 Emmy Award playing Detective Mick Belker on *Hill Street Blues*. He also appeared in the series casts of *Anything But Love* and *Byrds of Paradise*. The chilling Nick Chinlund—a lucky last-minute find—made his film debut in *Lethal Weapon 3* (1992). He appeared in the "Auto Erotica" episode of Duchovny's *Red Shoe Diaries*.

2.14 "DIE HAND DIE VERLETZT" January 27, 1995

Writers: James "Chargers" Wong & Glen "Bolts, Baby!" Morgan
Director: Kim Manners

CROWLEY HIGH SCHOOL, MILFORD HAVEN, NEW HAMPSHIRE, NIGHT: Four members of a PTA-like group, the PTC—Jim Ausbury, Deborah, Coach Paul, and the unnamed school psychologist—call for a group prayer. They solemnly beseech the "lord of darkness" to "bestow their infernal power upon me." In German, Deborah prays, "His is the hand that wounds! His is the place called Hell."

NIGHT: High-schoolers Jerry Stevens and Dave Duran bring classmates Kate/Shannon Ausbury [N] and Andrea to the woods. The boys plan to fake a Satanic ritual in order to scare the girls and then get them drunk. As Dave reads an incantation, spectral voices murmur and rats appear. The girls and Dave run off while a hand clutches Jerry's throat until he dies.

CRIME SCENE 8:55 A.M.: Sheriff Oakes tells Scully the teen's been dead about twelve hours; his eyes and heart were removed. Scully finds a book page with a partial title; Oakes goes to track it down. Then, toads rain from the sky. At the school library, Mulder looks up the book traced to the torn page: M. R. Krashewski's *Witch Hunt: A History of The Occult In America*—last borrowed January 16, 1995, by Dave Duran. Scully says tornadoes in northern Massachusetts probably accounted for the toads.

Substitute teacher Mrs. Phyllis H. Paddock greets the agent in a science-lab classroom. They interview Duran and let him go. Outside the room, Ausbury wants to know which of his compatriots killed Jerry, who was displayed in accordance with the Rites of the Azazel; the others insist it was some outside force. Mulder notices that a drinking fountain drains counterclockwise not clockwise, which he says the Coriolis effect dictates in the Northern Hemisphere [N]. Paddock files papers in a desk drawer containing two eyes and a heart.

The school psychologist dismisses Mulder's question about the large number of recent student psychological complaints. Shannon, in science class, suffers a hallucination upon dissecting a fetal pig. She bolts from the psychologist's office when told her stepdad is coming for her. She privately tells Mulder and Scully about unspeakable Satanic rites Ausbury and others conducted with her and her sister, whom Ausbury murdered at eight, making it appear like an accident. Ausbury and his occult colleagues held rituals at her home when mom was away—making her and her sister pregnant and then sacrificing the babies; Shannon says she's had three, all now buried in the basement. The agents question the Ausburys; mom tearfully swears fifteen-year-old Shannon has never been pregnant, and that Teresa died of crib death at eight weeks.

Paddock, the same day, prepares Shannon to dissect a fetal pig for her final exam. Paddock solicitously takes Shannon's bracelet—which she uses as a talisman to enchant Shannon into fatally slashing her wrists. A grieving Ausbury learns his compatriots' plan to blame Jerry's death on Shannon in order to get the police and FBI to close the case. Scully tells Mulder the regular science teacher—who'd taken only two sick days in fifteen years—had contracted the highly rare necrotizing fasciitis, or flesh-eating bacteria; no one at the school knows anything about Paddock or who hired her. During a power outage, Paddock swipes Scully's pen.

With a warrant, Mulder searches the seemingly empty Ausbury home where Jim Ausbury waits in the basement. The others' attempt to frame his step-daughter has made him renounce his dark faith. Paddock performs a ritual with Scully's pen. Ausbury admits to Mulder he forced Shannon to participate in watered-down rituals, but never hurt her, and hypnotized her to repress the memories. Scully phones Mulder for help; Mulder handcuffs Ausbury in the basement while he rushes to the school—leaving Ausbury helpless when a large Burmese python slithers toward him.

Mulder finds Scully perfectly fine, saying she never called him. They rush back to Ausbury, but find only digested meat and bones next to a snakeskin. At the school, Coach Paul tells the others he heard from Sheriff Oakes that Ausbury is dead. The psychologist argues they'll have to sacrifice Mulder, or the same fate will befall them. Scully and Mulder arrive to find an injured Paddock blaming the PTC officials for killing Ausbury and Jerry. Investigating, they're attacked and bound by Paul and the psychologist. Deborah, with a prayer, raises a knife, but she and Paul are killed by two blasts from the psychologist's rifle as Paddock, in another room, gloats. She blows a candle out, and the psychologist shoots himself. Mulder and Scully find Paddock gone, having written on her chalkboard: "Goodbye. It's been nice working with you."

145

Dan Butler	Jim Ausbury
Susan Blommaert	Phyllis H. Paddock
Heather McComb	Shannon Ausbury
Shaun Johnson	(School psychologist) Pete Calcagni (unnamed in episode)
P. Lynn Johnson	Deborah Brown (last name not given in episode)
Travis MacDonald	Dave Duran
Michele Goodger	Barbara Ausbury (unnamed in episode)
Larry Musser	Sheriff John Oakes (first name not given in episode)
Franky Czinege	Jerry Thomas (per end-credits; last name Stevens per episode dialog; spelling per script)
Laura Harris	Andrea
Doug Abrahams	Paul Vitaris (last name not given in episode)

The official Fox *X-Files* website neglects to list front-credit actor Heather McComb. The Lowry book misspells the first name of actress Michele Goodger as "Michelle."

X-actitude: Student production the PTC forbids performance of: *Jesus Christ Superstar*

Book that Mulder skims past in the card file: Stephen King's *Four Past Midnight*

Krashewski book's file number: 354KRA. Two other borrowers:

May 17, 1994	J. Schwartsky
Oct. 8, 1994	L. Lemenchik

Agents' license plate: 6987N5

Paddock's official background:

Grossmont Union High School District 1992–94 (substitute). Los Angeles Unified District 1988–89. St. Louis Municipal High School 1974–79. Education: University of California, Los Angeles, CA.

Prayer at the end (Latin):

Deborah: *Dominus Inferus vobiscum* [The Infernal Lord be with you]
Men, responding: *Et cum tuo* [And with you]
Deborah: *Sursum cordo*

What Scully finds during Internet research: Article from a 1934 Nazi newspaper, *Volkischer Beobachter*, blaming Jews for the type of ritual murders often blamed today on occultists.

X-otica: Title translation: German for "the hand that wounds."

Crowley High is named after the famous occultist, sybarite, and author Aleister Crowley (1875–1947).

Ausbury mentions that his family and religion have been in this town seven generations. In mysticism, eventful things happen to the seventh generation, in particular to the seventh son or seventh daughter.

The producers, no doubt fearing legal or bad-press repercussions, had Shannon specify that the parent-teacher group isn't the PTA but the "PTC."

There's a real-life Milford, NH, but no Milford Haven.

The character names "Deborah Brown" and "Paul Vitaris" are those of Internet *X*-fans. Other fans' names appeared in an airline manifest in the season opener, "Little Green Men."

The idiosyncratic writer credits refer to the then upcoming Super Bowl XXIX. San Diego natives Morgan and Wong were rooting for the Chargers, who lost to the San Francisco 49ers, 49–26.

Dan Butler plays Bob "Bulldog" Briscoe on *Frasier*. Heather McComb is familiar from *Beethoven's 2nd* (1993), and as the poor-little-rich-girl Zoe in the Francis Coppola segment of *New York Stories* (1989). She played the superhero Jubilee in the 1996 TV-movie/pilot *Generation X*. Susan (a.k.a. Susan J.) Blommaert has appeared in the films *Crossing Delancey* (1988), *Pet Sematary* (1989) and *Edward Scissorhands* (1990), and as one of *Murphy Brown*'s hapless secretaries.

2.15 "FRESH BONES"   February 3, 1995
Writer: Howard Gordon
Director: Rob Bowman

FOLKSTONE, NORTH CAROLINA: Marine private John "Jack" McAlpin explodes in anger at his wife and their baby boy, Luke. After two horrible visions, he slams his car into a tree adorned with a strange painted symbol.

COUNTY ROAD 10: Scully and Mulder investigate and find McAlpin's is the second suicide in two weeks among men stationed at the Folkstone INS

Processing Center, housing 12,000 Haitian refugees. A month ago, a ten-year-old boy was killed under vague circumstances. At the tree, the agents speculate the graffiti might be a Haitian voodoo symbol (called a *ve-ve* or *vever*, though the episode doesn't specify).

Mrs. McAlpin says Pvt. Harry Dunham had told her they'd found evidence of a voodoo curse—the same evidence found on a stool the ten-year-old had used to hang himself. At Folkstone, Mulder buys a voodoo charm from a kid named Chester Bonaparte. The commander, Colonel Wharton, says self-proclaimed revolutionary Pierre Bauvais instigated the riot in which the boy died.

Camp morgue: Dr. Foyle tells Scully that McAlpin had no cardiorespiratory function, and his head was "hanging on his shoulders like a peony." But when he pulls out the refrigerated slab, there's only a dog. Dunham, from McAlpin's squad, tells Mulder he'd seen McAlpin's head "hanging by a thread." At the brig, Bauvais tells Mulder the tree symbol represents a *loco-miroir* ("mirror of the soul"), which makes a person confront one's true self. Later, the agents's car nearly hits a dazed McAlpin.

At the psychiatric infirmary, the unresponsive McAlpin is diagnosed with amnesia. Scully says a gross error like Foyle's has been known to happen. The medical report lists trace levels of tetrodotoxin, a poison found in puffer fish. Mulder says Harvard ethnobotanist Wade Davis found that this drug, which can cause paralysis and depressed cardiorespiratory activity, is a part of zombification rituals. Folkstone Municipal Cemetery: The agents check the grave of previous "dead" marine private Manuel Guttierez; the corpse is missing, and the groundskeeper says body snatchers are a local problem. They find Chester collecting frogs. Later at a restaurant with them, he says, "Fresh bones, they pay good," but that he sticks to frogs, selling them to Bauvais for fifty cents each. Scully notes certain frog species secrete bufo-toxin, similar to tetrodotoxin.

Outside, a nervous Dunham says Bauvais had told Wharton the marines would have their souls taken one by one if the refugees weren't repatriated. Wharton responded by ordering his men to beat the refugees. Chester runs, but after the agents give chase, all they find is a cat. Wharton denies the beating allegations yet to his horror sees blood seep from his breakfast. In the car, Scully cuts herself on a ring of thorns left around the steering wheel column; when she drops it outside, it lands next to a *loco-miroir*. Wharton and his aide beat Bauvais, demanding to know his "secret."

Mr. X tells Mulder in twenty-four hours, Folkstone will be sealed from out-side eyes. He says during a recent Haiti involvement, three soldiers—two of them Wharton's—committed suicide. Mulder deduces the military is letting Wharton have his revenge—which Mr. X pointedly does not deny.

Scully discovers Dunham's been AWOL since last night. She finds him dead in a bloody tub; a zombie-like McAlpin holds a bloody knife. In the brig, McAlpin recalls little of the last few days, but he's signed a confession under

147

pressure from Wharton, who tells the agents Bauvais cut his wrists on a bedspring and died, and the FBI investigation is over. Unbeknownst to Mulder, Scully is growing oddly ill. Mrs. McAlpin gives the agents a photo Dunham left for them—Bauvais and Wharton, chummy in Haiti.

WHARTON'S EMPTY OFFICE: Wharton's aide detains the agents as they dig for evidence; they inform him Dunham and Guttierez were about to testify against Wharton, and show him both Guttierez's dog tags and his bones in a trunk. The aide confesses they buried Bauvais in a municipal graveyard. There, Wharton prepares Bauvais's casket for a voodoo rite. Mulder goes after a guttural-incanting Wharton, while an ill Scully waits in the car. As liquid pours from her hand wound, a Creole-speaking man grabs her throat. Mulder, approaching Wharton, falls in pain when Wharton plunges a knife into the ground. Bauvais appears, and downs Wharton with dusty breath. In the car, Scully desperately reaches for the protective charm; upon grabbing it, her blood and the assailant vanish and a black cat appears. The next day the refugees are being shipped out. Scully asks about Chester—a marine says the boy had died in a riot six weeks ago. As the groundskeeper's loud steam shovel pours dirt onto a casket, Wharton bangs and screams unheard inside.

148

Bruce Young	Pierre Bauvais
Daniel Benzali	Colonel Wharton
Jamil Walker Smith	Chester Bonaparte
Matt Hill	Private Harry Dunham
Callum Keith Rennie	Groundskeeper
Steven Williams	Mr. X
Kevin Conway	Private (Jack) McAlpin
Katya Gardner	Robin (McAlpin; first name not given in episode)
Roger Cross	Private Kittel (Wharton's aide; unnamed in episode)
Peter Kelamis	Lieutenant Foyle (rank not given in episode)
Uncredited:	
Adrien Malebranche	Skinny man accosting Scully

The child or children playing infant Luke are uncredited.

X-actitude: Mulder's hotel room number: 7

Foyle's assistant: Jackson. Unseen, he's heard from off-camera.

Code Mr. X left in Mulder's room: Ten of diamonds card. (The marker for County Road 10 is diamond-shaped.)

Dunham background: In his hometown of New Orleans, he was to marry the daughter of Clyde Jessamin, an associate of Dunham's father. Jessamin's crooked business dealings enraged a voodoo practitioner, and the man's daughter died of some mysterious ailment—her autopsy revealed snakes in her belly.

With a painted voodoo *loco-miroir*.

X-otica: Wade Davis is a real-life Harvard ethnobotanist and the author of *The Serpent and the Rainbow*.

Folkstone, NC, is a fictional locale.

The groundskeeper's Rottweiler is named Wong—a seemingly cutting reference to coexecutive producer James Wong, who with writing partner Glen Morgan had scripted the previous episode, then left *The X-Files* to create *Space: Above and Beyond*.

Daniel Benzali starred as attorney Ted Hoffman in *Murder One*.

2.16 "COLONY"   February 10, 1995
Teleplay: Chris Carter
Story: David Duchovny & Chris Carter
Director: Nick Marck

Part 1 of a 2-part episode

THE BEAUFORT SEA, THE ARCTIC, NIGHT: Over Mulder's voice-over, a medevac helicopter ferries him to a rescue ship. He tells himself that if he dies now, it'll be knowing his belief in alien visitation has been justified. Scully bursts in, seeing Mulder on monitors and a respirator, and immersed in a tub of water. She declares he can't be warmed—the cold is all that's keeping him alive. She argues with the doctors until, in horror, she hears his heart monitor flatline.

The remainder of this episode and next is in flashback. THE BEAUFORT SEA: A light has been hovering over a research vessel for twenty minutes; then it accelerates too rapidly for any helicopter, and crashes in a mushroom cloud.

TWO DAYS LATER, WOMAN'S CARE FAMILY SERVICES AND CLINIC, SCRANTON, PENNSYLVANIA: The TV news calls the "UFO" a Russian aircraft; the unnamed pilot miraculously survived, but escaped his Alaska hospital. After seeing the Pilot's face on TV, Dr. Landon Prince bolts in terror. But the Pilot himself arrives, stops him and demands, "Where is he?" When the doctor says he doesn't know, the Pilot stabs him with a stiletto-like weapon, drawing green "blood" from the doctor's neck. He then sets the building afire.

FBI HEADQUARTERS: Mulder's received three obits in his e-mail, all of doctors who've died in arson fires at their respective abortion clinics over the last two weeks. From their pictures, they could be triplets—except that Mulder can't find anything about their birth or past. In Scranton a police sergeant tells Scully and Mulder he's arrested the Reverend Calvin Sistrunk, a local antiabortion activist who's threatened Dr. Prince. The officer confirms no body was found at the fire site—just as in the last two cases. Sistrunk denies involvement, despite being arrested with a newspaper clipping of the doctor's photo in a classified ad: "Have you seen this man?"

THE GLOBE AND MAIL, BINGHAMTON, NEW YORK: A clerk remembers the ad-buyer paid in cash and refused to sign anything. The agents find twenty-four messages in his voice mail, the latest claiming the man in the photo is Dr. Aaron Baker of Syracuse, New York.

They contact Agent Barrett Weiss (whose first name isn't given until the next episode) at the Syracuse field office. Outside Baker's house, Weiss hears the Pilot warn Baker, "Your plans will not succeed." Weiss bursts in and to his horror sees Baker turn into green ooze; when he shoots the menacing Pilot, green "blood" harmlessly pours from the wounds. After Mulder and Scully arrive, Weiss tells them Baker's long gone. Then, out of sight, "Weiss" throws his car keys into his trunk—where the real Weiss lies dead. Morphing, the Pilot resumes his original form and leaves.

With an agent dead, an angry Skinner terminates the case. Mulder and Scully get e-mail showing yet another lookalike doctor: James Dickens, here in D.C. Outside Scully's apartment house, they're approached by a man identifying himself as Ambrose Chapel, CIA. He says the CIA has known of the identical people for ten years; he claims that early in the cold war, the Russians isolated genetic material in identical twins, learned to reproduce it, and eventually created human clones. The program was code-named "Gregor," the name given to each clone. The Gregors slowly emigrated to the U.S., obtained high-security clearances at government medical facilities, and now stand poised to contaminate the nation in event of war. In a secret agreement, the U.S. is allowing the clones to be killed in exchange for Russia ending the program and sharing the science. Chapel placed the classified ad to save the Gregors, asserting he, like Mulder and Scully, can't stomach state-sanctioned murder and wants the truth to come out.

Chapel accompanies the agents to Dickens's apartment in suburban Germantown, Maryland. Upon seeing Chapel, Dickens jumps three or four stories to the street and, incredibly, gets up and runs away. A woman acquaintance of Dickens's has kept herself hidden from the agents. Mulder and Chapel give chase; after Mulder's knocked down by a car, "Chapel" morphs into the Pilot. By the time the agents catch up, he's turned back into Chapel, saying Dickens escaped to a roof. He leaves to search the area as Scully notices green ooze underfoot.

MULDER'S OFFICE: Scully can't believe Mulder took the CIA man at his word. "Whatever happened to 'Trust no One'?" "Oh, I changed it to 'Trust Everyone.' I didn't tell you?" Scully, upon learning Chapel's a seventeen-year CIA veteran, wonders how someone so experienced could lose such an easy fugitive. She then displays an acid-like hole in one of her new shoes— evidently from the ooze she stepped in; they'll have it analyzed. Scully, doing an autopsy on Weiss, finds polycythemia, excessive production of red blood

On the rescue ship with, left to right, an extra, and frequent utility player Bonnie Hay.

cells—Weiss's blood had curdled—yet she can find no coagulating agent. Skinner informs Mulder of a family emergency involving his dad, William (whose name isn't given in this episode, but later in 2.25, "Anasazi"). Mulder's divorced mom answers the phone at his father's house. His father tells Fox to rush home.

Scully, finding an address tag on the briefcase she'd collected at Dickens's apartment, tracks it to a Germantown warehouse. Inside, she finds congealed ooze on the floor, and Chapel—either the Pilot or, perhaps, the *real* Chapel—knocking over a green cylindrical chamber and squishing the organs that fall out. When he notices her, Scully tears out and hides in her apartment [N]. West Tisbury, Martha's Vineyard, Massachusetts: Mulder's enigmatic father and emotionally scarred mother introduce him to a thirty-ish woman with reddish-brown hair—whom his father identifies as Fox's sister, Samantha. Mulder doesn't realize it, but it's evidently the woman from Dickens's apartment.

After hours of talking with the woman, Mulder assures his mother that it *is* Samantha; indeed, the young woman jokingly asks if Fox wants to play that game of Stratego they were about to start twenty-two years ago. She tells him she'd returned at age nine or ten with no memory, and was raised by adoptive parents; years ago, anxiety prompted her to try regression-hyp-notherapy—and everything about the abduction and testing came back. She says she's in danger from a bounty hunter who killed "my father and the other doctors . . . They're only visitors here—what people would call aliens." Though the hunter can change his appearance, she can always recognize him—one reason he's coming to kill her.

Scully, on a bus, calls Mulder saying she'll be hiding at the Vacation Village Motor Lodge off I-90 in Germantown. A few passengers away, the Pilot listens. She stops at the warehouse and finds a clone/alien fetus and four grown male clones, who say they're the last and ask for protection. Shortly thereafter, Scully hands them off to a federal marshal and police, for placement in maximum protective custody. The Pilot watches. Mulder phones the motel, just missing Scully as she checks in; the clerk forgets to give her the message. Mulder tries her cel phone a few minutes later, but she's in the shower and doesn't hear. Federal Stockade, Tilestown, Virginia 7:05 p.m.: The federal marshal appears at the clones' cells—it's the Pilot. At 11:21 p.m., Mulder arrives at Scully's room—or so it seems until her cel phone rings . . . and it's Mulder.

Mitch Pileggi	Assistant Director Walter S. Skinner
Peter Donat	William Mulder
Brian Thompson	The Pilot
Dana Gladstone	"Dr. Landon Prince"/"Dr. James Dickens"/other duplicates

Megan Leitch	Samantha Mulder (evidently)
Tom Butler	"CIA Agent Ambrose Chapel"
Tim Henry	Federal Marshal
Andrew Johnston	Agent Barrett Weiss
Rebecca Toolan	Mulder's Mother
Ken Roberts	Motel Proprietor
Michael Rogers	1st Crewman
Oliver Becker	2nd Doctor
James Leard	Sergeant Al Dixon (unnamed in episode)
Linden Banks	Rev. (Calvin) Sistrunk
Bonnie Hay	Field Doctor
Kim Restell	Newspaper Clerk
Richard Sargent	Captain
David L. Gordon	FBI Agent (who gets Mulder from autopsy room)
Uncredited:	
Capper McIntyre	First Jailer (nonspeaking role, just before end-of-shift changeover to moustached guard)
Michael McDonald	Military Policeman (not evident in episode; named in several print sources)

X-actitide: The doctors whose obits Mulder received: 153

Dr. Landon Prince, of Scranton, PA

Dr. Dale Gayhart, of New York City

Dr. Harvey Buchanon, of Teaneck, NJ

Voice-mail access number for the newspaper classified ad: 236

Dr. Aaron Baker's address: 737 26th St., Syracuse, NY

Tag on Dickens's briefcase, confirming his name and the warehouse address: Dr. James Dickens, 3243 Edmonton St., Germantown, MD 21401. (The Germantown zip code is in reality 29874.)

Mulder's medical condition: severe hypothermia—basal temperature 86°F, pupils dilated, heartbeat bare

X-otica: The green liquid that the clones and the Pilot bleed appears to be the same as that spilled by Dr. Secare when he's shot by police in the opening of episode 1.24, "The Erlenmeyer Flask." Secare wasn't an alien or a clone, but a terminally ill human who underwent treatment with a synthesized extraterrestrial virus. There's likely some deliberate connection, since the props and makeup people could have easily come up with another eerie color.

Note: Even after Scully had seen "Chapel" at the warehouse and left the scene, the man never morphed into the Pilot. Perhaps it really *is* CIA Agent Chapel, who's working in tandem with the alien.

Chris Carter had originally wanted Darren McGavin to play Mulder's father, but their schedules did not work out.

Scranton, PA; Binghamton and Syracuse, NY; Germantown, MD, and West Tisbury, MA, on Martha's Vineyard; are all actual locales. Tilestown, VA is fictional.

Peter Donat is the nephew of the late, Oscar-winning actor Robert Donat (*Goodbye, Mr. Chips*). The Lowry book erroneously says Peter is Robert's son. Donat, born in Kentville, Nova Scotia, was a longtime star of the Canadian stage before relocating to San Francisco and the American Conservatory Theater. Among his many TV and film roles, he played the evil Dr. Mordecai Sahmbi in the sci-fi series *Time Trax*.

2.17 "END GAME"   February 17, 1995
Writer: Frank Spotnitz
Director: Rob Bowman

Part 2 of a 2-part episode

NUCLEAR SUBMARINE USS *ALLEGIANCE*, BEAUFORT SEA, 87 MILES NORTH OF DEADHORSE, ALASKA: [in a probable flashback (N)] Sonar detects an object, eighty meters across, emitting an apparently random pattern of radio signals from 200 meters below the ice. After the captain informs Pacific Command of their discovery an admiral orders them to torpedo it. Once at the site, the sub's reactor goes down, stranding them below thirty-two feet of ice.

The present: VACATION VILLAGE MOTOR LODGE: With inhuman speed, "Mulder" disarms Scully and knocks her into a wall. When she doesn't say where Mulder is, he throws her through a glass table, knocking her unconscious. When Mulder breaks in later with Samantha, Scully's gone. Samantha says the alien bounty hunter is using Scully as bait to get her—since she knows the only way to kill him is by piercing the base of his skull. She warns Fox human exposure to the alien's blood is fatal (*a la* Weiss).

MULDER'S APARTMENT 12:38 A.M.: Samantha reveals the apparent aliens are the cloned progeny of two original visitors, and have been trying to form a colony since the 1940s. Since the clones look identical, the colony has dispersed. They work in abortion clinics for access to fetal tissue, so that they can combine human and alien DNA to create nonidentical progeny. The bounty hunter was sent to end this practice that dilutes the alien race. Mulder doubts her story. Skinner unexpectedly arrives, asking what Mulder knows about Scully putting four men into protective custody—because they've vanished. A wounded Scully calls from a pay phone, saying her captor wants "the woman who's with you." The Pilot demands Mulder meet him at Old Memorial Bridge in Bethesda, Maryland, in one hour.

Mulder asks Skinner for help. An hour later, near the bridge, Skinner hides with a sharpshooter. Mulder and Samantha make the exchange, and the Pilot orders Samantha, "Tell me where she is." The sharpshooter, finally getting a clear shot at the one vulnerable spot, fires, and the Pilot and Samantha fall into the river. Daylight: The FBI drags the water for bodies.

Scully arrives, having been discharged from the hospital. Mulder finally tells her and Skinner that her captor was an alien. Later, at his apartment, Mulder breaks the news to his father, who accuses him of trading his own sister for his partner. Mulder breaks down, and his father leaves—but not before dropping an envelope from Samantha for Fox: "If anything should happen to me or if we become separated, you must meet me here: 1235 91st Street, Rockville, Maryland." With it is an ID access card for the Women's Health Services Clinic.

As he arrives, Scully cel-phones to say Samantha's body was found, but not the man's. After a despondent Mulder hangs up, paramedics call Scully over to see "Samantha's" body dissolving into green ooze. Mulder, inside the seemingly deserted clinic, finds a woman in surgical scrubs—another "Samantha." She beckons Mulder to a room with green cylinders and yet another "Samantha." "We needed your help," the first one explains. "We knew you could be manipulated." They introduce him to the indispensable original "Samantha" (the "she" whom the Pilot asked Mulder's Samantha about). Mulder, devastated, declaring he's not their savior, walks away. But the original stops him: They know where Samantha is—how else would they have known so many intimate details? A fire alarm heralds the Pilot, who'd followed him and now beats Mulder up; when Mulder's rescued by firefighters later, he's informed they found no one else there.

FBI HEADQUARTERS: Scully writes in her report that Mulder was treated at Samaritan Hospital and released in satisfactory condition. Many aspects of the case "defy explanation," but she states Mulder's claim of alien involvement remains unsubstantiated. The mysterious man has now been charged with the murder of Weiss, whose body has been quarantined at the U.S. Medical Research Institute of Infectious Diseases. There, heat triggered mass production of red blood cells that the researcher controlled by lowering the temperature five degrees.

KENNEDY CENTER, WASHINGTON, D.C.: Mulder meets Mr. X, who says the aliens are all dead. Mulder replies there's still the bounty hunter, and that a nuclear sub had located his craft in the Beaufort Sea five days ago. X informs him an attack fleet is now on the way to destroy it. In Mulder's apartment, Scully finds e-mail addressed to her from him, asking her not to follow and risk her life. She goes to Skinner, but all he knows is Mulder wanted time off and warns her Mulder's unsanctioned actions put both his *and* her career and lives at risk. Back at Mulder's, Scully sleeps on his couch (evidently hoping for an e-mail or some other clue to his whereabouts). Mr. X, with whom Scully isn't familiar, knocks; he unconvincingly claims he's at the wrong door, and leaves. As he gets off the elevator on the ground floor, he's accosted by Skinner, who wants to know where Mulder is. After a vicious fight, Skinner appears at Mulder's to give Scully Mulder's Arctic coordinates.

In that wasteland, Mulder finds the stranded USS *Allegiance*'s conning tower above the ice. Inside, he finds one survivor, identifying himself as Lt. Terry Wilmer, who says a man came, sealed most of the crew below without air, and executed the rest. Wilder had survived by hiding under the chief petty officer's body. Mulder handcuffs himself to Wilmer. With his gun at the base of the man's neck, he demands to know where Samantha is; in exchange, Mulder will let him get to his ship before the Navy destroys it. "Wilmer" then starts slamming Mulder around, and morphs to his Pilot form. He says he could've killed Mulder several times over, and as he prepares to do it now, tauntingly says Samantha is alive.

Mulder retrieves his gun and fires, and is burned by the wounded Pilot's blood. Dragging Mulder out the tophatch, the Pilot breaks the handcuffs with it, then drops Mulder onto the ice. The Pilot gets back in, and the sub begins to submerge—nearly slicing Mulder with a tower fin.

PRESENT DAY: Returning to last episode's opening, Scully convinces the doctors Mulder's suffering hyperviscosity syndrome, and needs his cold-induced hypometabolic state to live. Eventually, she gets him stabilized.

In her report, Scully says blood tests confirmed Mulder's exposure to a mysterious retrovirus. Yet Scully writes she can't accept a paranormal explanation, since that means abandoning science [N]. Later, Mulder awakens with Scully at his bedside—and a renewed faith, he says, "to keep looking."

Mitch Pileggi	Assistant Director Walter S. Skinner
Steven Williams	Mr. X
Peter Donat	William Mulder
Brian Thompson	The Pilot
Megan Leitch	"Samantha Mulder"
Colin Cunningham	"Lt. Terry Wilmer"
Garry Davey	Captain
Andrew Johnston	Agent Barrett Weiss
Allan Lysell	Able Gardner (unnamed in episode)
J. B. Bivens	Sharpshooter
Oliver Becker	2nd Doctor
Beatrice Zeilinger	Paramedic
Bonnie Hay	Field Doctor

X-actitude: USS *Allegiance*: On cartography mission at cruising depth of 1,000 feet. Its course heading for the unknown craft: 0.47.

Samantha's access-card number for the women's clinic: 4A

Message number of Mulder's e-mail to Scully: 238479

Mulder's Arctic journey: Commercial flight to Tacoma, WA; military flight to Deadhorse, AK; chartered a Rollagon all-terrain vehicle; drove to within ten miles of destination, from where he hiked.

Mulder's latitude and longitude, respectively, in the Arctic, expressed in cartographic minutes and seconds:

When first we see him: North 71'41.619" West 146'37.287"

At submarine location: North 71'43.010" West 146'37.221"

X-otica: An unfilmed second-act scene in one draft of the script involved "Samantha" surviving the watery fall, riding with Mulder to the clinic, and having her be the Pilot in morphed disguise, who then grapples with Mulder until the car crashes in an explosion. Time, expense, and a desire for a more streamlined narrative nixed that notion.

The Canadian destroyer HMCS *Mackenzie* was scheduled to be sunk when construction coordinator Rob Maier leased it for use as the submarine interiors. The ship was then reused for both the interiors and exteriors of an even rustier old ship in 2.19, "Dod Kalm."

For the submarine conning tower, the producers rented the larger Stage 5 at North Shore Studios and had it refrigerated to hold 140 tons of snow; the crew built a fifteen-foot structure with hydraulic lifts so that it would descend several feet below the stage. Chris Carter had originally wanted to shoot this at a frozen lake, but that proved impractical.

The establishing long-shot of Mr. X in Washington, D.C.'s Kennedy Center used the real Kennedy Center but *not* the real Mr. X. Shot two days before the air-date, after it was realized in post-production a transition shot was needed, it required producer Paul Rabwin to have a small crew of local freelancers shoot the actual place with a stand-in Mr. X: the Washington, D.C. assistant film commissioner.

157

We say the clones are "apparent" aliens since the series has already established (in 1.11, "Eve") that the U.S. was involved in the "Litchfield Project" cloning experiment since the 1950s. Deep Throat truthfully admitted to the existence of psychotic Eves; he'd also said there were Adams, establishing that males were also being cloned.

What about the fact that the female clones intimately know Samantha? Doesn't *that* indicate they're aliens? Not necessarily—since Samantha may not even have *been* kidnapped by aliens. Consider we've learned that: A) in 1.02, "Deep Throat," the U.S. uses alien technology to build alien-like aircraft; B) in 3.10, "731," Scully is told by one of the shadow-government "elders" that she and assumedly other women (and perhaps Duane Barry) were abducted not by aliens but by the government; and C) in 3.01, "The Blessing Way," Fox's mother says Samantha's abduction was prearranged and agreed upon by William Mulder—confirming government involvement, and indicating that while Samantha may have been abducted by aliens in league with the government, it may *also* mean she was abducted by Earth forces alone, using recovered alien high-tech.

The Pilot seems to be a genuine alien. We've seen no indication of Earth-alien hybridization technology advancing beyond the relatively crude Purity Control that created Dr. Secare—a far cry from the astonishingly morphing and superhuman Pilot. As well, there's no reason whatsoever for an Earth-created assassin to have a working, flying, attention-getting, eighty-meter craft crash and be buried deep below an Arctic icecap, especially when his mission involves assassinations in the U.S. The fact he has green "blood" like the clones and Dr. Secare seems to confirm alien physiology and since all that spacecraft bother indicates he's not an Earth creation, then, *ipso facto*, he's an alien.

2.18 "FEARFUL SYMMETRY"   February 24, 1995
Writer: Steve DeJarnatt
Director: James Whitmore Jr.

IDAHO MUTUAL INSURANCE TRUST, FAIRFIELD, IDAHO: Two night janitors, Roberto and one other, watch an invisible behemoth rampage down the street. Upon reaching nearby Highway 24, the entity tramples to death a road worker on a federally funded project. The next morning, trucker Wesley Brewer barely avoids hitting an elephant. State police later find the animal—forty-three miles from a zoo—dying.

Mulder and Scully investigate the road-worker's death; his spine had been crushed, and there was a circular abrasion on his chest roughly resembling an elephant's foot. They speak with Ed Meecham, operations chief of the Fairfield Zoo, who has just returned elephant Ganesha there; she apparently died of exhaustion and her cage was found locked. Meecham's boss, Willa Ambrose, a naturalist hired last year, confirms the cage was locked and only she and Meecham have keys. They still use cages, rather than open habitats, since this impoverished 1940s zoo is close to closing. Additional pressure comes from anticaptivity activists the Wild Again Organization (WAO).

HIGHWAY 24: WAO spokesperson Kyle Lang denies he let Ganesha loose. At his office, accompanied by a silent man with short-cropped blond hair, he shows the agents a tape of elephants being torturously prodded. He reveals Ambrose is being sued by the Malawi government over a gorilla she rescued there ten years ago and raised as a child.

JO JO'S COPY SHOP: Mulder tele-conferences with Frohike and Byers. Byers says Fairfield is known for weird animal disappearances, and that Mountain Home Air Base—a UFO hot spot—is nearby.

Scully follows the WAO assistant into the closed zoo. She runs into Meecham, while the WAO guy videotapes a hard-to-see disturbance. A flash of light reveals a loose tigress; the man's camera records her fatal—and suddenly invisible—attack. The agents meet with Ambrose and her agitated gorilla, Sophie, who's been signing, "Light. Afraid." At Ganesha's autopsy, Scully discovers the elephant was pregnant.

BLAKE TOWERS CONSTRUCTION SITE, DOWNTOWN BOISE, IDAHO: A tigress has two men trapped. Meecham shoots it when the animal charges Ambrose. Next day, the zoo is shut down, and the board withdraws funding. The animals will be shipped to other zoos. Mulder informs Ambrose the tigress had been pregnant; Ambrose insists she would have known about it and laughs when he suggests alien abduction. She stops laughing when Mulder says Sophie may be pregnant and afraid of having her baby taken away. Sophie responds to Ambrose's questions by signing, "Baby. Go. Fly. Light."

Sheriff's deputies serve a court order to release Sophie into protective custody. Ambrose seeks Lang's help to find a private reserve, but Lang says Sophie should live in the wild. Mulder, at the zoo warehouse, watches Sophie being prepped for shipping. Scully shows him a newspaper clipping with the photo caption "Naturalists Willa Ambrose and Kyle Lang will bring animal back to the U.S."

Lang goes inside the warehouse looking for Ambrose. He finds Sophie's cage empty and then a force throws him across the room; a crate slams down, killing him. Scully questions Ambrose, who denies any connection to Lang until Scully shows a note he'd left: "Willa—Lets [*sic*] talk. Kyle." Mulder, finding Sophie's transport-cage unlocked, tails Meecham. Scully says Lang was hit by a cattle prod, and arrests Ambrose. Ambrose declares it was an accident, that Lang had surprised Meecham, who was helping to rescue Sophie. Sophie's now at a building between here and Boise; there Mulder learns Ambrose had paid Meecham for this. Sophie is hysterical in a locked room. Meecham manages to push Mulder inside with the terrified animal, though moments later, a bright light takes her away.

Scully later arrives with a police officer. Mulder says Sophie had tried to tell him something, and repeats her signing: "Man. Save. Man." The police radio announces a large animal on the road; the agents find Sophie has been killed by a car. Mulder's voice-over tells us Ambrose and Meecham were charged with Lang's manslaughter, and suggests alien conservationists may be involved on Earth.

Jayne Atkinson	Willa Ambrose
Lance Guest	Kyle Lang
Jack Rader	Ed Meecham
Bruce Harwood	Byers
Tom Braidwood	Frohike
Jody St. Michael	Sophie
Charles Andre	Ray Floyd (unnamed in episode)
Garvin Cross	Red Head Kid (apparently, the blond WAO person)
Tom Glass	Trucker (Wesley Brewer)

The actors playing Roberto and the other janitor are uncredited.

The official Fox *X-Files* website erroneously includes Dean Haglund as "Langley" (*sic*).

X-actitude: Ganesha: a twelve-year-old, female Indian elephant

Fairfield Zoo hours: 10 A.M.–5:30 P.M.

Newspaper headline appears to read: Couple Save Baby Gorilla from Black Market Smugglers

Church sign: "Man has no preeminence above a beast: For all is vanity."

X-otica: The elephant's name, Ganesha, is the female form of Ganesh, the popular Hindu household god.

The episode's title refers to the William Blake poem "The Tyger."

In-joke: Blake Towers is named after William Blake.

Fairfield, ID, is an actual town of a few hundred people—though Highway 20, not 24, passes through it.

Mime Jody St. Michael had previously played a simian in *Gorillas in the Mist.* In this episode, St. Michael worked under the auspices of the famed special-effects-makeup firm Rick Baker and Company.

2.19 "DOD KALM"   March 10, 1995

Teleplay: Howard Gordon & Alex Gansa

Story: Howard Gordon

Director: Rob Bowman

Norwegian Sea, 66° latitude, 8° East Longitude: Captain Barclay of the destroyer USS *Ardent* pulls a gun on a Lt. Richard Harper, trying in vain to keep several men from abandoning ship. Eighteen hours later, lifeboat 925 is picked up by Canadian fishing vessel *The Lisette.* All on board the lifeboat are seemingly very old.

Bethesda Naval Hospital: Scully informs Mulder the *Ardent* had apparently vanished for forty-two hours. Last night, eighteen crew-members were found alive, but now only Harper survives. When Scully questions a nurse why the twenty-eight-year-old Harper looks so aged, the attending physician claims Scully's clearance code is invalid, and throws her out.

Mulder's office: Mulder says the X-Files have recorded nine ships disappearing in the 65th-parallel area. Citing the Philadelphia Experiment, he suggests "wormholes"—postulated portals where matter interfaces with time at an accelerated or decelerated rate. At 8:30 P.M., the agents leave for Norway.

Tildeskan, Norway: At a bar, Mulder and Scully, looking to hire a ship to reach the sea north of Beerenberg, roughly ten hours away, meet trawler captain Henry Trondheim. He berates the other sailors for their superstition about an evil god's stone that crashed through the ice. Twelve hours later—bad weather having slowed the voyage—Mulder is seasick. Trondheim and mate Halverson crash into a ship that's been in and out of radar—the *Ardent,* looking old and rusted though only commissioned in 1991. They find mummified-looking remains, covered with residue. Then someone, to their horror, steals Trondheim's ship.

The *Ardent's* radio and engines are dead. Halverson has his skull fatally fractured. Mulder finds a terrified and aged Captain Barclay clutching a Jack Daniels bottle. Per Barclay's log, the navigation system had failed; then crew members saw a light in the sea and the ship began to "bleed." As Trondheim sends Halverson's body out to sea, he's attacked by a man whom Mulder captures: pirate/black-marketeer Olafsson, who speaks only Norwegian. Below, Barclay is dead, and appears to be decomposing into a crystalline substance. Per his log, the ship had picked up four Norwegian sailors whose own ship had sunk, accounting for Olafsson, whom they bind, and the men who stole Trondheim's ship.

They sleep, but when Mulder wakes Scully for her turn at the watch, both the agents and Trondheim have aged. Scully suspects free radicals—highly reactive chemicals with extra electrons, that attack DNA proteins and theoretically cause bodies to age. If the ship is approaching another massive metallic source, like a meteor, the two might (with the ocean as the "battery") act as terminals to electromagnetically excite free radicals.

Trondheim notices the ship "bleeding" rust. The agents follow an oddly uncorroded yellow pipe. Olafsson tells Trondheim he'll trade the secret of his youth in exchange for freedom. The agents follow the pipe to the Sewage Processing Hold, where they see the "campsite" of Olafsson's men, and what Mulder deduces is the only drinkable water on the ship; the regular desalinated water must've gotten contaminated, and this recycled water may be the key. When they seek to question Olafsson (whom Trondheim has killed), Trondheim claims he escaped.

Eighteen hours, forty-five minutes since the onset of symptoms, blood and urine tests show impossibly high salt levels: The contaminated water apparently catalyzes body fluids to cause rapid, massive cellular degeneration. The recycled water has slowed the aging in Trondheim and Scully, but less so in Mulder, who'd gotten dehydrated when seasick. Trondheim wants Scully to stop giving the doomed Mulder his ration of water; Scully will not, but does note Mulder's kidneys aren't secreting what she's calling "heavy salt." Trondheim barricades the door to the sewage hold, and the last remaining water.

Later, the ship's outer hull corrodes through; as the ocean bursts into the sewage hold, Trondheim can't escape through the barricade. Fourteen hours later, Scully tells Mulder the one thing she remembers from her abduction is thinking there's nothing to fear when life is over. Later, she writes Mulder lost consciousness at 4:30 A.M., March 12. Food and water ran out twenty-four hours previous. Rescuers eventually reach them and Scully finds herself being treated by the doctor who'd thrown her out before. Thirty-six hours

161

later, Scully is on dialysis with a high-flux filter and responding well and Mulder is given a successful course of synthetic hormones. Scully wants to return for further research, but the doctor informs her the ship sank an hour after their rescue.

John Savage	Henry Trondheim
David Cubitt	Captain Barclay
Vladimir Kulich	Olafsson
Mar Anderson	Halverson
John McConnach	Sailor (on *The Lisette*)
Stephen Dimopoulos	Ionesco (on *The Lisette*; unnamed in episode)
Claire Riley	Dr. Laskos (unnamed in episode)
Robert Metcalfe	Nurse
Dmitry Chepovetsky	Lieutenant (Richard) Harper

The official Fox *X-Files* website erroneously lists the character Dr. Laskos as "Burke."

X-actitude: *The Lisette* registry number: CV233

Lt. Harper's hospital room: 3G

Capt. Barclay's age: 35

City where, Trondheim says, "everybody knows" Olafsson: Gildeskal

Other ship disappearances, per Mulder:

British Royal Navy battleship, on Dec. 12, 1949, between Leeds and Cape Perry

Fleet of Soviet mine-sweepers in 1963, enroute to Havana

Nearest land to the area where the *Ardent* went missing: Lofoton Island

Trondheim's background: former Pensacola, FL, charter-boat operator; now runs fifty-ton double-hulled trawler, *The Zehar*

Only liquids Scully can find after Trondheim barricades sewage hold: snow-globe water, sardine-can liquid, juice of a half dozen lemons

Mulder's take on the Philadelphia Experiment: WWII project designed to render ships invisible to radar; when the Manhattan Project kicked in, most of the scientists were ostensibly shifted to Los Alamos, NM, but actually shifted to Roswell, NM. Nine months after the alleged crash of a UFO there, the USS *Eldridge* vanished from a Philadelphia naval yard and reappeared minutes later in Norfolk, VA. Mulder claims the scientists were experimenting with the theory of "wormholes."

X-otica: "We were working on the show with John Savage where we aged to, like, ninety years old in a couple of days," Duchovny remembers. "And John Savage was playing a Norwegian guy who kept coming back to this word . . . He was yelling at a guy [Olafsson] and he said, '*bleaver!*' And for some reason, it struck Gillian and [me] as the funniest thing. You know he kept on saying, '[gibberish, gibberish] *bleaver!*' And we kept cracking up every time! We were supposed to be huddled in a corner, dying of old age

162

at the age of thirty, and every time he'd say '*bleaver!*' we'd go [desperate stifled laugh]. And so we started saying, 'Leave it to bleaver!'"

John Savage is best known for his powerful work in *The Deer Hunter* (1978). He's crafted indelible performances in *The Onion Field*, *Hair*, *Salvador*, and *The Godfather*, *Part III*.

2.20 "HUMBUG"   March 24, 1995

Writer: Darin Morgan
Director: Kim Manners

CIRCUS-PERFORMER HAVEN GIBSONTON, FLORIDA: At his pool at home, Jerald Glazebrook, a circus "Alligator Man," is attacked and killed.

FBI HEADQUARTERS: Mulder tells Scully that Glazebrook had ichthyosis, the scale-like shedding of skin. His murder is the latest of forty-eight such mutilations in twenty-eight years, occurring in nearly every state in the continental U.S.

Mulder, Scully, and the cooperative Sheriff James Hamilton attend Glazebrook's funeral, where an armless pastor eulogizes Jerry as a renowned escape artist. Suddenly, the ground trembles and a man emerges, crazily declaring that in honor of the deceased, he'll drive a metal stake into his chest—which he does. The funeral erupts in bedlam. PHIL'S DINER: Mulder asks about a mermaid illustration on the menu, by local artist Hepcat Helm. Hamilton takes them to Hepcat's studio. Helm's offended by Hamilton's referring to his nearby "Tabernacle of Terror" as a funhouse, but he identifies the figure as a "Feejee Mermaid"—a "humbug" P. T. Barnum pulled in the nineteenth century, with a mummified monkey sewn onto the tail of a fish. Mulder says a trail of possibly simian tracks were found at several of the crime scenes.

GULF BREEZE TRAILER COURT: Little-person proprietor Mr. Nutt takes exception to Mulder's innocent question as to whether he'd worked for a circus, lecturing him about his degree in hotel management. A slow-witted but pleasant tippler, Lanny, takes their bags to their separate trailers. Lanny used to headline, showing audiences his attached brother, Leonard, but Nutt convinced him that lacked dignity—so now he carries people's luggage. Hepcat is killed in his studio by a tiny, crawling, bald, apelike creature.

The next day Mulder spots a bald man with jigsaw tattoos all over his body, catching a fish from a stream and eating it raw. At 7:15 A.M., Lanny awakens Scully to report Hepcat's murder. Mulder notices blood on the outside of one of Hepcat's small windows. The agents come across funeral disrupter Dr. Blockhead; as they chat, he taps a nail into his nose, which Mulder helpfully retrieves. Mulder will have the lab compare the blood on the nail to that on the window. Dr. Blockhead introduces his friend "The Conundrum," whom he says will eat anything; Scully wonders if that includes human flesh.

GIBSONTON MUSEUM OF CURIOSITIES, 3:14 P.M.: The proprietor gives Scully a tour, offers her a poster of Jim-Jim the Dog-Faced Boy, and for an additional five dollars promises an authentic Barnum exhibit, "The Great Unknown," which turns out to be an empty chest. Mulder tells Scully the blood samples match, so he's running further tests. A background check on Dr. Blockhead reveals him as Jeffrey Swaim, born in Milwaukee and not Yemen (as he'd claimed); he also doesn't hold a doctorate. Scully's check on Jim-Jim reveals he grew up to become . . . Sheriff Hamilton! He'd suffered hypertrichosis, which Mulder accurately notes does not mean lycanthropy.

They spy Hamilton in his backyard, digging beneath a full moon. When they investigate, he sheepishly admits burying a potato as an old-wives' remedy for warts; he concedes he was, indeed, Jim-Jim. That same night, after the Conundrum pays his rent, a creature squeezes through Nutt's doggy door and kills Nutt. As the agents investigate, Hamilton takes a highly distraught Lanny to the drunk tank. The agents and Hamilton arrest Dr. Blockhead.

At the station house, Lanny screams in his cell. Scully and Mulder see a blood trail leading out the tiny window: Lanny's attached twin has extracted itself. Lanny pitifully says Leonard doesn't know he's hurting anyone—he's merely seeking another brother. That rejection has made Lanny miserable. The sheriff calls for paramedics; the agents chase Leonard into the Tabernacle of Terror. Leonard escapes to attack the Conundrum, whom the agents shortly thereafter find prone but unhurt. When they leave, he rubs his belly and burps.

Morning: Scully finds Blockhead and the Conundrum packing to leave. Scully informs Dr. Blockhead that Lanny died last night of cirrhosis of the liver; his autopsy showed some offshoots of his esophagus and trachea that seemed umbilical. She inquires about the Conundrum's being so drowsy and logy. "Probably," he suggests, "something I ate."

Jim Rose	Dr. Blockhead/Jeffrey Swaim
Wayne Grace	Sheriff James Hamilton
Michael Anderson	Nutt
The Enigma (Paul Lawrence)	The Conundrum
Vincent Schiavelli	Lanny
Blair Slater	Glazebrook (older)
Devin Walker	Glazebrook (younger)
John Payne	Jerald Glazebrook
Debis Simpson	Waiter
Alex Diakun	Curator
George Tipple	Hepcat Helm
Alvin Law	Reverend

The deputy, who has one line, is uncredited.

The official Fox *X-Files* website erroneously refers to the Glazebrook character as retired, and neglects to list front-credit performer The Enigma.

Jim Rose, right, as Dr. Blockhead, driving a nail into his nose. Don't try this at home.

***X*-actitude:**   Site of first mutilation attack: Oregon. Site of last five: Florida
Glazebrook's family: Bearded-lady wife; two normal sons, approximately eight and ten years old.

Biblical passage read at Glazebrook's funeral: Psalm 23 ("The Lord is my Shepherd . . .")

Gibsonton's founding: In 1920s, when Barnum and Bailey performers came there during the off-season.

Copyright date of Hepcat Helm's menu illustration: 1992

Museum admission charge: "Freaks Free . . . Others please leave donation."

Blood samples: both O-positive

Conundrum's rent check: The Conundrum, P.O. Box 6071, Gibsonton, FL 180203 (*sic*); City Trust and Savings Bank, Main Branch, Corner 3rd and Main.

Nutt's mutt: Commodore

Jim-Jim the Dog-Faced Boy background: orphan discovered in an Albanian forest, 1943; became sideshow attraction, then ran away, supported himself, and eventually became Gibsonton's four-term sheriff.

***X*-otica:**   Gibsonton, FL, is a real town, just south of Tampa, on Tampa Bay.

Jim Rose and The Enigma come from the Jim Rose Circus Sideshow, a popular, Seattle-based performance-art troupe founded in 1991. The Enigma was formerly known as Slug the Sword Swallower. Michael (a.k.a. Michael J.) Anderson became famous as "The Man From Another Place" on *Twin Peaks*. Character actor Vincent Schiavelli appeared in *Amadeus*, *Batman Returns,* and countless other films and TV shows, and played the recurring role of Reverent Gorky on *Taxi*.

In-joke: The Gulf Breeze trailer court is named after the famous 1987–88 "sightings" made near Gulf Breeze, FL. For more on this, see episode 1.10, "Fallen Angel."

2.21 "THE CALUSARI"　　　　　　　　　　　　　　April 14, 1995
Writer: Sara B. Charno
Director: Michael Vejar

At a park, State Department employee Steven Holvey and wife Maggie are with sons Charlie, nine, and Teddy, two. When Teddy accidentally loses his helium balloon and starts crying, dad gives him Charlie's; the older boy demands another. Minutes later, in the restroom with Maggie, Teddy mysteriously escapes his baby harness and follows his new balloon to his death at a kiddie-railroad track. Three months later, Mulder and Scully visit Dr. Charles "Chuck" Burks at his University of Maryland lab, where he uses digital-imaging software on a photo of Teddy taken seconds before the tragedy. It raises an image of electromagnetic concentration seemingly pulling the balloon's string.

ARLINGTON, VIRGINIA: Maggie's old-world mother, Golda, declares in Romanian, "*Diavol lol. . . . Nu ieste el cauza. . . . No asta este problema ta biatud este blestemat*." She adds (subtitled), "We must perform the ritual or the killings will continue. . . . Ye Dracul!" Mulder notices a swastika with dots painted on Charlie's hand. Golda, both protective and fearful of Charlie, tells her daughter, "You marry a devil. You have devil child!"

MULDER'S OFFICE: Mulder says a swastika, a.k.a. a gammadion or fylfot, is an ancient good-luck symbol. Scully notes Teddy was hospitalized ten times in two years, and suggests Golda has the psychological illness Münchausen's syndrome by proxy, in which a person induces medical symptoms in their children. Holvey, at work, tells the agents he'd met Maggie in Romania in 1984; the highly superstitious Golda objected to the marriage. He agrees to let Scully and Karen F. Kosseff, LCSW, an FBI psychiatric social worker (whom Scully had consulted in 2.13, "Irresistible") interview Charlie.

Later, Steve, with Charlie in the car, tries to undo a stuck garage door; some unseen force grabs his tie and catches it in the garage-opener mechanism, choking him to death before Charlie's tear-filled eyes. During the police investigation, Scully notices Golda speaking with three men, telling them, in subtitled Romanian, "We must act quickly. It is getting stronger."

Mulder finds ash all over the garage; the lab report later says it contains nothing organic *or* inorganic—technically, it doesn't exist.

Burks saw this material in India, 1979, in his hippie days: *vibuti*—holy ash. He calls it an *apport*—something that materializes out of thin air. *Vibuti* is created during either the presence of spirit beings or of bilocation—wherein a person's energy is transferred to a different place. Scully suggests someone activated the garage door by remote control.

GOLDA'S ROOM: As Golda and the Romanians conduct a ritual, an angry child's ghostly visage appears. Maggie and Kosseff, who's arrived to file a court report, run upstairs when Charlie screams. Golda locks Charlie into the room and raises a knife. Kosseff calls 911 and runs downstairs to alert Mulder and Scully, who are meeting her here. Something invisible attacks Golda; Charlie, incanting *"E siti din mina trup pertiti,"* drops two roosters on her who claw and peck her to death. Scully and Mulder burst in too late to help.

Later, Charlie remembers nothing, and the room contains more holy ash and a mugwort herb. The Romanian men say the ritual must be completed; Maggie throws them out, and explains to the agents that in Romania, such men—"Calusari"—ensure correct observance of rites. The white-bearded elder tells Mulder the evil here has existed throughout history under many names.

ST. MATTHEWS MEDICAL CENTER, ARLINGTON: Kosseff interviews Charlie, who denies being in Golda's room and blames it all on "Michael." Maggie says they'd never told Charlie about Michael—his twin who died at birth—and Golda had wanted to perform a ritual to divide their souls. Afterward, when Nurse Castor comes to give Charlie a shot, Michael materializes, bludgeons Castor, then wakes Maggie in the waiting room, and insists they go home *now*. Mulder and Scully notice "Charlie" getting into Maggie's red station wagon—yet Charlie's still in bed, and Castor says another boy hit her. Mulder rushes to get the Calusari, and dispatches Scully to the Holveys's.

After Michael has taunted her, Maggie slips away to perform some ritual—but Michael, spotting her, raises a knife. At the hospital, the Calusari perform a rite that makes the walls "bleed." At the Holveys's, Michael growls in an unearthly language as a gale pitches Scully through the air. As Michael prepares to kill her, the Calusari's ritual climaxes and he disappears. Maggie rushes to the hospital, where the whitebeard-elder warns Mulder, "You must be careful. It knows you."

167

Helene Clarkson	Maggie Holvey
Joel Palmer	Charlie and Michael Holvey
Lilyan Chauvin	Golda
Kay E. Kuter	Calusari Elder
Ric Reid	Steve Holvey
Christine Willes	Karen (F.) Kosseff

Bill Dow	(Dr.) Chuck Burk (*sic*) (Closed captioning gives last name as "Burks," which appears to agree with audio pronunciation.)
Jacqueline Danieneau	Nurse Castor
Bill Croft	2nd Calusari
Campbell Lane	3rd Calusari
George Josef	4th Calusari
Oliver and Jeremy Isaac Wildsmith	Teddy Holvey

The official Fox *X-Files* site neglects to list front-credit actor Kay E. Kuter.

X-actitude: Kosseff's business card: Karen F. Kosseff, LCSW, Psychiatric Social Worker, J. Edgar Hoover Building, Tenth Street and Pennsylvania Ave., Washington, D.C. 205354 (*sic*). The address is accurate, except for that last, extra digit in the zip code.

Calusari license plate: Virginia KH7-356

Mulder and Scully's FBI motor-pool plate: FS4-291

Guru whom Burk insists created a feast from thin air: Sai Baba

X-otica: Lilyan Chauvin played the recurring role of Madame Dussolier in the Valerie Bertinelli series *Cafe Americain*; her endless film credits include Elvis Presley's *Tickle Me*, *Private Benjamin*, *Universal Soldier*, and of course, *Pumpkinhead II: Blood Wings*. No baby-boomer could ever forget Kay E. Kuter as *Green Acres*'s Newt Kiley—though the classically trained Shakespearean actor wishes they would.

2.22 "F. EMASCULATA"   April 28, 1995

Writers: Chris Carter & Howard Gordon

Director: Rob Bowman

A COSTA RICA RAIN FOREST: Dr. Robert Torrence finds a dead boar with pulsing red sores, and a strange insect. As he examines a sore, using surgical gloves [N], it spurts onto his face. That night, deathly ill, he shortwaves the "R.B.P. Field Base" requesting immediate evacuation. Seven hours later, soldiers find him dead.

CUMBERLAND STATE CORRECTIONAL FACILITY, DINWIDDIE COUNTY, VIRGINIA: Guard Winston delivers an overnight-mail package to solitary prisoner Bobby Torrence. The original address has been blacked-out and the package re-addressed. Inside is a body part with a pulsating sore. Eighteen hours later, Paul and Steve, murder convicts who are cleaning Bobby's empty cell, say someone named McGuire told them the infirmary was full and all the bedsheets are to be incinerated.

A federal marshal tells Mulder to stay out of his way during the manhunt for the escaped Paul and Steve. Mulder, noticing men in contamination suits, asks Scully to stay and investigate. At a rest stop, vacationing dad Robert is killed and the family camper stolen. Scully finds a Dr. Osborne of the CDC, who reluctantly says a "flu-like illness," invariably fatal after thirty-six hours, has killed ten of fourteen men infected. He's unsure if the escapees are infected; Scully cel-phones Mulder to warn him. Another man in a clean-suit demands Scully leave.

At a gas station, Paul phones Elizabeth, who has a baby boy. Station-attendant Angelo Garza discovers Steve in the rest room, splotched with sores. Paul knocks Angelo out. At the prison incinerator, Scully finds body bags—one marked "001 Torrence." She cuts it to examine inside; as Osborne desperately tries to close it, a pustule explodes in his face.

Back at the gas station, Mulder informs the marshal that the fugitives may be infectious. Mulder, figuring the men might head for a girlfriend's, has an operator tell him the last call made on the pay phone. A helicopter with no registry number—just RESCUE—dispatches four clean-suited persons to whisk away the terrified Garza.

The fugitives take Garza's stolen car to Elizabeth's home. Scully learns the overnight package came from Pinck Pharmaceuticals, and plucks an insect from Torrence's corpse. Marshals arrest Elizabeth, just after a boil erupts onto her. Steve's dead; Paul's missing.

Osborne—infected—confides the prison is quarantined not by the CDC but by Pinck, for whom he works. Three months ago, an entomologist seeking new species for drug applications "disappeared," though his samples were retrieved. One is the insect Scully shows him: *Faciphaga emasculata*, a parasitoid (parasite carrier) that secretes a dilating enzyme. The pustules hold its larvae, which upon eruption burrow into their new host. Since Scully was next to Osborne when the Torrence boil burst, she may be infected herself.

FBI HEADQUARTERS: Mulder, Skinner, and the Smoking Man argue over the latter keeping information about the disease from the public. Back at the prison Osborne tests Scully by having her bitten by an uninfected insect, which then acts as incubator; any parasite in her blood will take thirty minutes to get into the bug, and another two hours to grow large enough to see.

DINWIDDIE COUNTY HOSPITAL: Quarantined Elizabeth tells Mulder that Paul will take the 10 P.M. bus to Toronto. Scully puts Osborne in an oxygen tent. When she returns from the lab upon finding she's uninfected, he's gone.

THE BUS DEPOT: A mom puts her young-teen son on the Toronto bus; he gives Paul the time (9:40). At the prison incinerator, the brusque clean-suited man from earlier tells Scully they're destroying material in accordance with CDC procedure; he doesn't reply when Scully says he doesn't work for the CDC. Osborne's body gets loaded in. THE BUS DEPOT: Mulder, having learned Paul's infected, tries to slip on as a passenger, take Paul at gunpoint, and bring him out safely as proof of the disease and cover-up. But

Paul takes the boy as hostage. After Mulder convinces him to give up and get medical treatment, a sniper shoots Paul dead.

Mulder tells Skinner that Pinck used prisoners as guinea pigs to circumvent FDA testing. Mulder plans to tell the media, but Scully arrives to report the scientist in Costa Rica was also named Robert Torrence; Pinck arranged it this way as a fail-safe, to blame "postal error." Mulder, defeated, demands to know where Skinner stands. "I stand right on the line you keep crossing," he answers . . . and adds, "as a friend—watch your back."

Mitch Pileggi	Assistant Director Walter S. Skinner
Charles Martin Smith	Dr. Osborne
Dean Norris	U.S. Marshal
John Pyper-Ferguson	Paul
William B. Davis	Smoking Man
Angelo Vacco	Angelo Garza
Morris Paynch	Dr. Simon Auerbach (unnamed in episode; the other doctor at the prison)
Lynda Boyd	Elizabeth
John Tench	Steve
Alvin Sanders	Bus Driver
Kim Kondrashoff	Bobby (Torrence)
Chilton Crane	Mother (at bus station)
Bill Rowat	Dr. (Robert) Torrence
Jude Zachary	Winston

The actors playing the boy on the bus; the camper dad (Robert); the camper mom, and the ticket agent are all uncredited.

The official Fox *X-Files* website erroneously lists the character Dr. Simon Auerbach as "Dr. Barber," and neglects to list front-credit performers Charles Martin Smith, Dean Morris, and John Pyper-Ferguson.

X-actitude: The federal marshal is named Tapia per the closed captioning, but not per episode dialogue.

Name listed on Dr. Torrence's locked case: Bio Diversity. Section he wants evacuation from: Z-15

Overnight-mail package: Transcontinental Express no. DDP112148, sent from Pinck Pharmaceuticals in Wichita, KS

Elizabeth's address: 925 August St., somewhere in Dinwiddie County, VA; telephone 555-6936.

Prisoner Bobby Torrence: neck sore measures 5cm; body temperature 103.5°; oxygen saturation 81

Bus depot: Paul in line to buy Greyhound ticket at 9:25 P.M.; Toronto bus (no. 943) at Gate 20; boy visiting his Uncle Jake

X-otica: Dinwiddie County, VA, south of Richmond, offers close access to Interstates 85 and 95 for the fugitive in a hurry.

Self-testing for *F. emasculata* infection.

Angelo Vacco was an *X-Files* production assistant with no prior film or TV acting credits; Chris Carter wrote the part of Angelo Garza specifically for him.

2.23 "SOFT LIGHT"   May 5, 1995
Writer: Vince Gilligan
Director: James Contner

RICHMOND, VA: In a hotel hallway, a distraught man insistently knocks on the door of a man named Morris, saying it's Chester. Across the hall, businessperson Patrick Newirth watches the commotion through his peephole until Chester's shadow slips beneath the door and evaporates him. Chester, hearing Newirth's scream, unscrews a hallway lightbulb and flees.

At the scene, Scully tells Mulder that Kelly Ryan, one of her Academy students, now with the Richmond Police, called last night asking for help with her first case. When Newirth didn't answer his wake-up call, Security came up three hours later to find him gone from a locked and chained room with no other means of exit. A blotch on the floor is similar to those at three other crime scenes; it's mostly carbon, with some potassium and trace minerals, which Scully says sounds like residue from burnt flesh. Mulder taps the unaccountably loosened bulb in the hallway, and when it appears to work, asks Ryan to check it for prints. He's thinking spontaneous human combustion.

Outside the home of the last missing person, Margaret Wysnecki, Mulder finds a similar loose bulb [N]. Scully notes the first victim, Gail Anne Lambert, was an engineer with Polarity Magnetics, Inc. Mulder finds a round-trip train ticket with a return date of the day Wysnecki disappeared; Newirth had also arrived by train. Ryan sends cops to check the station, where Chester accidentally evaporates two officers.

MORNING: Ryan tells the agents the lightbulb prints didn't match those of any hotel employee or guest [N]—but two scorch marks in the alley indicate the killer was here. The agents examine security-camera tapes, finally noticing a man "always" sitting in the train terminal. A blow-up reveals the Polarity Magnetics logo. Mulder and Scully find Polarity Magnetics closed. Dr. Christopher Davey finally answers, and says the man in the March 22 security-video print is former business partner Dr. Chester Ray Banton. Davey thought he'd died after an accident here five weeks ago: Chester had gotten locked inside their particle generator, receiving a quanta bombardment equal to a 2 billion megawatt X-ray.

TRAIN STATION: Mulder notices the diffused, soft light casts no shadows. He and Scully find and capture Chester. YALOFF PSYCHIATRIC HOSPITAL, PIEDMONT, VIRGINIA: They question a devastated Chester, who's insisted on soft light rather than darkness. He says his shadow is like a black hole that splits molecules into component atoms; Lambert had died by his just standing in her doorway. He's convinced the government wants to subject him to a "brain suck" to steal his ideas and commandeer the shadow. Ryan officiously tells the agents to stop; her superior, Detective Barron, wants to know why they're here. Scully lies for the scheming, manipulative Ryan. Barron says he's transferring Chester to county jail and compliments Ryan on *her* good work.

Mulder meets with Mr. X, who's never heard of Chester and won't help Mulder appropriate him from the Richmond P.D. He says not to contact him again unless absolutely necessary. At 3:24 A.M., amid a power outage, Mr. X tells a nurse they're here for Chester. Two associates start to bind and gag him, but when the lights return, they're killed. Chester escapes.

The agents learn power was selectively disconnected at a substation two blocks away by someone posing as a city engineer. Mulder, convinced Chester only wants to control his power, deduces he'd flee to his lab. There Ryan, ignoring Chester's pleads, evaporates in the shadow. Chester has Davey lock him in the accelerator to try and rid himself of the dark matter and discovers Davey is working for "them." As Davey phones someone to report Chester's been caught, Mr. X kills him. Mulder and Scully arrive to see a man in the accelerator disappearing and leaving behind a dark outline.

Later, Mulder confronts Mr. X, whose description the nurse gave; he'd lied about not knowing Chester. Mr. X says, "Despite my loyalty to my predecessors, I've never made you any promises," and adds, "I didn't kill

[Chester]." Later, Mulder says Dr. Morris West, a physicist affiliated with Polarity, had filed a missing-person report on Davey; Mulder suggests it wasn't Chester in the accelerator. Elsewhere, a scientist tells Mr. X Davey's expertise would've been helpful. A brain-monitored Chester sits wide-eyed in terror.

Tony Shalhoub	Dr. Chester Ray Banton
Kate Twa	Detective Kelly Ryan
Kevin McNulty	Dr. Christopher Davey
Steven Williams	Mr. X
Nathaniel Deveaux	Detective Barron
Robert Rozen	Doctor
Donna Yamamoto	Night Nurse
Forbes Angus	Government Scientist
Guyle Frazier	Officer #1 (Barney)
Steve Bacic	Officer #2
Craig Brunanski	Security Guard

The actor playing Patrick Newirth is uncredited.

X-actitude: Newirth background: age fifty-two; executive with Morley Tobacco of Raleigh-Durham, NC; in Richmond for meetings. His hotel room: 606. His wakeup call: 6 A.M. Date of disappearance: March 31.

Margaret Wysnecki background: age sixty-six; retired production-line worker with Laramie Tobacco, where she worked approximately thirty-six years. Train destination: Hampton Roads, VA. Date of disappearance: March 17.

First police car license plate: 48 (police dept. symbol) 759

Second police car license plate: 26 (police dept. symbol) 578

Polarity Magnetics's particle accelerator: one-fifth the power of the Texas Supercollider.

Code to unlock the particle-accelerator target chamber: 8292

X-otica: Morley Tobacco, the company for which Newirth worked, makes the cigarette brand Morley—a fictional knockoff of Marlboro. A box of Morleys is a key element in 2.08, "One Breath," and other episodes.

Hampton, not Hampton Roads, is a small city on the Virginia coast where Langley Air Force Base is located.

In-joke: When the agents are confounded by how Newirth vanished from a locked room, Scully glances at the tiny heating vent. "You never know," Mulder cracks—a reference to mutant Eugene Tooms's preferred method of entrance in 1.03, "Squeeze."

Tony Shalhoub's unforgettably funny guest appearance as an Italian waiter on *Wings* led to his Antonio Scarpacci character joining the hit series as a cabbie. Outside that show, he's winged it in films including *Quick Change*, *Barton Fink*, *Honeymoon in Vegas,* and *Addams Family Values.*

2.24 "OUR TOWN"   May 12, 1995

Writer: Frank Spotnitz

Director: Rob Bowman

DUDLEY, ARKANSAS, COUNTY ROAD A7: Lovely young Paula Gray leads lusty middle-aged George Kearns to a woodsy, torch-lit site where a figure in a carved mask slays him.

FBI HEADQUARTERS: Ten weeks later, Federal poultry inspector Kearns is listed as missing. Mulder says a woman driving on I-40 that night saw what she called a foxfire spirit in a field. Mulder and Scully go to Dudley, home of Chaco Chicken. There the agents find a twelve-foot-diameter burn and a witch's peg, used to ward off evil spirits. Sheriff Arens tells the agents there's no body and no evidence of a crime, that the fields are full of witch's pegs, and the fire was an illegal trash burning.

Doris Kearns says her adulterous husband probably ran off. Mulder notices a report Kearns was going to file with the Department of Agriculture, recommending that Chaco be closed for health violations. At Chaco, floor manager Jess Harold tells the agents and Arens that Kearns was always trying to shut them down; "troublemaker" Kearns had even sued the government over work-related headaches. Suddenly Paula, a Chaco worker, grabs Harold and puts a blade to his head. Arens shoots her dead, and she falls into a feed grinder. Staff physician Dr. Randolph tells the agents that Paula had complained last week of headaches and irritability. Kearns had similar symptoms. Scully wants to do an autopsy on Paula, and obtains permission from company owner Walter Chaco—Paula's grandfather and legal guardian.

SETH COUNTY MORGUE: Prenaturally young Paula, born January 6, 1948, suffered from the rare, hereditary, and noncommunicable Creutzfeldt-Jacob disease, in which brain tissue develops spongelike holes, causing dementia and death. Scully suspects Kearns also had the disease. The agents, on their way to check courthouse records, are run off the road by a Chaco Chicken truck that swerves into a small lake; they learn the driver exhibited the same symptoms as Paula and Kearns. Arens resists Mulder's request to drag the lake, but acquiesces when Mulder suggests the FBI do it [N]. The dragging produces a pile of human bones. Scully IDs nine skeletal remains, including Kearns's; some may be twenty to thirty years old. There are no skulls, and the bones are all smooth at the ends. At the Chaco plant, Randolph and Harold discuss the bones, and say a Clayton Walsh has become the fourth to exhibit symptoms. Randolph complains Chaco's doing nothing about it.

Danny at the FBI faxes a list showing that in the last fifty years, eighty-seven people have disappeared within a 200-mile radius. Scully, who walked into the sheriff's station house with a bucket of fried chicken, suggests a cult. Mulder thinks cannibals, since the polished bone-ends suggest boiling—as, he claims, anthropologists found in studying the cannibalistic Anasazi tribe of New Mexico.

At Chaco's home, Chaco warns Harold the townsfolk are losing their faith. Doris arrives, saying she can't lie anymore, but Chaco reassures her. Harold doesn't trust her, but Chaco reminds him it's the FBI who are the problem.

THE COURTHOUSE: The birth records have been burned—recently. Doris calls Mulder, fearful Chaco will kill her. Mulder goes to arrest him, while Scully leaves to help Doris—whom a masked figures kills.

While a maid goes to get Chaco, Mulder looks at memorabilia: pictures of Chaco in WWII flying regalia (including a shot of him posing with spear-wielding South Pacific aborigines), and a human skull labeled "Jale Tribe, New Guinea, 1944." When the maid says Chaco's unavailable, and that she has no key to a memorabilia cabinet, Mulder breaks into it to find shrunken heads. The maid and Chaco vanish; Mulder calls Scully at Doris's, but after a moment on the phone, she's knocked unconscious.

A BONFIRE-LIT FIELD: The townsfolk line up for ladles of soup. Chaco arrives, enraged at what they've done to Doris. He's brought Scully, bound and gagged. Harold accuses Chaco of bringing in "the outsider [Kearns] who made us all sick," then brings out the masked man, who beheads Chaco. Mulder, driving by, sees the fire, and Scully on the chopping block. He kills the masked man with two gunshots; panic ensues, allowing Mulder to free Scully. The masked man is Arens; Harold has been trampled to death.

175

In the morning, state police raid the Chaco plant; Scully's report says the USDA then closed it. Twenty-seven townsfolk have died of Creutzfeldt-Jacob. The remains of Chaco, who'd spent time with the ostensibly cannibalistic Jale tribe, are missing.

Caroline Kava	Doris Kearns
John Milford	Walter "Chic" Chaco
Gary Grubbs	Sheriff Arens (print sources, though not the episode, give his first name as "Tom")
Timothy Webber	Jess Harold
John MacLaren	George Kearns
Robin Mossley	Dr. Vance Randolph (first name not given in episode)
Gabrielle Miller	Paula (Gray)
Hrothgar Mathews	Mental Patient (Creighton Jones)
Robert Moloney	Worker
Carrie Cain Sparks	Maid

The official Fox *X-Files* website erroneously gives actor Timothy Webber's name as "Weber."

X-actitude: Chaco Chicken motto: "Good People, Good Food!" Indeed.

Walter "Chic" Chaco's background: born 1902; during WWII, transport plane carrying him was shot down over New Guinea (1944). The only survivor, he spent six months with the Jale tribe.

Paul Gray's background: born Jan. 6, 1948; high school graduate; phone 555-7265

Agents' rental car license plate: R89 495

Foxfire spirit: associated with massacred Indians in nineteenth-century Ozark folktales, and of people taken away by fireballs.

Person whom Arens goes to speak with at Chaco plant: Logan

How Scully IDs Kearns's bones: His medical records indicate a metal pin in his femur from a bone break four years ago.

X-otica: While I-40 does run east-west through Arkansas, there's no town of Dudley in the state.

Caroline Kava—who played NYPD Detective Jean Harp in three of the Richard Crenna "Janek" telefilms, wrote, directed, and produced the eighteen-minute short *Polio Water* (1995), shown at Columbia University's Ninth Annual Evening of Film: Faculty Choice of the Best Student Films in New York City. John Milford played LAPD Captain Dempsey in the *Dukes of Hazzard* spinoff, *Enos*.

176

2.25 "ANASAZI"   May 19, 1995

Teleplay: Chris Carter
Story: David Duchovny & Chris Carter
Director: R. W. Goodwin

Part 1 of a 3-part episode

The opening credo this episode: Ei Aaniigoo 'Ahoot'e. (Navajo for "The Truth Is Out There.")

NAVAJO RESERVATION, TWO GREY HILLS, NEW MEXICO: A 5.6 earthquake hits, waking a teenaged Eric Hosteen. His grandfather, Albert Hosteen, tells Eric's father, "the Earth has a secret it needs to tell." A motorcycling Eric spies metal oddly visible from a quarry floor. He later shows his family and neighbors the skeletal, barely fleshy remains of some humanoid creature. Albert says it should be returned: "*They* will be coming."

DOVER, DELAWARE: Kenneth Soona's computer, going through key sequences, beeps "Access Granted."

UNITED NATIONS BUILDING, NEW YORK CITY: A worried-looking Antonio tells an Italian diplomat someone's broken into the "MJ Files." Soon, word spreads through shadowy power echelons of Japan, Germany, and the U.S.—including the German-speaking Smoking Man. Masked assassins burst into Soona's empty apartment.

WASHINGTON, D.C.: The Lone Gunmen appear at Mulder's apartment. He's not happy to see them here, particularly since he hadn't slept last night. They tell Mulder about a multinational "black ops" unit known as Garnet—"School of The Americas" alumni—which is after Soona, a.k.a. The Thinker (who'd helped Mulder in 2.08, "One Breath"). Soona had hacked into the Department of Defense (DOD) computer net; now everyone including Customs and Immigration seek to block his escape. In his last communiqué, Soona named a place and a three-hour window in which to meet Mulder. A gunshot sounds, and the men race to see a woman in another apartment has gone crazy and shot her husband.

U.S. BOTANIC GARDEN, WASHINGTON, D.C., NIGHT: Soona (a possible psuedonym) tells Mulder that killers are tracking him—and that he believes he has the DOD's UFO intelligence files, with information about Roswell, MJ 12, and everything from the 1940s on. He gives Mulder a digital audiotape (DAT) of the files, which he didn't have to time to copy before high-tailing it. FBI HEADQUARTERS: Mulder tells Scully he finally has the Holy Grail: proof that the government's known of extraterrestrial existence for fifty years. They find it marked "DOD Top Secret" and written in code Scully recognizes as Navajo, which her military father had told her was the only language the Japanese couldn't break during WWII. She'll try to find a Navajo speaker. Mulder meets with Skinner, who's investigating rumors Mulder's receiving secret files. Mulder denies it and they briefly brawl.

177

Scully meets with Skinner and four of the usual mysterious higher-ups: the silver-haired man from her first meeting with Blevins (identified in the credits as second Senior Agent), a sharp-featured man with tall, blown-dry charcoal hair (identified in the credits as Senior FBI Agent), a silver/brown-haired man (series creator Chris Carter, in an uncredited cameo), and a silent, red-haired woman. Scully can't explain Mulder's behavior. One senior agent asks pointedly, "Weren't you originally assigned to agent Mulder to debunk his work?" Skinner warns her if there's anything she's not telling them, she faces the same summary fate as Mulder: dismissal without chance of reinstatement.

WEST TISBURY, MARTHA'S VINEYARD, MASSACHUSETTS: Smoking Man visits Mulder's father, greeting him as Bill. Mulder's dad is surprised and disturbed; over scotch, they discuss the files. Smoking Man claims the hacker "has come forward" and fingered Fox. Bill's agitated since his *own* name is in those files, which Smoking Man assures are encrypted. "You wouldn't harm *him*?" Bill asks. "I've protected him this long, haven't I?" Smoking Man replies, not entirely convincingly.

MULDER'S APARTMENT: Scully tells a strangely snappish Mulder she's meeting with a Navajo speaker in an hour; after she leaves, Mulder tapes an X to his window. OFFICE OF THE NAVAJO NATION, WASHINGTON, D.C.: A woman there can only make out bits and pieces of the sample Scully's given her, and says Scully needs an actual "code-talker." She'll ask one to contact Scully. The words she does recognize, she says, are those for "goods, merchandise," and "vaccination." Mulder's dad summons Fox but when Scully returns to Mulder's apartment, he's already gone and a bullet pierces his window and grazes her.

A seemingly repentant William tries to tell Fox about "the choices that needed to be made." He warns that the meaning of words like "the merchandise" will become horribly clear. William excuses himself to use the bathroom—where the shadow-government assassin Mulder knew as "Krycek" hides in the shower; he kills William with a single shot and escapes unseen. William's dying words to a tearful Fox: "Forgive me." Mulder calls Scully with the news. They're both afraid he'll be blamed; Scully tells him to run, since a shot had been fired through *his* apartment window, and his life may be in immediate danger. A feverish Mulder agrees to rest at her place while they plan how to find the assassin.

Mulder awakens to find Scully's taken his gun to the FBI Firearms Unit for comparison with the bullets [*sic*] removed from William. Scully later removes the bullet from Fox's wall and notices a workman outside loading a tank into an unmarked van. She finds a row of water-softener tanks in the basement; one, with new valves, is unmarked. Mulder, arriving home, sees an armed "Krycek." Mulder surprises him, takes his gun, and—certain "Krycek" killed his father—angrily assures "Krycek" he's going to kill him anyway, and to just give up the truth. Scully rushes to the scene and after warning Mulder not to kill "Krycek," shoots Mulder in the shoulder before he can commit vigilante murder. "Krycek" escapes.

Farmington, New Mexico: The two agents are at a hotel; Mulder has been out for thirty-six hours. Scully tended to the bullet wound and now gives him water, saying he hasn't had any in all this time, and shows him a valve from the unmarked tank. She says the tank was probably used to put drugs into his drinking water, explaining his erratic behavior.

Scully introduces him to Albert, a WWII Navajo code-talker, who claims an omen had told him Mulder was coming. Albert had told Scully that while most of the files are in jargon, they do refer to an international conspiracy dating to the 1940s. He'll take Mulder to where evidence of this conspiracy lies. Scully must return to Washington. She says her *own* name is in those files along with references to Duane Barry (who'd been instrumental in her seemingly alien abduction in 2.06, "Ascension"), and to some "test."

At the reservation, Albert tells Mulder about a tribe who lived here 600 years ago—the Anasazi, whose name means "the ancient aliens." Historians believe they disappeared without a trace. And the truth, Mulder asks?

"Nothing disappears without a trace." Albert believes they were abducted "by visitors who come here still." Mulder rides with Eric to the quarry; as they climb down toward the exposed metal, Smoking Man calls Mulder on his cel phone. He tells Mulder not to listen to everything his father said— that "he authorized the project, that's what he couldn't live with." "He couldn't live with it," Mulder retorts, taking the bait and staying on the line, "because you had him killed." Smoking Man says he wasn't involved; Mulder doesn't believe him. By the time he's hung up, a soldier tells Smoking Man they've gotten a coordinate on Mulder; they enter a waiting black helicopter.

Mulder dusts off a plaque showing this is a railroad refrigeration car. Mulder calls Scully from inside—where bodies like the one Eric had retrieved are stacked floor to ceiling. Scully tells Mulder the coded documents refer to U.S. experiments conducted by Axis scientists granted amnesty after WWII—tests on humans referred to as "the merchandise." Yet Mulder sees these remains look *in*human—and one has what appears to be a vaccination scar. Eric slams down the hatch, as a black helicopter descends and soldiers emerge. Eric won't talk, and a soldier checking out the boxcar says Mulder's not inside—he's vanished without a trace. Smoking Man yells, in ironic counterpoint to Albert, "Nothing vanishes without a trace!" Then he orders, "Burn it!" Taking Eric, the chopper ascends as fire explodes from the hole.

179

Mitch Pileggi	Assistant Director Walter S. Skinner
Peter Donat	William Mulder
Floyd Red Crow Westerman	Albert Hosteen
Nicholas Lea	"Alex Krycek"
William B. Davis	Smoking Man
Bruce Harwood	Byers
Dean Haglund	Langly
Tom Braidwood	Frohike
Michael David Simms	Senior FBI Agent
Renae Morriseau	Josephine Doane (woman at Navajo Nation office; unnamed in episode)
Ken Camroux	2nd Senior Agent
Dakota House	Eric (Hosteen)
Bernie Coulson	The Thinker (Kenneth Soona)
Mitchell Davies	Stealth Man
Paul McLean	Agent Kautz (unnamed in episode; evidently the Firearms Unit agent)
Uncredited:	
Aurelio Dinunzios	Antonio
Chris Carter	3rd Senior Agent
Byron Chief Moon	Father

(Note: Tim Michael is listed as "Albert's son"—Eric's father—in the subsequent two parts)

The official Fox *X-Files* website erroneously lists the character played by Renae Morriseau as Joseph, rather than Josephine, Doane.

X-actitude: Buried boxcar plaque: Sierra Pacific Railroad RTC-567490

Taxi that Mulder took home from Scully's apartment: Capitol Cab; phone 555-4987.

Book Soona is reading: *The 50 Greatest Conspiracies of All Time,* by Jonathan Vankin and John Whalen.

X-otica: Farmington, NM, is a real-life small city just outside the Navajo Reservation.

Floyd Red Crow Westerman played Uncle Ray Firewalker in *Walker, Texas Ranger.* He twice appeared on *Northern Exposure* as the spirit guide One Who Waits.

3.01 "THE BLESSING WAY"   September 22, 1995

Writer: Chris Carter
Director: R. W. Goodwin

Part 2 of a 3-part episode

NAVAJO RESERVATION, TWO GREY HILLS, NEW MEXICO: Albert Hosteen reflects on history being controlled by eliminating witnesses and their memories. The Smoking Man and camouflaged soldiers burst in, having seen Mulder's car outside, and beat up Albert, his son, and grandson, vainly seeking Mulder and the MJ Files. After the soldiers leave, the bloodied Hosteens direct Scully to the smoldering boxcar. No sign of Mulder. Driving across the Navajo Reservation northwest of Los Alamos, New Mexico, Scully's menaced by a helicopter; soldiers take her paper files and leave when she tells them Mulder has the DAT version.

THE OPC: Four of the usual higher-ups put Scully on mandatory leave. She turns in her badge and gun, and complains to Skinner about being rail-roaded. Then, in Mulder's office, she finds that the DAT is missing.

NEW YORK CITY, (EAST) 46TH STREET: Smoking Man meets with a cabal of mysterious power-brokers, including men end-credited as Elders no. 1, no. 2, and no. 3, and the Well-Manicured Man. Elder no. 2 wants assurance that "forty years of work" haven't been compromised. Smoking Man half-truth-fully assures the files have been recovered, and that the pilferers—includ-ing Mulder—have been "removed." Elder no. 1 says, "[A]ll the pertinent parties should be informed, that we may continue with our work." At her mom's house, Scully breaks down.

Albert finds a barely living Mulder beneath some rocks at the quarry, where he'd somehow hidden underground [N]. He transfers the unconscious agent to a hogan, and brings in Navajo holy men to perform the healing, days-long Blessing Way Chant.

SCULLY'S APARTMENT: A saddened Frohike arrives, having heard of Mulder's apparent death. He shows Scully a newspaper article from two days ago about the execution-style slaying of Kenneth J. Soona, a.k.a. The Thinker, who'd hacked into the DOD's MJ files and given Mulder the DAT.

Mulder hovers between life and death in a spectral starfield, where Deep Throat tells him, "There is truth here, my old friend, if that's all you seek. But there's no justice or judgment, without which truth is a vast, dead hollow." Mulder's father, William, laments the lies "I thought might bury forever the truth I could not live with." They urge Fox to keep his memory—and thus the truth—alive.

FBI HEADQUARTERS: Scully, at the front entrance, sets off a metal detector; the friendly guard, who knows her, figures it's just some stray pin. Scully

181

shows Skinner the Soona obit, and asks to compare the Trenton P.D. ballistic record against that of Mulder's father. Skinner replies any match would have been noted already, and he won't double-check; he also tells her he's executed a warrant to search her apartment for the DAT. As she leaves, Scully and the guard narrow the source of the alarm to something embedded in her neck. A doctor later extracts what he at first suspects is buckshot.

On the third day of the ritual at the reservation, Mulder awakens and asks for water, and over the following days recuperates. Scully's doctor now tells her that the metal object is a computer chip. At her sister Melissa's urging, Scully sees a regression-hypnosis specialist, psychotherapist Dr. Mark Pomerantz. She hazily recalls her "lost" abduction time: There were men, a light, and distorted sounds—including that of an alarm and of someone wondering if she were all right. Panicked, she cuts the session short. Later, she sees Skinner leaving her apartment house and driving away.

Albert tells Mulder that as part of the ritual, he cannot bathe or change clothes for four days, and explains Mulder had gone to the "origin place" in each of us—was it all a dream? Scully phones Skinner, who, with Smoking Man in his office, denies being at her apartment. That night, Scully dreams Mulder is alive and speaking to her. GARDEN OF REFLECTION, PARKWAY CEMETERY, BOSTON: At William Mulder's funeral, Scully tells Fox's mother she believes her son is alive. The Well-Manicured Man approaches Scully; he's from a consortium representing "global interests . . . that would be extremely threatened" by the DAT being leaked. He tells her Mulder's dead and she herself is scheduled to die one of two ways: by men at her home with an unregistered weapon or by someone close to her, at an unscheduled meeting. He warns her only because her murder will draw problematic attention to his group. Its business? "We predict the future. And the best way to predict the future is to invent it."

GREENWICH, CONNECTICUT: Mrs. Mulder is ecstatic to see Fox alive. Yet she only reluctantly takes him to the attic to find artifacts of his father—and unconvincingly swears she doesn't recognize any of the other seven men in a photo taken in 1972 (per Mulder this episode) or "about 1973" (per Mulder next episode), though we can clearly see one of them is Smoking Man. Mulder pulls a gun from a trunk and leaves. At Scully's apartment, a worried Melissa phones that she's coming over; Scully agrees, but then, recalling the warning, decides to go to Melissa's instead—with an automatic pistol. Yet as she leaves, Skinner pulls up, claiming he needs to speak with her in private; warily, she takes him to Mulder's apartment and at gunpoint demands to know who sent him.

At Scully's, assassin Luis Cardinal (identified only as "Hispanic Man" until 3.16, "Apocrypha") shoots Melissa in the head; his partner, the man known as Alex Krycek, realizes their horrible error and the two quickly vanish.

Back at Mulder's, Skinner says it was he who'd taken the DAT from Mulder's desk, and insists he, too, wants justice done. Scully hears footsteps outside the door, and in that split-second of distraction, Skinner draws *his* gun on *her*. They stare down each other's barrels in a standoff.

"In Memoriam: Larry Wells, 1946–1995"

Mitch Pileggi	Assistant Director Walter S. Skinner
Peter Donat	William Mulder
Floyd "Red Crow" Westerman	Albert Hosteen
Melinda McGraw	Melissa Scully
Sheila Larken	Margaret (Maggie) Scully
Nicholas Lea	"Alex Krycek"
William B. Davis	Smoking Man
John Neville	Well-Manicured Man
Tom Braidwood	Frohike
Jerry Hardin	Deep Throat
Alf Humphreys	Dr. (Mark(Pomerantz
Dakota House	Eric (Hosteen)
Michael David Simms	Senior FBI Agent
Rebecca Toolan	Mrs. Mulder
Don S. Williams	Elder #1 (Heavyset man)
Forbes Angus	(Scully's) M.D.
Mitchell Davies	Camouflage Man
Benita Ha	Tour Guide
Victor Ian	Minister
Ernie Foort	Security Guard
Lenno Britos	Hispanic Man (Luis Cardinal)
Uncredited:	
Stanely Walsh	Elder #2
John Moore	Elder #3
Martin Evans	Major Domo (goateed man)*

183

*Actor name and character designation given in episode 3.16, "Apocrypha"

Note: The Lowry book lists Tim Michael as playing Albert's Son (Eric's father) this episode—yet for the previous episode, Lowry lists Byron Chief Moon in the role. Neither are credited on-screen, but Moon, who appears in *White Fang 2: Myth of the White Wolf* (1994), appears to be correct.

***X*-actitude:**   Men in the old photo, from statements and evidence in this and the following episode, left to right:
   Smoking Man, William Mulder, Victor Klemper, unknown, unknown, Deep Throat, unknown, Well-Manicured Man
   Apartment across from Scully's: no. 3. Since Scully's apartment is no. 35, it's likely that a digit is missing from the door across the hall.

License plate on Scully's personal car: 2N9-521 (state indecipherable). Since Scully is on mandatory leave with no access to motor-pool vehicles, this two-door car must be her own.

Melissa's family nickname: Missy

Newspaper article: (paper) *The Examiner*; (headline) HOMICIDE VICTIM BODY DISCOVERED AT CITY DUMP; (article highlights) body of Kenneth J. Soona discovered April 16 in the Trenton landfill by landfill worker Sparky Sinclair; Soona was raised in Youngstown, PA, and went to college on an academic scholarship; survived by mother Jane, sisters Isabel and Elsbeth, and brother Mike.

X-otica: Since Scully walks to her mother's house we must assume they live close by.

The division usually referred to as the Office of Professional Responsibility is here called the Office of Professional Conduct.

Larry Wells was the series's costume designer.

London native and now Canadian citizen John Neville is a distinguished Shakespearean great. He costarred on the American sitcom *Grand* and as the title character in Terry Gilliam's *The Adventures of Baron Munchausen* (1988). Neville was awarded the Order of the British Empire in 1965.

Rebecca Toolan, beginning her recurring role as Mulder's mother, is a local Vancouver actress whose films include *Little Women* (1994).

184

3.02 "PAPER CLIP"   September 29, 1995

Writer: Chris Carter

Director: Rob Bowman

Part 3 of a 3-part episode

In a voice-over, Albert Hosteen describes Mulder's recuperation, and of news from Native Americans in the Great Plains of a white buffalo's birth—a major omen of change. MULDER'S APARTMENT: Mulder, gun drawn, bursts into the standoff and forces Skinner to hand Scully his gun.

Scully complains about her death threat; Skinner asks Mulder what's in the DAT. After telling Skinner "your cigarette-smoking friend" had his dad assassinated and then "killed me . . . I was a dead man and now I'm back," Mulder explains that the tape holds the secret DOD "MJ" documents confirming the existence of alien life on Earth. They let Skinner hold on to it for safekeeping when he insists it's their only leverage to bring the conspirators to justice.

D.C. GENERAL HOSPITAL: A doctor tells a frantic Margaret Scully that her daughter just out of surgery for a cranial gunshot wound isn't Dana, but

Melissa. OFFICE OF *THE LONE GUNMAN*: The agents show Langly and Byers the photo of Mulder's dad and others. They discuss Project Paper Clip, in which Nazi scientists were granted immunity in the U.S. after World War II. Langly recognizes one such war criminal in the photo: Victor Klemper, who conducted inhuman experimentation on Jews. Frohike gently breaks the news about Melissa; Scully bolts to go, but Mulder convinces her that whomever's responsible will be gunning for *her* there.

NEW YORK CITY, (EAST) 46TH STREET, 7:09 A.M.: Elder no. 1 cautions Smoking Man about the repercussions of an innocent woman being shot; another elder confirms the assassins work for Smoking Man. The Well-Manicured Man wants the DAT, which Smoking Man, lying, says he has in safekeeping and will bring tomorrow. At a greenhouse, the agents speak with Klemper, who says only that the photo was taken at the Strughold Mining Company in West Virginia, and then asks if they know the formula of Napier's Constant. After they leave, Klemper phones the Well-Manicured Man to taunt that he's been visited by "the son of one of our old colleagues." The Well-Manicured Man, now aware Mulder's alive, arranges for more satisfactory killers.

As an ominous man in a blue suit paces outside Melissa's room, Albert arrives to tell Margaret that Dana's fine, but can't come; he stays to pray over the comatose Melissa. WEST VIRGINIA: Inside an abandoned coal-mining facility, Scully and Mulder find an incongruous set of security doors with numeric-keypad locks. They punch in the first five digits of Napier's Constant [N], until Scully gets one door open.

FBI HEADQUARTERS: Skinner tells Smoking Man he may have the DAT, and wants to keep it from the wrong hands. Smoking Man hisses he doesn't make deals and insinuates that Skinner's own assassination is not impossible. At the mine, Scully and Mulder find countless rows of file cabinets containing medical files—each including a smallpox vaccination record and a tissue sample. They find records both for Scully and for Mulder's sister, Samantha—the latter originally earmarked for Mulder himself. A rumbling brings Mulder upstairs, where he sees a majestic apparent spacecraft. Inside the mine, small apparent aliens scurry past an astonished Scully. Suddenly, unmarked cars arrive. Gun-toting men chase Mulder downstairs but the agents slip out a back door.

CHARLOTTE'S DINER, ROUTE 320A, CRAIGER, MARYLAND: Meeting with Skinner, the agents reveal their find. Skinner wants to turn over the DAT in exchange for their safety; Mulder objects, but Scully says the truth won't do them any good if they're fugitives. Skinner—who confirms that "whoever downloaded" the files copy-protected them against either digital or hard copies [N]—assures them the conspirators will honor the deal, or else he'll turn State's evidence and they'd have to kill him, too. The agents agree to the trade, and Skinner gives them a lift.

185

MELISSA'S HOSPITAL ROOM: Albert has been praying for two days. Skinner, arriving, introduces himself to Albert and Margaret. Blue-Suit Man still hovers ominously; a suspicious Skinner chases him into a stairwell, where he's ambushed and beaten by Blue-Suit and two others—Luis Cardinal and "Alex Krycek," who takes the DAT. SOUTHEAST WASHINGTON, D.C.: Krycek and the others stop for gas and beer; after the others leave the car, a wary Krycek sees the clock oddly blinking, and escapes just before the car blows up.

KLEMPER'S GREENHOUSE: The agents find Well-Manicured Man, who tells them Klemper's dead, and doesn't deny complicity; he admits to being in the 1972 photo, and to knowing Mulder's dad. He offers three disconnected bits of information—a 1947 spaceship crash in New Mexico (e.g. Roswell); Dr. Josef Mengele's Nazi wartime supersoldier experiments, also worked on by scientists granted amnesty under Operation Paper Clip; and Klemper's orchid hybrids. Mulder deduces Klemper was working to create an alien-human hybrid. Well-Manicured Man continues: During the cold war, men like Mulder's father collected genetic data for, ostensibly, post-apocalyptic identification; he lets these medical records gave Klemper access to a DNA database of hundreds of millions of vaccinated Americans. When William Mulder learned of this misuse, he threatened to expose this eugenics project—so they took Samantha hostage.

Krycek phones Smoking Man at the cabal's suite, and promises exposure if ever threatened. GREENWICH, CONNECTICUT, 2 A.M.: Mulder's mother painfully reveals to Fox that his father was told to make a choice between their children. At FBI headquarters, Skinner tells Smoking Man he'll trade the DAT (which he doesn't have) for Scully and Mulder's safety. Smoking Man knows he's bluffing, and suggests he may have Skinner killed for trying. But Skinner reveals Albert, and informs Smoking Man that Albert's memorized the MJ Files's contents, and has carried on the Navajo oral tradition by teaching it to twenty others: Unless Smoking Man can have every Navajo in four states killed, he'd better leave them alone. At the hospital, Scully tells Mulder that Melissa died three hours ago—as with Mulder, they've taken away her sister. Even the skeptical Scully admits she's heard the truth—and wants answers.

"In Memoriam: Mario Mark Kennedy, 1966–1995"

Mitch Pileggi	Assistant Director Walter S. Skinner
Walter Gotell	Victor Klemper
Melinda McGraw	Melissa Scully
Sheila Larken	Margaret (Maggie) Scully
Nicholas Lea	"Alex Krycek"
William B. Davis	Smoking Man
John Neville	Well-Manicured Man
Tom Braidwood	Frohike

Dean Haglund	Langly
Bruce Harwood	Byers
Floyd Red Crow Westerman	Albert Hosteen
Rebecca Toolan	Mrs. Mulder
Don S. Williams	Elder #1 (Heavyset man)
Robert Lewis	ER Doctor
Lenno Britos	Hispanic Man (Luis Cardinal)
Uncredited:	
Stanley Walsh	Elder #2
Peta Brookstone	ICU Nurse
Martin Evans	Major Domo*

*Actor name and character designation given in episode 3.16, "Apocrypha"

The official Fox *X-Files* website erroneously spells Langly as "Langley," and neglects to list front-credit performer Floyd Red Crow Westerman.

X-actitude: Samantha's medical-record file: Samantha Ann Mulder, born Nov. 21, 1965. The police report, in the pilot episode, gives her middle initial as "T.," but then, the report also showed a typo in the spelling of her hometown. Her medical records here seem more credible.

License plate on the assassins' car: 3CB-502

Dr. Josef Mengele's genetic-experimentation center: Institute of Hereditary Biology and Racial Hygiene

X-otica: Walter Gotell is familiar as the KGB chief, General Anatol Gogol, in six James Bond movies from *The Spy Who Loved Me* to *The Living Daylights* (plus minor baddie Morzeny in 1962's *Dr. No*).

Mario Mark Kennedy was a prominent on-line X-Phile.

3.03 "DPO"   October 6, 1995
Writer: Howard Gordon
Director: Kim Manners

CONNERVILLE, OKLAHOMA: At a strip-mall video arcade, off-duty pizza-deliverer Jack Hammond declines to let Darren Oswald have back the "Virtua Fighter 2" game which Darren had left for a minute. A fight brews, as Darren's arcade-clerk friend Zero watches. But then Jack, seemingly not in control of his body, leaves and gets into his car—where he's killed by some strange electrical surge.

LLOYD P. WHARTON COUNTY BUILDING: Scully examines Hammond's body as Stan, the county coroner, and Johnston County Sheriff Teller watch. This latest in a pattern of odd electrocution deaths shows, curiously, no contact point, and the coroner defensively insists it's just lightning—though he admits the five recent Connerville strikes (four fatal) are statistically "improbable." Teller asserts there's nothing unusual: The nearby Astadourian Lightning Observatory has 100 ionized rods designed specifically to stimulate lightning. Mulder wonders why the lightning only strikes seventeen- to twenty-one-year-old males.

Checking the only shop open after Jack quit work, they question Zero; he noticed nothing, he says, what with the noise and flashing lights here. An on-screen display alerts Mulder that the ten-game record-holder on "Virtua Fighter 2" is initialed DPO—as in Darren Peter Oswald, the only survivor of the lightning strikes. The notations place DPO here at the time of the incident. KIVEAT AUTO BODY: Darren, working there, nervously greets Sharon Kiveat, the beautiful wife of garage owner Frank. He has a crush on her. Frank returns from a towing job, soon followed by Mulder and Scully. As the agents fruitlessly question Darren, Mulder's cel phone mysteriously heats and starts to melt.

At the dilapidated Oswald house, Darren's couch-potato mother belittles him, and doesn't bat an eye when he changes channels from across the room without the remote. When Zero comes by, Darren goes to a pasture next door to "barbecue" some cows. Zero begs him not to, but Darren calls lightning down to hit him, and the next morning, Teller is there as three dead cows are towed away. He shows the agents a fulgarite—a place where lightning strikes sandy soil to form glass—and declares their investigation over. Mulder finds a partial footprint incongruously in the fulgarite. FORENSIC LAB, JOHNSTON COUNTY SHERIFF'S OFFICE: Scully finds it's from a size 8 1/2 standard military boot; she also found traces of antifreeze. They go seek auto mechanic Darren.

COUNTY ROAD A-7: Darren manipulates traffic lights, planning to cause an accident. Zero suggests he stop all this, and use his power to make a killing in Vegas. But Darren won't go anywhere without Mrs. Kiveat. At the Oswald house, the agents find an 8 1/2-size shoe and a clipped picture that fits the cut-out yearbook space for Mrs. Kiveat. ACCIDENT SCENE: Darren causes tow-trucker Frank to have a heart attack; when the two EMS workers find their portable defibrillator unaccountably chargeless, Darren "heroically" rescues Frank by defibrillating him by hand.

COMMUNITY HOSPITAL, FELTON, OKLAHOMA: As Frank recuperates, the agents learn Darren was admitted here five months ago in cardiac arrest after his lightning-strike and that he has acute hypokalemia, an electrolyte imbalance of high sodium and low potassium, which Mulder theorizes, somehow explains his ability to generate electricity. They question Darren at the Johnston County Jail, but he admits nothing and thinks Zero squealed on him. They try to get Mrs. Kiveat to press harassment charges. She'd been afraid to, but the agents say they can hold Darren seventy-two hours on suspicion of murder, so she and Frank will be safe. Yet Teller's decided the feds have a weak case, and has let Darren go.

The agents rush to the hospital, but Darren's stopped at the arcade first to kill Zero. Darren eludes Mulder to get to Frank's room, where Scully draws her gun but Sharon, wanting no danger near Frank, agrees to walk out with Darren. Outside, she runs away when Teller pulls up. Darren kills Teller before Mulder can fire, then Darren falls in a lightning-crumpled heap himself. OKLAHOMA STATE PSYCHIATRIC HOSPITAL: Scully tells Mulder the coroner's ruled Teller's death accidental, by lightning, and the DA can't fathom how to prosecute for murder. Darren, inside his cell, stares blankly at a TV screen that's channel-changing either to his whim or in his mind.

Jack Black	Zero*
Giovanni Ribisi	Darren Peter Oswald
Ernie Lively	Sherrif Teller
Karen Witter	Sharon Kiveat
Steve Makaj	Frank Kiveat
Peter Anderson	Stan Buxton (last name not given in episode)
Kate Robbins	Mrs. Oswald
Mar Andersons**	Jack Hammond
Brent Chapman	Traffic Cop
Jason Anthony Griffith	Paramedic #1
Uncredited, each with one or more speaking lines:	
Cavan Cunningham	Paramedic #2
Bonnie Hay	Night Nurse

189

*Character's full name (given in print sources but not in the episode) is Bart Liquori.

** Credited as Mar Anderson in 2.19.

***X*-actitude:** Darren's "Virtua Fighter 2" records (rank/initials/date/time):

1.	DPO	09-12-95	11:41 P.M.
2.	DPO	09-11-95	11:35 P.M.
3.	DPO	09-11-95	10:50 P.M.
4.	DPO	09-11-95	10:30 P.M.
5.	DPO	09-10-95	10:15 P.M.
6.	DPO	09-10-95	11:04 P.M.
7.	DPO	09-10-95	11:18 P.M.
8.	DPO	09-10-95	11:33 P.M.
9.	DPO	09-08-95	10:37 P.M.
10.	DPO	09-08-95	10:56 P.M.

Darren's other three victims: Corey Huffar, Burke Roberts, Billy (no last name given)

Mrs. Oswald's TV shows: A talk show with a heavily tattooed man discussing rebellion and S&M; and a (fictional) music video Darren switches to—The Rosemarys, "Mary Beth Clark I Love You."

J. Hartling Records, Director: Deb Brown. The latter is an X-Phile also referred to in 2.14, "Die Hand Die Verletz."

Radio frequency of lightning, per Mulder: 8Hz; called the Schuman Resonance

Lettering on Frank Kiveat's tow truck: Kiveat 24 Hr. Towing Auto Service

Sharon Kiveat: Remedial reading teacher at Gravenhurst High School; Darren failed her class

Frank's hospital room: 404

Darren's t-shirt when he's taken in for questioning: Vandals (front); Nitro Records (back)

Specified charge level of the portable defibrillator: 300 joules

---

3.04 "CLYDE BRUCKMAN'S FINAL REPOSE" October 13, 1995
Writer: Darin Morgan
Director: Rob Bowman

ST. PAUL, MINNESOTA, SEPTEMBER 16: [N] Insurance salesman Clyde Bruckman buys a Lotto ticket in a liquor store. Outside, he passes a thin, balding, redheaded man going to see palm reader Madame Zelma. The man (later identified as "Puppet" in print sources but not in episode) asks Zelma why he envisions and then carries out terrible things. Then he murders her.

NORTH MINNEAPOLIS: A doll collector and amateur tasseographer (tea-leaf reader) is the latest in a string of prognosticator serial murders. Detective Cline tells Detective Havez he's asked the help of someone highly recommended but unorthodox and, per the police photographer, "spooky." And it's . . . famous psychic "The Stupendous Yappi!" Mulder and Scully, who have also arrived to investigate, are amused.

Elsewhere, Bruckman tries to sell a life-insurance policy to young marrieds the Gordons before envisioning Gordon, two years from now, suffering a fatal head-on collision with a drunk in a blue 1987 Mustang. Later, Bruckman helps senile apartment-house neighbor Mrs. Lowell with her garbage. He has a momentary vision of her Pomeranian eating entrails; moments before, he'd envisioned a human head in a bag of lettuce. At the dumpster, he finds Madame Zelma's body.

Scully and Mulder question him since he knows details the police hadn't divulged. Mulder suspects he may be psychic, and they take him to the tea-reader's apartment. The reluctant Bruckman says the killer feels so not-in-control of his life, he's like a puppet and he states they'll find the victim's

Peter Boyle, left, standing, looking more
spiffy than Clyde Bruckman, in the cable movie
The Tragedy of Flight 103.

body tomorrow morning at Glenview Lake. After the agents do so, Mulder
returns to Bruckman (who's just lost at Lotto) and convinces him to be tested
for psychic ability, which they discover is limited to foretelling death.

Scully arrives with one of three identical keychains found on the victims;
it has a logo she's traced to Uranus Unlimited, which sells astrology-based
marketing advice. Bruckman says Uranus owner Claude Dukenfield's been
murdered; they find his body near some woods to which Bruckman directs
them. On the way, Bruckman has shut up the inquisitive Mulder by suggesting there are worse, if more dignified, ways to die than autoerotic asphyxiation. Why are you telling *me*, Mulder worriedly asks. Later, Bruckman says
the killer is a psychic himself, and Bruckman sees what *he* sees: Mulder
being stalked in a kitchen, getting his throat slashed after stepping in a
banana-cream pie. He explains the vision came after touching a letter from
the killer, in which he vows to kill Bruckman and—though the letter's post-
marked the day before the agents met Bruckman to tell the feds hi.

LE DAMFINO HOTEL: Scully guards Bruckman in protective custody, and
asks him about how she'll die. Bruckman enigmatically replies, "You don't."

Mulder relieves Scully, and gets an earful from Bruckman about his recurring dream of being dead and decomposing. Morning: Detective Havez relieves Mulder, who accompanies Scully to the murder site of yet another tarot reader. While Havez uses the bathroom, Bruckman lets in a bellhop who'd just bumped into Scully and Mulder. It's the killer, who is astonished to find Bruckman there. Coincidence or destiny? Brandishing a steak knife, the killer asks why he does what he does. Because, Bruckman replies, "You're a homicidal maniac," adding, "You don't kill me now." Havez isn't so lucky.

At the tarot reader's, Scully concludes that the bellhop did it. At the hotel, she finds Havez dead and Bruckman gone. Mulder grapples with the bellhop in the kitchen, and though the predication's specifics are a bit off, the killer is about to knife Mulder when Scully kills the man with a single shot. They find Bruckman in his apartment, dead or about to die of autoerotic asphyxiation. He's left a note asking Scully to care for Mrs. Lowell's remains and maybe adopt her dog. Later, at home, Scully watches a late-night Laurel and Hardy short with the pooch (which we learn in 3.22, "Quagmire," she's named Queegqueg)—and when a Yappi infomercial comes on, throws her phone at the screen.

192

Peter Boyle	Clyde Bruckman
Stu Charno	The Killer ("Puppet")
Frank Cassini	(Detective) Cline
Dwight McFee	(Detective) Havez
Alex Diakun	Tarot Dealer
Karin Konoval	Madame Zelma
Ken Roberts	(Liquor-store) Clerk
Jaap Broeker	The Stupendous Yappi
David McKay	Young Husband (Mr. Gordon)
Greg Anderson	(Police) Photographer
Uncredited (no lines, but prominent presence):	
Doris Rands	Mrs. Lowell

Yappi's lovely assistant (who has no lines but appears in Yappi's scenes and in his infomercial) is uncredited, as is the animal-performer.

X-actitude: Bruckman's apartment: 503; Mrs. Lowell's is 504.

Doll collector's apartment: 66

Minneapolis police APB, based on Yappi's "psychic reading": While male, 17–34, with or without facial hair, with or without a tattoo

Value of life insurance policy Bruckman wants to sell the Gordon's: $200,000, for $2,400 net annual cost.

Bruckman's scotch: J&P

Claude Dukenfield data: forty-three years old, divorced with two kids, lives at 316 Roundview Lane, nonsmoker, makes about $87,000 a year

Winning Lotto numbers: 8, 12, 36 (by extrapolation), 38, 40, 44. Bruckman's numbers: 9, 13, 37, 39, 41, 45.

X-otica: World-class character-actor Peter Boyle was a Christian Brothers monk before turning to comedy with Chicago's Second City troupe. After an inauspicious movie debut in *The Virgin President* (1968), he found fame as the title character of *Joe* (1970). Among his classic screen portrayals are Robert Redford's campaign manager in *The Candidate*, the sympathetic monster in *Young Frankenstein*, and the cabbie-guru Wizard in *Taxi Driver*.

3.05 "THE LIST"   October 20, 1995
Writer-Director: Chris Carter

NIGHT: On a remote road, a car picks up a waiting man. EASTPOINT STATE PENITENTIARY, LEON COUNTY, FL: Warden Leo Brodeur begins the execution of Napoleon "Neech" Manley. Manley's wife Danielle swears that she'll never love again. The waiting man appears inside the electric-chair chamber wearing a black hood. As Manley dies he swears he'll be reincarnated, and that five men will die to pay for his mistreatment. FBI HEADQUARTERS: Mulder tells Scully that Manley was convicted in 1984 for driving the getaway car in a Florida liquor store double-murder. Mulder has discovered that Manley appears to be making good on his threat. The guard who'd led him to the chair was found dead of suffocation in Manley's cell.

At the prison, Brodeur figures Manley had help from confederates. As he, Mulder, and Scully approach the guard's body they find it already covered with maggots. Mulder questions convict John Speranza, who'd known Manley well. Speranza is convinced that Manley has returned. The whole prison's nervous. A guard, Fornier, takes Scully to examine Manley's cell and leaves her alone there [N]. She's then pulled into the shadows by guard Vincent Parmelly, who tells her a con named Roque has Manley's hit list.

7:03 A.M.: Fornier's maggoty head is found inside a paint can. The state coroner explains to Scully that *Lucilia cuprina*, or the green bottle fly, can lay eggs within a minute after death occurs, and hot, humid environments promote rapid growth. Roque privately tells Mulder he'd overheard Manley giving Speranza the names; now Roque will exchange them for transfer to another prison. But Brodeur, later, tells Mulder he won't deal. Moments afterward, he walks into his office to find Fornier's headless body in his chair. MANLEY'S CELL, 3:45 P.M.: Scully and Mulder find evidence of Manley's obsession with soul-transmigration, and a letter from his wife. They visit Danielle at her home; she's genuinely terrified that Manley has returned. At the prison, the warden beats Roque to death while demanding he reveal who's on the list. All Roque will say is that Brodeur is number five.

193

Danielle's lover, Parmelly, assures her that Manley is not coming back. At the prison, Mulder pressures Brodeur into revealing the executioner's name—Perry Simon—to save him from becoming one of the next victims. But the agents find Simon dead in his attic, covered with maggots. Speranza refuses to give Mulder the list, but reveals that Roque was not on it. Two more will die. Scully alerts Mulder that in the last two months, Manley made thirty calls to a Danny Charez, who's been to see Speranza three times since the first murder. Questioning Charez, the agents learn that he was Manley's twenty-six-year-old court-appointed lawyer, whom Manley always blamed for his conviction. Charez hopes to get Speranza a retrial and avoid Manley's supernatural wrath. He'd even sought Danielle's help, but her boyfriend Parmelly had threatened him with a gun. At the prison, Speranza agrees to Brodeur's deal: Stop the murders, and Brodeur will pull strings with the governor. That night, Charez brushes away a large fly, just before some blurry African-American man—Manley? Or Parmelly?—smothers him with a pillow.

The agents then stake out Danielle's place, and Scully later picks Parmelly out of a prison-guard mug book, identifying him as the unnamed guard who'd told her about Roque's list. When Brodeur tells them Charez has been murdered, they go to arrest Parmelly. Danielle, at home, wakes to see Manley in her room; she follows him to the living room, but sees only Parmelly. Convinced he's actually Manley, she kills him with two shots as the agents and cops burst in. At the prison, the sadistic Brodeur beats a bound Speranza as he'd beaten Roque.

As the agents drive away, aspects of the "closed" case still bother Mulder—there are too many unanswered questions about how and why Parmelly could have been the killer. Brodeur drives by in the opposite direction, calmly swatting a large fly. To his horror, he sees Manley in the back seat reaching over to wrestle with the wheel until the car smashes into a tree, killing Brodeur. The backseat's already infested with maggots.

J. T. Walsh	Warden Leo Brodeur
Bokeem Woodbine	Roque (print sources, but not the episode, give his first name as Sammom)
Badja Djola	Napoleon "Neech" Manley
John Toles-Bey	John Speranza
Ken Foree	Vincent Parmelly
April Grace	Danielle Manley
Greg Rogers	Daniel Charez
Mitch Kosterman	Fornier
Paul Raskin	Ullrich (coroner; name not given in episode)
Denny Arnold	Key Guard
Craig Brunanski	Guard
Joseph Patrick Finn	Chaplain

Uncredited:
Bruce Pinard   Executioner Perry Simon
Listed in print sources, but not evident in episode:
Don McKay   Oates
Michael Andaluz   Tattooed Prisoner

***X*-actitude:**   Manley's mug shot/arrest number: 50416. Prison time: eleven years, fifty-six days. His wife was allowed only three visits in that time. Two stays of execution.

Death-row cell block: Q

Agent's Lariat rental car license plate: Florida plate OKE 46J

Guards visible in mug-shot book: Sgt. S. Gold no. 4151; Guard V. Parmelly no. 4310

***X*-otica:**   Tony Award-winner J. T. Walsh (*Glengarry Glen Ross*) has been memorable in such films as *Hannah and Her Sisters*; *Tin Men*; *Good Morning, Vietnam*; *Hoffa*; *The Client,* and *The Last Seduction*. Badja Djola's films include *A Rage in Harlem*, written by fellow guest John Toles-Bay. Guest Joseph Patrick Finn is one of the series' producers.

3.06 "2SHY"   November 3, 1995
Writer: Jeffrey Vlaming
Director: David Nutter

CLEVELAND, OHIO, NIGHT: A man and woman talk in a car, against a romantic skyline. Lauren MacKalvey is a plain-looking, somewhat overweight woman; her date is an attractive, charming man she met on-line three months earlier. When he kisses her, she gags up a gelatinous substance. In the morning, a cop finds a grotesque, goo-covered, fleshy mass in the car. Detective Alan Cross contacts Mulder and Scully, recommended as FBI experts in the unusual. A couple of months earlier in Aberdeen, Mississippi, four women who'd answered personals ads had disappeared in less than a month. The sole body found was too decomposed for an autopsy.

The killer, going by the alias Virgil Incanto, chats on-line with overweight Ellen Kaminsky, whose computer handle is "Huggs." His is "Timid," and he wants to meet. Incanto's interrupted by his landlady, who, thinking him a novelist or editor, asks him to critique her poems sometime. CUYAHOGA COUNTY MORGUE, SAME DAY: [N] Scully discovers Lauren's remains have degenerated into a skeleton and a pool of red glop. Mulder learns the man Lauren had dated last night had been communicating with her on-line, handled "2Shy"; Lauren's roommate gives Mulder copies of the romantic letters 2Shy had sent Lauren. Mulder calls Scully to say 2Shy's their serial killer—he'd opened his on-line account with one of the Aberdeen victims' credit cards.

At the morgue, Scully tells Mulder the crime-scene goo is mostly hydrochloric acid, similar to stomach acid; it also contains traces of the digestive enzyme pepsin. The red glop is composed of normal body chemicals, except for extremely low amounts of adipose—fatty tissue. Ellen is nervous about meeting "Timid"—all the more so when her friend Joanne reminds her about the general warning the FBI's just issued. Ellen rationalizes she's been chatting with Timid every day for a month, but she ultimately doesn't show up at a French restaurant, where he waits. Incanto finds a chunky streetwalker, Holly McClain, who scratches him savagely before he kills her in an alley. Incanto runs when another hooker and her john come by.

Scully finds all air passages in McClain's body blocked with the viscous hydrochloric goo. Mulder tells Cross that 2Shy's e-mail to Lauren quoted from obscure sixteenth-century Italian poems found only in controlled-circulation academic libraries; he asks Cross to compile a list of literary professors and such. Incanto—a translator of Italian literature—signs for a package at his apartment house, running across the landlady and her blind preteen daughter, Jesse.

CLEVELAND P.D. 1ST DISTRICT: Mulder arrives with an FBI analysis of the killer's skin, found under McClain's nails. There's no match in the DNA database of known offenders but the report does note the samples contained no oils or essential fatty acids. Mulder thinks the killer is (in Scully's sardonic words) "a fat-sucking vampire." Cross arrives with a list of thirty-eight names. Ellen e-mails Incanto asking for another chance. Cross, canvassing, questions Incanto. Night: Ellen gives Incanto a lift home after dinner. The landlady, with her poems, has let herself into his apartment, where she finds Cross's body. Incanto, seeing the light on, leaves Ellen to investigate. Jesse comes by, looking for her mom; Incanto lies he hasn't seen her. But Jesse, who's smelled her mother's perfume, calls 911.

When the agents and police burst in Incanto is gone, and Cross and the landlady are dead. FBI REGIONAL OFFICE, COMPUTER CRIME SECTION: An agent restores the erased files on Incanto's hard drive, and breaks the password and encryption to retrieve a list of Incanto's on-line chat-room women [N]. Incanto, meantime, talks his way into Ellen's apartment. The agents e-mail a warning and a sketch to everyone on Incanto's list, then go to check on two women unreachable by phone—including Ellen, who's excused herself to excitedly e-mail Joanne. Doing so, she finds the FBI sketch in her bin; Incanto sees it, too, and attacks.

The agents break in when Ellen doesn't answer, and neighbor Joanne confirms she's home. Ellen's injured but alive; Mulder chases a man he sees fleeing down the street, who turns out to be just a graffiti-tagger. Incanto, hidden, attacks Scully in the bathroom but Ellen shoots him with Scully's gun, left behind in the bedroom [N]. Cᴜʏᴀʜᴏɢᴀ Cᴏᴜɴᴛʏ Jᴀɪʟ, ᴏɴᴇ ᴡᴇᴇᴋ ʟᴀᴛᴇʀ: Incanto, his skin mottled and curdling, confesses to forty-seven murders in five states. He insists he's no monster: "I gave them what they wanted. They gave me what I needed." In Italian he adds, "The dead are no longer lonely."

James Handy	Detective Alan Cross
Timothy Carhart	"Virgil Incanto"
Catherine Paolone	Ellen Kaminsky
Kerry Sandomirsky	Joanne (Jo) Steffen
Aloka McLean	Jesse
Suzy Joachim	Jennifer (Lauren's roommate; unnamed in episode)
Glynis Davies	Monica (landlady; unnamed in episode)
Randi Lynne	Lauren (MacKalvey)
William MacDonald	Agent Kazanjian (unnamed in episode)
Uncredited:	
Brad Wattum	Patrolman
P. J. Prinsloo	(Graffiti) Tagger
Jan Bailey Mattia	Second Hooker
Lindsay Bourne	Second Hooker's John
Dean McKenzie	Lt. Blaine (African-American detective; unnamed in episode)

The man playing Brennan (no lines) is uncredited.
Listed on the official *X-Files* website, but not evident in episode:
Beverly Elliot, Raven.

The official *X-Files* website neglects to list antagonist Timothy Carhart.

X-actitude: Incanto's apartment: no. 27

On-line chat-room where Timid and Huggs meet: "Big and Beautiful"

Two unseen people to whom Det. Cross refers: Wendy Sparks, the Cleveland P.D.'s liaison with the FBI; and Dr. Kramer, the county coroner.

Unseen social worker in whose care Scully places Jesse: Mrs. Shepherd

Restaurant where Incanto is stood up: Les Trois Etoile ("The Three Stars")

Lauren's weight on driver's license: 165; at death: 122.

Lab container with the acid found on Lauren: no. 43978

Ellen's address: 658 South Hudson Ave., no. 23; her license plate: DUF 274

Numbers on cover of FBI DNA-report folder (top-to-bottom): 458790; 477998; 45879V

FBI hotline number: 800-555-0132

Per Mulder, the poems Incanto quotes from include: Guinzelle's "Lavitanova"; Casteona's "Il Courtagiano." Poem Incanto says he'll read to Ellen: "E Cazzone." Book Incanto receives from Strautcher Publishing, via the FedEx-like Transcontinental Express (seen in episode 2.22, "F. Emasculata"): *Poeti Italiani Del Novecento*.

197

Church where landlady takes a poetry class: St. Frank's

Man whom a canvassing Scully questions: Mr. Brennan

Computer-handles of women on Incanto's list (ostensibly all in the "Big and Beautiful" chat room) include: Big Heart, OperaGirl, Jenni, KSmithe, louise, Delphine, Friend, Jeannie, Marsha, LoriG, Badgrrr, Riosha, Care Bear, Huggs, NightenGail, Gina L., BarDoe. Real names include: Rhonda Jahnitz, Tara Jarrette, Alison Pritchard.

***X*-actitude:** Three victims: Jennifer Flackert, Kathy Miller, Hillary Turk

***X*-otica:** The Cleveland police station is the First District Police Headquarters Building in Washington, D.C., on Virginia Avenue.

Timothy Carhart played Geena Davis's would-be rapist in *Thelma and Louise*, and the villain in *Beverly Hills Cop III*.

3.07 "THE WALK"   November 10, 1995

Writer: John Shiban

Director: Rob Bowman

ARMY HOSPITAL PSYCHIATRIC WARD, FORT EVANSTON, MARYLAND: Lt. Col. Victor Stans has tried to commit suicide three times in three weeks, and tells a doctor some phantom figure "won't let me die." Stans goes alone to the hydrotherapy room, where he sets a whirlpool to almost 200°F, then jumps in holding weights. An alarm goes off and a manually bolted door unlocks by itself. He's rescued, but horribly burned. Later he tells investigators Mulder and Scully about the phantom, who appears to be a soldier and had burned alive Stan's wife and children three months ago. Captain Janet Draper informs the agents that Gen. Thomas Callahan is quashing their inquiry. A take-charge Scully threatens to have Callahan investigated for obstruction. Mail clerk Quinton "Roach" Freely watches suspiciously.

At a therapy session for wheelchair-bound veterans, bitterly obnoxious quadruple amputee Leonard "Rappo" Trimble berates a single amputee describing "The Walk," an apparently common recurring dream about having working legs. Trimble's flunky, Roach—a fellow combat vet whom Leonard blames for a mistake that cost him his limbs—is worried about the FBI.

Callahan tells the agents he's reported their "gross misconduct" to the Justice Department; the agents fire back with questions about germane facts strangely missing from Stans's file, plus the lackadaisical army investigation of the family's house fire. Scully notes similar underreported circumstances in the case of a Staff Sergeant Kevin Aiklen six months ago; both served under Callahan in the Gulf War. Investigating the hydrotherapy room, Mulder suspects some Gulf War biological weapon as the root cause, and Scully suspects the general is protecting men who murdered their families.

That night the phantom soldier momentarily materializes in Callahan's office, then leaves a garbled message on the answering machine—even though Callahan turns it off. Minutes later (10:32 P.M.), Draper, swimming at the officers' gym, is murdered by some invisible force; the agents later find bruises consistent with a struggle. Callahan tells them about the phantom, who'd left two previous garbled messages on his home answering machine.

ROSSLYN, VIRGINIA: Eight-year-old Trevor Callahan screams for his mom, Frances, that a stranger's in the house; Roach surreptitiously leaves. The agents arrive with Callahan, who plays them the one microcassette he's saved of the phantom voice. They see a man fleeing through the yard, and later find fingerprints that direct them to Roach at his apartment; there they find mail addressed to Aiklen, Draper, Stans, and Callahan. At the Callahan home, while a uniformed guard sneaks a smoke, something kills young Trevor in his sandbox—burying him alive.

Roach, under questioning, says he's only a "mailman" for Trimble. Later, Roach in his cell cries in terror to a guard that Rappo's going to kill him; the guard and Scully find Roach suffocated to death with a bedsheet. Mulder shows Scully dental plates he's been carrying; each reveal radiation exposure—from, Mulder theorizes, astral projections, with supposed psychokinetic capabilities. He's convinced it's Trimble; Freely's mail-gathering may have provided a necessary connection to people and places to which he could project. As for the tapes, they're backward-masked, saying, "Your time has come, killer." The agents confront Trimble, who laughs in their faces.

That night, Callahan sees the phantom in combat uniform and follows bloody bootprints upstairs to find Frances dead. Callahan loads his .45 and goes to Stans; admitting Stans was right, Callahan puts the gun to his own head but gets only clicks. Stans tells him Trimble's the phantom killer, and indeed, the unspeakably evil Rappo gleefully admits killing Frances "and the boy, too." He urges Callahan to kill him, but the general lets him live, to "suffer like the rest of us." After the agents arrive and take Callahan's gun, the general rides an elevator that deposits him against his will in the sub-basement. There the phantom traps him amid bursting steampipes. Mulder tries to help, but the phantom tosses him away. Trimble goes into cardiac arrest, and as Scully goes to fetch a crash cart, Stans suffocates Trimble. Mulder's report says the murders remain officially unsolved. The disfigured Stans, now a mail clerk, brings letters to the tragedy-stricken Callahan's desk.

Thomas Kopache	Gen. Thomas Callahan
Willie Garson	Quinton "Roach" Freely
Don Thompson	Lt. Col. Victor Stans
Nancy Sorel	Capt. Janet Draper
Ian Tracey	Leonard "Rappo" Trimble
Paula Shaw	Ward Nurse

Deryl Hayes	Army Doctor
Rob Lee	Amputee
Andrea Barclay	Mrs. (Frances) Callahan
Beatrice Zeilinger	Burly Nurse
Uncredited (each with speaking lines):	
Pat Bermel	Therapist in group session
Brennan Kotowich	Trevor Callahan
Paul Dickson	Uniformed Guard
D. Harlan Cutshall	Guard

***X*-actitude:** Agents' license plate: Virginia ND4-729

Roach's fingerprints: two matching index fingers and a thumb, on the mailbox and on the backyard door.

Trimble's remains: cremated, and ashes interred at Tannersville, PA, cemetery; the army refused him burial at Arlington.

Type of bugs in Roach's drawer: ants

***X*-otica:** On the soundtrack, the final sentence of Mulder's report is, "What destroyed those parts of [Trimble] that make us human beings—those better angels of our nature—I cannot say." The original shooting script of Mulder's final voiceover seemed, incredibly, to partially excuse Trimble for his inexcusable crimes: "The Army Board of Inquiry declined to press charges against Lt. Col. Victor Stans. After a lengthy investigation, Stans was released from the hospital and posted under medical supervision at Fort Marlene, MD. Leonard Trimble was a casualty of the Gulf War, a victim of friendly fire. The wounds of war, however, can go beyond the physical and mental injuries of battle. There is a spiritual toll on the combatants—the attack against the psyche that leaves in its wake only bitterness and anger. It was war that destroyed Leonard Trimble's body and war that unleased his phantom soul. And it was war that destroyed those parts of himself that make us civilized human beings, those better angels of our nature."

200

3.08 "OUBLIETTE" November 17, 1995
Writer: Charles Grant Craig
Director: Kim Manners

VALLEY WOODS HIGH SCHOOL, SEATTLE, WASHINGTON: Amy Jacobs, fifteen, has her class picture taken. The photographer, Larken, berates his creepy assistant, Carl Wade, who's fixated on the girl. That night at 10:05 P.M., Wade abducts Amy from her room, as her sister calls out for Mom. That same moment, at a fast-food restaurant twenty miles away, thirty-year-old counterwoman Lucy Householder starts bleeding inexplicably, and collapses—repeating exactly what Wade had told Amy: "Nobody's going to spoil us."

JACOBS HOUSE, NEXT DAY: Special Agent in Charge Walt Eubanks tells Mulder he'll be happy to have him interview Lucy and explore this vague connection.

University Medical Center, Seattle, 10:31 a.m.: Mulder meets Scully, who's flown in separately. The doctors say Lucy has glossolalia, or incoherent speech. Mulder notes that when Lucy was eight, she, too, was kidnapped; she'd spent five years locked in a basement before escaping. Now the troubled Lucy—who has a criminal record of prostitution and narcotics and whose boyfriend is doing time for assault and child endangerment—is belligerent and unhelpful to the agents. Elsewhere, with his car disabled on a road, a tire iron-wielding Wade threatens a tow-truck driver who'd stopped to help.

FBI Regional Field Office, 1:53 p.m.: Lucy's blood is O-positive, yet Forensics found both that and B-positive—Amy's blood type—on her clothes; Scully will run a PCR to see if that blood's DNA matches Amy's.

Bright Angel Halfway House, 7:19 p.m.: Lucy's shivering, has fresh scars on her face, and tells housemate Henry it's dark and she can't see. Amy, at that moment, in a basement cell, shivers in the dark, with the same scars. 8:30 p.m.: A paramedic pronounces Lucy fine, yet a sympathetic Mulder—who sees his sister Samantha's plight in Lucy—still can't get her to talk. At the Seattle FBI office Scully and Mulder see a tape of thirteen-year-old Lucy, made a week after she was found in 1978; like Amy, she'd been kept in the dark by a largely unspeaking captor. Scully finds that school photos taken by Larken Scholastic had been sent to all students except Amy; Larken himself had checked out, but Wade—whom he'd fired the next day—had spent most of the last fifteen years institutionalized with a bipolar condition.

Day: When Wade drives away, Amy escapes from the basement. When Wade returns and gives chase, Amy runs—as does Lucy the moment Mulder shows her Wade's photo. When Amy stumbles and hurts her wrist, so does Lucy. After Mulder returns Lucy to her room, Scully, Eubanks, and another agent arrive to arrest her: The blood on her uniform matched Amy's DNA. But Lucy's fled. Eubanks, though acknowledging Lucy was twenty miles from Amy, thinks she and Wade are in league. At the Seattle office, 5:35 p.m., the tow-truck driver, responding to a police-bulletin photo of Wade, shows on a map where he'd encountered Wade; Mulder, checking the available roads, spots nearby Easton, where Lucy had been taken fifteen years ago [N]. Soon, three unmarked cars speed through the small town; Mulder and Scully check Bilton Photo to see if Wade has an account and an address. Agents storm Wade's house; he's gone, but Lucy is in the cell, sobbing, not knowing why she came back to her place of imprisonment.

Lucy starts shivering, and says Amy is cold and wet. With most of the agents heading north, to where Wade's car has been spotted, Mulder and Scully head east, toward the river; they leave Lucy with a young Agent Kreski. In the river, Wade hears distant police sirens and starts to drown Amy. Lucy, simultaneously, starts vomiting water and stops breathing; Kreski calls EMS. Wade ignores Mulder's demand to stop, and Mulder shoots him dead. Scully and Mulder try to resuscitate Amy to no avail. Yet moments after Scully convinces an obsessed Mulder that it's futile, Amy starts to breathe—as Lucy, at that same moment, dies. The next day, at the halfway house, Scully tells Mulder that Amy hasn't even a cut on her—and the state pathologist found five liters of water in Lucy's lungs. Even skeptic Scully says that Lucy died for Amy. A downhearted Mulder suspects this was Lucy's way of finally putting her past to rest.

Tracey Ellis	Lucy Householder
Michael Chieffo	Carl Wade
Jewel Staite	Amy Jacobs
Ken Ryan	Eubanks
Dean Wray	Tow-Truck Driver
Jaques LaLonde	Henry
David Fredericks	Larken
Sidonie Boll	Myra Jacobs (first name not given in episode)
Robert Underwood	Paramedic
Dolly Scarr	Fast-Food Supervisor
Bonnie Hay	Woman
David Lewis	Young Agent (Kreski)
Uncredited:	
Alexa Mardon	Sadie Jacobs (Amy's sister; name not given in episode)

The African-American cop, who has a line, is uncredited.

The official Fox *X-Files* website erroneously lists the character Carl Wade as John Wade, and Eubanks as Banks.

X-actitude: Roads near where tow-truck driver found the west-bound Wade: Interstate 12; County Road 15 North; Route 903
   Name of driver who'd called for tow truck: Gary Mosier
   Tow-truck driver's call to Eubanks: Line 3
X-otica: An oubliette (from the French *oublier*, "to forget") is a dungeon with a trap door on top as the only way in or out.

3.09 "NISEI"   November 24, 1995
Writers: Chris Carter, Howard Gordon, Frank Spotnitz
Director: David Nutter

Part 1 of a 2-part episode

KNOXVILLE, TENNESSEE: At a railroad yard, an older Japanese man steps out of a train car uncoupled there that day, as four other Japanese men go inside to a surgical suite where a videocamera records them operating on someone receiving transfusions of green "blood." Gas-masked soldiers brandishing automatic weapons slaughter the unarmed men, and body bag an apparent alien or alien-human hybrid.

FBI HEADQUARTERS: Mulder plays Scully an "alien autopsy" video he'd ordered from a magazine; someone in Allentown, Pennsylvania, had recorded it off a satellite dish at 2 A.M. It shows the scene we've just witnessed, up to the soldiers' arrival.

ALLENTOWN: Scully and Mulder find Steven Zinnszer bound and executed in his bedroom, his body still warm. Mulder captures a fleeing Japanese man, Kazuo Sakurai, and takes his briefcase. POLICE SUBSTATION C, NIGHT: Skinner unexpectedly arrives with a federal attorney to free Sakurai—a high-ranking Japanese official with diplomatic immunity. Outside, the briefcase Mulder "forgot" to turn in contains satellite photos of a ship and a list of local members of the UFO–buff group MUFON, headed by Zinnszer. Scully goes to the home of the circled Betsy Hagopian, while Mulder takes the photos to the Lone Gunmen. WASHINGTON, D.C.: Byers, Frohike, and Langly say the ship in these probably Japanese photos is the *Talapus*, a salvage vessel out of San Diego. It had supposedly been searching for a Japanese ship sunk during World War II. Nothing was reported found, yet the ship returned not home, but to a Naval yard in Newport News, Virginia. NIGHT: A well-dressed, hawk-like man kills Sakurai in his limo as Sakurai's driver remains impassive.

DAY: At Hagopian's, Scully is greeted with eerie recognition by two women who tell each other, "She's one . . . one of us." She later meets several "alien-abductee" women each taken repeatedly to what they call "the bright, white place." COAST GUARD HEADQUARTERS, NEWPORT NEWS: An official tells Mulder the DEA wouldn't let the *Talapus* into port, and the ship put out to sea next morning. Mulder finds an unmarked ship with a *Talapus* jacket inside; when a squadron of black ops storms aboard, he dives to safety. The women show Scully they have, like her, neck scars where a computer chip was extracted. They take her to the Allentown Medical Center's Oncology Department, where a tumor-filled Hagopian is dying—a result, the women contend, of repeated abduction and testing since her teens. They say it's their and Scully's fate.

Mulder looks inside a shipyard building guarded by black ops; inside is an obscured, blimp-shaped vessel surrounded by scientists and soldiers. At home, Mulder finds his apartment ransacked; Skinner, who'd arrived afterward, demands the briefcase, citing pressure from higher-ups. Mulder says Scully has it, and he doesn't know where she is; Skinner leaves, seething that Mulder's on his own. OFFICE OF SENATOR RICHARD MATHESON: Mulder's benefactor provides the names of the four murdered doctors and hints of "monsters begetting monsters." Mulder matches the names to a WWII photo of a (real-life) Japanese medical corps code-named 731, which performed

203

heinous human experimentation. One member is Dr. Takeo Ishimaru, reported dead in 1965 yet whom Scully insists she's seen. Mulder's certain this all involves the alien-human hybrid project Deep Throat spoke of (in 1.24, "The Erlenmeyer Flask") and the Well-Manicured Man hinted at (in 3.02, "Paper Clip"). Mulder receives a fax (evidently but not definitively from Matheson) showing car 82517 of a secret government railroad.

An FBI scientist, Pendrell, tells Scully her mysterious computer chip has state-of-the-art microlithography and an unknown purpose; he'll keep checking. QUINNIMONT, WEST VIRGINIA: As Mulder watches, several Japanese men place into the train car a living, alien-like figure in an anticontamination suit. The train pulls away before Mulder can catch it. Scully, back in Washington, reviews the "autopsy" video, recognizes Ishimaru, and envisions him peering over her in the bright, white place. Mulder calls to say the surgical car will connect with a Canadian passenger train outside Cincinnati; Scully apprises him of Ishimaru.

EDWARDS TERMINAL, QUEENSGATE, OHIO: One of the men who'd ushered the "alien" into the train car is killed by the hawklike assassin. A distinguished Japanese man (Dr. Shiro Zama, a.k.a. Dr. Takeo Ishimaru, per next episode) arrives for the Vancouver-bound train, which Mulder just misses. Scully, arriving at an apartment door, finds Mr. X outside in the hall, saying Mulder's in danger if he boards that train. Scully cel-phones Mulder with the warning; disregarding her, he jumps from an overpass onto the train's roof, losing his phone.

Mitch Pileggi	Assistant Director Walter S. Skinner
Stephen McHattie	Assassin*
Steven Williams	Mr. X
Raymond J. Barry	Senator Richard Matheson
Robert Ito	"Dr. Shiro Zama"/Dr. Takeo Ishimaru
Tom Braidwood	Frohike
Dean Haglund	Langly
Bruce Harwood	Byers
Gillian Barber	Penny (last name Northern per Fox *X-Files* website, but not per end-credits or dialogue)
Corrine Koslo	Lottie Holloway (name not given in episode; first name given in closed-caption only)
Lori Triolo	Diane (name not given in episode)
Paul McLean	Coast Guard Officer
Brendan Beiser	Agent Pendrell (name not given in this episode, but in next)
Yasuo Sakurai	Kazuo Sakurai

Uncredited (with speaking lines or notable presence):

Carrie Cain Sparks	Train Station Clerk
Warren Takeuchi	Man killed at train station
Bob Wilde	Limo Driver

The actors playing the murdered doctors are uncredited.

Listed in print sources, but not evident in episode:
Roger Allford   Harbormaster

The official Fox *X-Files* website erroneously gives the character name of Agent Pendrell as Agent Comox, and the character Kazuo Sakurai as Kazeo Takeo.

*Print sources refer to the character as "Red-Haired Man," but McHattie demonstrably does not have red hair; compare his brown locks with Scully or Agent Pendrell's red hair.

X-actitude: Allentown MUFON (Mutual UFO Network) members noted here:
   Steven Zinnszer (deceased)
   Betsy Hagopian (hospitalized, terminal)
   Edna Cooper
   Doug St _____ (rest of name obscured on list)
   Penny
   Cathy (woman whom Penny phones)
   unnamed woman ("Lottie" per closed-caption) who opens door

205

   Doctors murdered in surgical train car: Naofomi Sakaguchi, Shigeru Takeuchi, Matanaru Shimizu, Daisuke Nishigaba
   Senate committee of which Matheson is a member: Intelligence
   Agent's Lariat rental car license plate: Washington, D.C. 4S7 573
   "Alien-autopsy" train car: 82594; second surgical car: 82517; train engine that uncouples the former: 756
   "Alien-autopsy" tape: $29.95 plus shipping, from Rat Tail Productions, Allentown, PA
   Dialogue: When Scully sees the alien-autopsy video, she comments humorously, "This is even hokier than the one they ran on the Fox network!"
   Where Sakurai was found dead: C&O (Chesapeake & Ohio Railroad) Canal
   Announcement at Queensgate station: "Your attention, please: All passengers for Canadian Northwest Express to Vancouver, prepare for boarding on track four."
   Apartment Scully has keys to: no. 5, off an apartment-house hallway. Either she's no longer in the subdivided house with a private entrance to her apartment, or she's got keys to a friend's place.

X-otica: Scully recognizes Ishimaru as one of the doctors in the autopsy video, and Senator Matheson confirms to Mulder the doctors were killed, not wounded. Yet *Ishimaru is alive to catch the train.* What's going on? The answer—neglectfully unaddressed in the episode itself—is that Mulder's autopsy video began *before* the operation, and that Ishimaru is the man leaving the train car when the other four doctors arrive. (While it's true that Ishimaru's name isn't among those of the four dead doctors, that's no indication Ishimaru hadn't been one of them, since we know he uses aliases.)

Quinnimont, WV, is a fictional town; the other towns and cities are real.

The Japanese word *nisei* translates literally to "second generation," and refers to the U.S./Canada–born and –educated children of immigrant Japanese (*issei*); those born here of immigrants and educated in Japan are *kibei*. Metaphorically, the title apparently refers to the second generation of Japanese-conducted human (and by extension human/alien) experimentation.

3.10 "731" A.K.A. "NISEI (PART 2)"   December 1, 1995
Writer: Frank Spotnitz
Director: Rob Bowman

Part 2 of a 2-part episode

Opening credo this episode: Apology is Policy

PERKEY, WEST VIRGINIA: At the seemingly abandoned Hansen's Disease Research Facility, soldiers roust several frightened, alien-looking figures in concentration-camp attire, brutally shoot them in the backs, and dump their bodies into a mass grave.

Scully confronts Mr. X at gunpoint for answers, but he snatches her weapon away and tells her cryptically that her extracted microchip-implant "holds more than I could ever tell you." Mulder finds the surgical train car locked, with a quarantine sign. The conductor can't open it; the railroad picks up such cars sporadically without knowing what's inside. The conductor does say a Dr. Shiro Zama, who'd come aboard at Queensgate, was checking it earlier. At Zama's compartment, there's only a briefcase with handwritten Japanese journals; Mulder gives it to the conductor for safekeeping, along with an empty .45 pistol with which to bluffingly restrain Zama till Mulder returns.

FBI HEADQUARTERS, 8:25 P.M.: Agent Pendrell informs Scully that the microchip's neural network appears capable of storing biological information traveling to and from a person's nervous system and mimicking memory formation, so that it could, theoretically, reproduce a person's mental processes. Studying the chip effectively destroyed it, but the good news is that a manufacturer's name was printed on the silicon matrix. Pendrell's search through U.S. and Japanese records turned up a courier mailing-label to a Dr. Zama in Perkey, West Virginia.

The hawk-like assassin from last episode garrotes Zama in a restroom, where Mulder later finds him. At the Hansen's facility, Scully finds terrified leprosy victims hiding beneath a trapdoor. Their spokesman says they've lived here most of their lives—they're among the last to contract Hansen's before treatment was developed. He says Zama and his medical staff haven't been here for a long time, and that death squads have killed hundreds of people who began arriving several years ago, and were kept segregated from the lepers. The spokesman shows Scully an open mass grave, saying others have been filled. Suddenly, a helicopter death squad arrives. Scully and the man dart for the woods; captured, Scully hears two shots close by.

Mulder instructs the conductor not to stop the train until he captures Zama's killer. The surgical car's now open, and behind a second locked door is a frightened apparent alien. Then the assassin loops a garrote around Mulder's neck, nearly killing him before the conductor, at gunpoint, orders him to stop. The assassin does so and asserts he's a law-enforcement agent; the nervous conductor runs and closes the door, locking the two men in. Mulder gets the drop on the assassin, who has National Security Agency (NSA) ID; Mulder, knowing garrotes aren't standard-issue, doesn't buy it. The assassin says there's a bomb on the train "because of what's in that room. Because if the man responsible for it couldn't get it out of the country, he would rather kill it than let it live."

PERKEY, WEST VIRGINIA: Scully is brought to the heavyset, shadow-government "elder" last seen in 3.02, "Paper Clip." He claims the (evidently liquidated) lepers had been "exposed" to something vague from "an inhuman project" by Dr. Zama—a.k.a. Ishimaru—who'd begun working on his own agenda. Mulder, on the train, tries the assassin's key-card on the door, risking that the entry code, when used to try exiting, won't detonate the bomb. As he's about to press the last number, the assassin's cel-phone rings—it's the elder, who puts Scully on with Mulder.

She declares the being in the car with them isn't alien, and that the leper colony was a front for Ishimaru's disease and radiation experiments on the homeless and the insane. Scully believes the man because she's in a train car like the one in the "alien-autopsy" video—the very room in which *she* was tested during her disappearance. Following some momentary phone static, a skeptical Mulder asks if Zama/Ishimaru abducted the women. Scully says alien abduction is a smoke screen to cover the doctor's experiments, and that the "UFO" in Newport News was part of a Russian nuclear sub. Scully says the president even apologized for the tests, which supposedly ended in 1974. She says if the bomb on Mulder's train explodes, then thousands might contract hemorrhagic fever, to which the being has been exposed. She tells Mulder precisely where the bomb is; the timer counts down from 01:42:00.4.

They want him to stop the train at the next station, but Mulder pretends the call's staticky again and hangs up. He tells the conductor to route the train to an unpopulated area, and uncouple the car. At dawn (5:59 A.M., per Mulder's watch) they do so; time to detonation is now 01:11:06.3. Mulder calls Scully, who's driving back to D.C., telling her he's sure the train car's on satellite surveillance; if the being is important, someone will rescue them.

207

By 00:38:16.1, however, Mulder's convinced no one's coming. Threatening to make the assassin's last half hour excruciating, he compels the man to admit the creature is "a weapon"; Mulder takes his hints to mean it's a prototype for soldiers immune to the effects of laser, nuclear, or biological arms. Mulder suggests it's an alien-human hybrid; the assassin suggests if that were true, someone would have rescued them by now.

MULDER'S APARTMENT: Scully, reviewing the "autopsy" tape, sees Ishimaru punching the exit code; she calls it in to Mulder. It works—but distracts Mulder so that the assassin beats him. The assassin starts to exit, knowing the explosion's only seconds away, and is shot by Mr. X, who steps over the still-living killer. With 59.3 seconds left, X looks in on the creature (who may or may not still be alive). He carries out Mulder as the car explodes.

ONE WEEK LATER: Mulder can find no trace of the train car; Matheson is ostensibly out of the country and not returning calls. Scully has the briefcase from the train—but it's a fake. In some darkened room, a white-bearded Japanese man translates the real journals, as the Smoking Man lights up.

208

Stephen McHattie	Assassin
Steven Williams	Mr. X
William B. Davis	Smoking Man
Michael Puttonen	Conductor
Robert Ito	"Dr. Shiro Zama"/Dr. Takeo Ishimaru
Colin Cunningham	Escalante (name not given in episode, except in closed-caption)
Don S. Williams	Elder
Brenden Beiser	Agent Pendrell

X-actitude: Railroad car door codes: entry—1111471; exit—101331
Mailing label:
> From: (label obscured) a company on Constitution Way, Washington, D.C. 20005
> To: Dr. Shiro Zama, R.R. 214, Perkey, WV 26301; (304) 555-0103

Location of train when Mulder tells conductor to find unpopulated area: twenty minutes past Murray Station, IA

Location of train when it blows up: near the town of Blue Earth, IA

X-otica: Cult-favorite actor Stephen McHattie, a Nova Scotia native, is best known as crime lord Gabriel from the final season of CBS's *Beauty and the Beast*, and as psychiatrist Dr. Reston in episodes of *Seinfeld*. Robert Ito played assistant coroner Dr. Sam Fujiyama on Jack Klugman's *Quincy, M.E.*

Perkey, WV, is a fictional town.

For this episode, John Bartley garnered an American Society of Cinematographers Award nomination for Episodic TV Series.

3.11 "REVELATIONS"   December 15, 1995

Writer: Kim Newton

Director: David Nutter

A demonic industrialist (Welsh) who's murdered eleven false prophets now stalks an Ohio boy (Zegers) who may be a genuine stigmatic. While Mulder proves skeptical of the case's religious apparent-miracles, the Catholic-reared Scully finds her faith both tested and renewed. Kenneth Welsh played *Twin Peaks*'s evil mad-genius Windom Earle. Michael Berryman is a cult-favorite horror-movie figure (*The Hills Have Eyes*, etc.). R. Lee Ermey is a former military man and now an actor (*Dead Man Walking*) and TV/film military consultant; he did the voice of the toy soldier Sarge in *Toy Story*.

Kevin Zegers	Kevin Kryder
Sam Bottoms	Mr. Kryder
Kenneth Welsh	Millenium Man
Michael Berryman	Owen Jarvis
Hayley Tyson	Susan Kryder
R. Lee Ermey	Reverend Findley
Lesley Swan	Carina Maywald
Fulvio Cecere	Priest
Nicole Robert	Mr. Tynes
Uncredited:	
Selina Williams	School Nurse

209

3.12 "WAR OF THE COPROPHAGES"   January 5, 1996

Writer: Darin Morgan

Director: Kim Manners

In a seeming self-parody—written by the scripter of the tongue-in-cheek "Humbug" and the often blackly comic "Clyde Bruckman's Final Repose"—the agents try to counter a *War of the Worlds*–like panic brought on by possibly extraterrestrial insects—specifically, coprophages (dung–eaters), which in this case are cockroaches. Among the surreal touches: a Dr. Strangelovian scientist, and a town called Miller's Grove (a play on *WOTW*'s Grover's Mill).

Bobbie Phillips	Dr. Bambi Berenbaum
Raye Birk	Dr. Jeff Eckerle
Dion Anderson	Sheriff Frass
Bill Dow	Dr. Newton
Alex Bruhanski	Dr. Bugger (exterminator)
Ken Kramer	Dr. (Alexander) Inanov
Nicole Parker	Chick
Alan Buckley	Dude

Tyler Labine	Stoner
Maria Herrera	Customer #1
Shaw Allan	Customer #2
Norma Wick	Reporter
Wren Robertz	Orderly
Tom Heaton	Resident #1
Bobby L. Stewart	Resident #2
Dawn Stofer	Customer #4
Fiona Robertz	Customer #5
Uncredited:	
Tony Marr	Motel Manager

Note: No role is listed as "Customer #3"

3.13 "SYZYGY"

January 26, 1996

Writer: Chris Carter
Director: Rob Bowman

When a planetary alignment causes demonic changes in two small-town high school girls, turning them into powerful, witch-like harpies, Scully and Mulder find panicked townsfolk marching on supposed Satanists, and that even they themselves are acting out-of-character: Scully gets angry at Mulder's supposed flirting with police detective White, and teetotaler Mulder gets tipsy on vodka and almost succumbs to a close encounter with the comely cop.

In-joke: The cross-dressing local doctor is named R. W. Godfrey—close to R. W. Goodwin, the coexecutive producer.

Dana Wheeler-Robinson	Detective White
Wendy Benson	Margi Kleinjan
Lisa Robin Kelly	Terri Roberts
Garry Davey	Principal Bob Spitz
Denalda Williams	Zirinka
Gabrielle Miller	Brenda (J. Summerfield)
Ryan Reynolds	Jay "Boom" De Boom
Tim Dixon	Dr. R. W. (Richard) Godfrey
Ryk Brown	Minister
Jeremy Radock	Young Man
Russell Porter	Scott Simmons

3.14 "GROTESQUE"

February 2, 1996

Writer: Howard Gordon
Director: Kim Manners

The mean-spirited Behavioral Sciences agent who literally wrote the book on the field brings Mulder in to help solve the apparent copycat crimes following the arrest of an artist/serial-killer, and he won't stand for Mulder's agreeing with the suspect that demonic possession is involved. Kurtwood Smith is best known as bad-guy Clarence in *RoboCop* (1987).

Mitch Pileggi	Assistant Director Walter S. Skinner
Kurtwood Smith	Agent Bill Patterson
Levani (Outchaneichvili)	John Mostow
Greg Thirloway	Agent (Greg) Nemhauser
Susan Bain	Agent Sheherlis
Kasper Michaels	Young Agent
Zoran Vukelic	Model
Uncredited:	
John Milton Brandon	Aguirre
James McDonnell	Glass Blower
Paul J. Anderson	Paramedic
Amanda O'Leary	Doctor

3.15 "PIPER MARU"   February 9, 1996

Writers: Frank Spotnitz & Chris Carter
Director: Rob Bowman

Part 1 of a 2-part episode

Members of a secret French mission to salvage a sunken World War II plane in the Pacific Ocean meet slow radiation-burn death after an unknowing encounter with a demonstrably alien lifeform—one that exists in an oil medium, and can take over human bodies. Mulder's investigation uncovers an export firm trading in government secrets with the help, in Hong Kong, of a desperate "Alex Krycek," who still possess the DAT of the government UFO files (stolen from Skinner in 3.02, "Paper Clip"). Skinner—who's maintained an unofficial investigation into Melissa's Scully death after higher-ups mysteriously ordered the case closed—is gunned down in a restaurant. Mulder prepares to escort traitor Krycek back to the U.S.—unaware Krycek's been possessed by the alien.

Background: We discover Dana and Melissa spent part of their early childhoods living on a San Diego Naval Base. This is in addition to their Annapolis home, where they were living when Dana got her childhood smallpox vaccination.

The episode title comprises the first and middle names of Gillian Anderson's daughter. Bit-player Robert F. Maier is the series's construction coordinator.

Mitch Pileggi	Assistant Director Walter S. Skinner
Nicholas Lea	"Alex Krycek"
Robert Clothier	Chris Johansen

Jo Bates	Jeraldine Kallenchuk
Morris Panych	Gray-Haired Man
Stephen E. Miller	Wayne Morgan
Ari Solomon	Gauthier
Paul Batten	Dr. Seizer
Russell Ferrier	Medic
Lenno Britos	Hispanic Man (Luis Cardinal)
Kimberly Unger	Joan Gauthier
Rochelle Greenwood	Waitress
Joel Silverstone	Engineer #1
David Neale	Navy Base Guard
Tom Scholte	Young (Chris) Johansen
Robert F. Maier	WW II Pilot
Young Dana Scully	Tegan Moss
Uncredited:	
Darcy Laurie	Engineer #2
Richard Hersley	Capt. Kyle Sanford
Peter Scoular	Sick Crewman
Christine Viner	Young Melissa Scully

3.16 "APOCRYPHA"   February 16, 1996

Writers: Frank Spotnitz & Chris Carter

Director: Kim Manners

Part 2 of a 2-part episode

Skinner barely survives the shooting, and only Scully's fortunate intervention during his transfer to a new hospital saves him from a second attempt—both made by the Hispanic assassin who killed Scully's sister Melissa, and who is himself killed in jail. Mulder is nearly killed by agents ambushing him and Krycek—who, possessed by the alien, eventually reaches Smoking Man, who calmly promises to give him what he wants. That proves to be a spacecraft, hidden deep in an abandoned nuclear-missile silo where Mulder and Scully nearly find this hard proof of alien life before being captured by the Smoking Man's soldiers. Krycek is left locked and forgotten in an underground vault, after having painfully spewed out the alien through his mouth, nose, and eyes.

In-joke: The vault number is 1013, like the name of the production company (and Chris Carter's 10/13 birthday, sans year).

Mitch Pileggi	Assistant Director Walter S. Skinner
John Neville	Well-Manicured Man
William B. Davis	Smoking Man
Tom Braidwood	Frohike
Dean Haglund	Langly
Bruce Harwood	Byers

Nicholas Lea	"Alex Krycek"
Kevin McNulty	Agent Fuller
Barry Levy	Navy Doctor
Dmitry Chepovetsky	1st Government Man (Young William Mulder)
Sue Mathew	Agent Caleca
Don S. Williams	Elder #1
Lenno Britos	Hispanic Man (Luis Cardinal)
Frances Flanagan	Nurse
Brenden Beiser	Agent Pendrell
Peter Scoular	Sick Crewman
Jeff Chivers	Armed Man
Martin Evans	Major Domo
Uncredited:	
Eric Breker	Ambulance Driver
Harrison R. Coe	3rd Government Man
Richard Hersley	Capt. Kyle Sanford
David Kaye	Doctor
Stanley Walsh	Elder #2
Craig Warkentin	Young Smoking Man

3.17 "PUSHER"   February 23, 1996   213

Writer: Vince Gilligan
Director: Row Bowman

A brain tumor has apparently given a cold-blooded killer psychic powers, allowing him to induce his "perfect-crime" victims to commit suicide or otherwise bring on their own deaths. Calling himself "Pusher," he chooses Mulder for a cat-and-mouse game leading to a round of Russian roulette across a hospital table.

Scully and Mulder hold hands at the end, in what seems not at all a hail-fellow-well-met manner. Whether caused by relief Mulder wasn't killed or by something else is unclear at this point.

Mitch Pileggi	Assistant Director Walter S. Skinner
Robert Wisden	Robert Modell/"Pusher"
Vic Polizos	Agent Frank Burst
Julia Arkos	Holly
Steve Bacic	Agent Collins
Meredith Bain-Woodward	Defense Attorney
Roger R. Cross	SWAT Lieutenant
Ernie Foort	Lobby Guard
Janyse Jaud	Nurse
Darren Lucas	Lead SWAT Cop
Don MacKay	Judge
D. Neil Mark	Deputy Scott Kerber
Bret J. D. Sheppard	Prosecutor
Henry Watson	Bailiff

3.18 "TESO DOS BICHOS"   March 8, 1996
Writer: John Shiban
Director: Kim Manners

After a recently unearthed, Ecuadorian female-shaman mummy (an *amaru*) is shipped to a Boston museum despite warnings from the native Secona Indians, strange deaths occur. A jaguar-spirit curse at work? Or political terrorism to force the return of the artifacts? Mulder and Scully suspect expedition-member Dr. Bilac, who returned from the site, called Teso Dos Bichos, a strangely changed man.

Vic Trevino	Dr. Alonzo Bilac
Janne Mortil	Mona Wustner
Gordon Tootoosis	Shaman
Garrison Chrisjohn	Dr. Winters
Tom McBeath	Dr. Lewton
Ron Sauve	(Security Guard Tim) Decker
Alan Robertson	(Dr.) Carl Roosevelt
Frank Welker	Special Vocal Effects

214

3.19 "HELL MONEY"   March 29, 1996
Writer: Jeffrey Vlaming
Director: Tucker Gates

During the Chinese Festival of the Hungry Ghosts, Mulder and Scully investigate the burning alive of an immigrant whose death is linked to a mysterious Chinatown lottery where bettors risk losing their organs to vicious black marketeers. A Chinese-American police officer, Detective Chao, is caught between ancient traditions and modern law, while a desperate Chinese father hopes a lottery jackpot will help him pay for his daughter's needed medical care. This is one of the rare *X-Files* episodes without paranormal components.

B. D. Wong	Detective Chao
James Hong	Hard-Faced Man
Michael Yama	Hsin
Lucy Liu	Kim
Doug Abrahams	Lt. Neary
Diana Ha	Dr. Wu
Stephen Chang	Large Man
Donald Fong	Vase Man
Ed Hong-Louie	Money Man
Graham Shiels	Night Watchman
Paul Wong	Wiry Man

3.20 "JOSE CHUNG'S FROM OUTER SPACE" April 12, 1996

Working Title: "ETH SNAFU"
Writer: Darin Morgan
Director: Rob Bowman

In a surreal take on *Rashomon*, bestselling author Jose Chung interviews Scully and other, wackier participants who claim to have seen or been involved in an alien abduction of two smalltown teens—plus an abduction of one of the apparent aliens by the monstrous Lord Kinboat of the Earth's Core. An Air Force cover-up and mysterious men in black also figure, as the interviewees' stories conflict and the details grow ever more ludicrous. It all culminates in a book: Jose Chung's *From Outer Space.*

Charles Nelson Reilly	Jose Chung
William Lucking	Roky
Jason Gaffney	Harold
Sarah Sawatsky	Chrissy
Jesse Ventura	1st Man in Black
Larry Musser	Detective Manners
Alex Diakun	Dr. Fingers
Terry Arrowsmith	Air Force Man
Andrew Turner	CIA Man
Mina Mina	Dr. Hand
Allan Zinyk	Blaine
Michael Dobson	Lt. Schaeffer
Jaap Broeker	The Stupendous Yappi

The official Fox *X-Files* website erroneously lists professional wrestler-guest Jesse Ventura as "Jesse Venture."

3.21 "AVATAR" April 26, 1996

Teleplay: Howard Gordon
Story: David Duchovny and Howard Gordon
Director: James Charleston

His seventeen-year marriage dissolving, Assistant Director Skinner picks up a woman in a bar and later wakes up with her dead beside him. Mulder and Scully must investigate not only the crime, but Skinner's claim that he is being haunted by an apparition of an old woman, which had first appeared to him in Vietnam. When the agents delve into the dead woman's past in an effort to clear Skinner, they find her a member of a call-girl ring and find themselves targeted by mysterious assassins.

Mitch Pileggi	Assistant Director Walter S. Skinner
William B. Davis	Smoking Man

Tasha Simms	Jay Cassal
Amanda Tapping	Carina Sayles
Bethoe Shirkoff	Old Woman
Tom Mason	Detective Waltos
Cal Traversy	Young Detective
Stacy Grant	Judy Fairly
Janie Woods-Morris	Lorraine Kelleher
Jennifer Hetrick	Sharon Skinner
Malcolm Stewart	Agent Bonnecaze
Brendan Beiser	Dr. Rick Newton
Michael David Simms	Senior Agent
Morris Paynch	Grey-Haired Man

3.22 "QUAGMIRE"
May 3, 1996

Writer: Kim Newton

Director: Kim Manners

Following a rash of deaths at Rigdon, GA's, Heuvelmans Lake, a tourist site famed for a supposed Loch Ness Monster-type beast named Big Blue, Mulder explores the nature and limits of his Ahab-like obsession with truth, while Scully's pet Pomeranian, Queegqueg, gets eaten by a mysterious something. As human deaths mount, the agents' boat is sunk by some powerful lake creature, stranding Mulder and Scully on a rock where they spend time examining their lives. Onshore later, Mulder comes face to face with the flesh-eating leviathan—which turns out to be a very large 'gator. Yet there is still, it seems, something in the lake. . . .

Guest cast includes: Chris Ellis, Timothy Webber

3.23 "WETWIRED"
May 10, 1996

Writer: Mat Beck

Director: Rob Bowman

APRIL 29: A shadowy new source lures Mulder to investigate murders in small-town Braddock Heights, MD, where the unlikely killers each mistook their victims for someone they hated or feared. Mulder and Scully discover each of the killers was subjected to subliminal messages transmitted covertly through their TV sets. Scully finds herself victim to this cathode-ray coercion, and believes Mulder is out to get her—and that she has to kill him first. After Mulder tracks a cable installer and a psychiatrist to a rural house, the two conspirators are killed by Mr. X. He was the one who'd sent the shadowy source to Mulder, in hopes that Mulder might uncover the conspiracy before X had to kill the two men—under orders from the Cigarette-Smoking Man, to whom X, it is revealed, reports.

Mat Beck is the series's Visual Effects Producer.

Mitch Pileggi	Assistant Director Walter S. Skinner
Sheila Larken	Margaret (Maggie) Scully
William B. Davis	Smoking Man
Tom Braidwood	Frohike
Dean Haglund	Langly
Bruce Harwood	Byers
Steven Williams	Mr. X

Also in guest cast: Colin Cunningham, Tim Henry

3.24 "TALITHA CUMI"   May 17, 1996

Story: David Duchovny & Chris Carter
Teleplay: Chris Carter
Director: R. W. Goodwin

Part 1 of 2

After a shooting at a fast-food restaurant, a mysterious Jeremiah Smith miraculously heals the wounds of the shooter and his three victims, then disappears. Mulder and Scully discover that identical "Jeremiah Smiths" exist all over the country, working for the Social Security Administration. At the abandoned Quonochontaug, Rhode Island, summer home of Mulder's parents, the Cigarette-Smoking Man argues with Mulder's mother over the whereabouts of some mysterious object, while alluding to an intimate relationship with her since before Mulder was born. Shortly thereafter, she suffers a stroke yet still gives Mulder a clue to find a weapon like that used by the Pilot to kill the clones in episodes 2.16–2.17, "Colony" and "End Game." Cigarette-Smoking Man captures the Jeremiah Smith, who appeared at the restaurant, with plans to have the Pilot execute him for drawing unwanted attention that may threaten "The Project": alien colonization of Earth, for which a date has already been set. Mr. X battles Mulder for the weapon, the only thing that can kill the clones, yet retreats empty-handed. Smith, who'd rattled the Cigarette-Smoking Man by morphing into Deep Throat and Mulder's father, escapes or is let free; he goes to Mulder and Scully to reveal all about The Project—just as the Pilot appears, his weapon in hand.

Roy Thinnes starred in the cult-classic, 1967–68 UFO/conspiracy-theory series, *The Invaders*.

Mitch Pileggi	Assistant Director Walter S. Skinner
Roy Thinnes	Jeremiah Smith
William B. Davis	Cigarette-Smoking Man

Peter Donat	"William Mulder"
Jerry Hardin	"Deep Throat"
Brian Thompson	The Pilot
Angelo Vacco	Man Shot at Restaurant Door
Steven Williams	Mr. X
Hrothgar Mathews	Galen Muntz (first name not given in episode)
Rebecca Toolan	Mrs. Mulder
Stephen Dimopoulos	Detective
John MacLaren	Doctor
Cam Cronin	Paramedic
Bonnie Hay	Night Nurse
Uncredited:	
Brian Barry	Last Man
Ross Clarke	Pleasant Man

X-TRAS

• DOSSIER: THE MULDER FILE •

Address: Street address and city unknown; Apartment no. 42
Phone (area code NA): 555-0199
E-mail address: Fox Mulder, 000517
Apartment-house neighbors include (family names): Glaniceanu;
Pao/Hu; Dommann

Born: Oct. 13, 1961, probably Chilmark, MA (Martha's Vineyard)
Raised: 2790 Vine Street, Chilmark, MA

Religion: NA
Family (parents divorced):
Mother: name NA, Greenwich, CT
Father: William Mulder (d. April 1995, West Tisbury, MA)
Sibling: Samantha Ann Mulder, b. Nov. 21, 1965, Chilmark,
MA; abducted Nov. 27, 1973

Education:
High school: NA
College: Oxford University, Oxford, England; degree in
psychology (whether graduate or undergraduate degree
uncertain); attended c. 1983
FBI Academy, Quantico, VA
Wrote monograph on topic of serial killers and the occult,
1988
Academy nickname: "Spooky"

FBI: Joined age 28
Current Status: Special Agent

Partner: Dana Scully (as of 3/21/92)
Badge number: JTT047101111
Office: Basement, former copier room
Prior assignments:
Briefly in Violent Crimes, partnered with Jerry
Lamana. First case: Under ASAC Reggie Purdue,
helped to capture John Barnett.
Behavioral Science unit, profiling serial killers
(1989-92)
Blood type: O-negative
Smallpox vaccination certificate number: 378671
Misc. Personal Data:
Wears glasses for reading and close-up work
Used pseudonym "M. F. Luder" on *Omni* article
Recreational pursuits include: Washington Redskins;
pornography; basketball; running; pet fish
Enjoys eating sunflower seeds

• DOSSIER: THE SCULLY FILE •

Dana Katherine Scully
Address: 107 E. Cordova, Apartment no. 35*
Washington, D.C.
Phone: (202) 555-6431 (home); (202) 555-3564
(cellular) (703) 555-2804 (while stationed at FBI
Academy, Quantico, VA)
E-mail address: Dana Scully, 001013
* per police report; per visual examination, house
number is 1419; multiple-dwelling residence with
possible entrances on two perpendicular streets (if
a corner building) or on parallel streets (if
building is one-block deep).

Born: Feb. 23, 1964
Raised: San Diego, CA; 3170 W. 53 Road, Annapolis,
MD, and possibly elsewhere
Religion: Catholic

Family:
Mother: Margaret (Maggie) Scully

Father: Captain William Scully, USN (d. December 1993)
Siblings:
Older brother: William Jr.
Older sister: Melissa
Younger brother: name NA
Pets:
Dog: Queegqueg (Pomeranian; adopted October 1995; killed by alligator attack, spring 1996)

Education:
University of Maryland (B.S. Physics)
Senior thesis: "Einstein's Twin Paradox: A New Interpretation"
Medical school: NA; MD, specialty NA
FBI Academy, Quantico, VA
Recruited immediately after medical school
Class included: Tom Colton, Marty Neil

FBI: Joined 1990
Current status: Special Agent
Partner: Fox Mulder (as of 3/21/92)
ID#: 2317-616 (badge number NA)

Prior FBI assignment:
Instructor, FBI Academy, Quantico, VA (1990-92)

Misc. Personal Data:
Wears gold-cross necklace given by mother on 15th birthday
Wears glasses for reading and close-up work
While instructor at Academy, had year-long relationship with Agent Jack Willis; gave him engraved watch Feb. 23, 1992.
Smallpox vaccination certificate number: 29510

• TIME-X: THE *X-FILES* TIMELINE •

All times relative to their time zone. Primary sources are on-screen time-stamps, clocks, and dated printed matter such as tickets, newspapers, and police reports. An additional factor used in assessing whether a day has passed is a clearly visible change (or not) of clothing.

1992

1.01 PILOT: "THE X-FILES"

Agents meet	March 6 (Sat.)
Agents fly to Oregon	March 7, 8 A.M.
Scully beings autopsy on exhumed body	March 7, 10:56 P.M.
Scully writes report in hotel room	March 8, 4:37 A.M.
Agents speak with doctor at Raymon County State Psychiatric Hospital	March 8, day
Blinding light; Mulder checks watch	March 8, 9:03 P.M.
Agents at cemetery decide to see Billy	March 9, 5:07 A.M.
Agents see Billy, speak with woman orderly	March 9, day
Billy interviewed at FBI headquarters	March 22
Mulder calls Scully	date NA, probably March 22; 11:21-22 P.M.

1993

1.03 "SQUEEZE"

Tooms arrested (per police report in 1.21)	July 23

1.04 "CONDUIT"

Pre-episode: Greg killed	approx. three weeks ago; probably before Aug. 7

Note: Episode probably occurs late August, after episode 1.05.

1.05 "THE JERSEY DEVIL"

Dead vagrant Roger Crockett found	Aug. 9, 1993 (Mon.)
Agents meet with Atlantic City coroner	Friday (probably Aug. 13, possibly a later Fri.)

Mulder arrested	Friday, approx. 3 A.M.
Mulder released from jail	following Monday
Scully's date with Rob	Monday, 7:30 P.M.
Brouillet calls Mulder	Monday, 7:55 P.M.
Agents, Brouillet, Diamond at coroner's	Day; evidently Tuesday
Autopsy reports on beast-people arrive	one week later

1.06 "SHADOWS"

Lauren Kyte ATM mugging on security video; mugger's bodies found	Sept. 22 (Wed.), 9:45 P.M.
Agents at coroner's	Sept. 23, approx. 4 A.M.

Note: Per headstone, Graves died Oct. 5. This is a continuity error, as it was established he died approximately two weeks before Sept. 22. Police officer confirmed bodies found on a Wed.

1.07 "GHOST IN THE MACHINE"

Scully writes in field journal, night of the day agents question Wilczek	Oct. 24 (Sun.)

1.08 "ICE"

Ice-Core transmission sent	Nov. 5 (Fri.)
Agents arrive in Nome	Wed. (possibly Nov. 10)

1.13 "BEYOND THE SEA"

Scully has dinner with parents	c. Dec. 15–25
William Scully suffers fatal coronary	hours later, c. 12:45 A.M.
Boggs's executed	one week after ashes-scattering

1994

1.18 "MIRACLE MAN"

Scully begins autopsy	March 7 (Mon.), 11:21 P.M.
Scully gives Mulder preliminary results	March 8, 12:29 A.M.

223

1.22 "BORN AGAIN"

Barbala killed; agents arrive in Buffalo	March 28 (Mon.)
Fiore takes out Morris homicide file	March 29, 2-2:15 P.M.
Felder killed	March 29, evening
Charlie/Michelle attacks Fiore at home	March 30, night
Post-episode; Fiore pleads guilty	April 18

Note: When Mrs. Bishop on March 28 speaks of her fourth nanny this year and it being only April, she's speaking casually and alluding to March being nearly over.

1.23 "ROLAND"

Pre-episode: Grable car accident	November 1993
Dr. Surnow killed in wind tunnel	April 23, 1994 (Sun.)
Agents arrive at crime scene	April 24
Dr. Keats killed	April 25, 12:31 A.M.
Roland/Arthur closes Grable file	April 25, 5:23 A.M.

1.24 "THE ERLENMEYER FLASK"

Dr. Secare leaps into harbor	May 7 (Sat.), day
Deep Throat phones sleeping Mulder	May 8, very early A.M.
Agents speak with police at harbor	eighteen hours after Secare leap
Mulder interviews Dr. Berube	May 8, 5 P.M.
Mulder breaks into Berube's house	May 8, 6:30 P.M.
Secare phones Mulder at Berube's house	May 8, 7:45 P.M.
Carpenter shows Scully her DNA analysis	May 8, 11:45 P.M.
Agents finds Zeus Storage empty	May 9, 7:30 A.M.
Crew-Cut Man abducts Mulder, kills Secare	May 9, night or May 10, early A.M.
Deep Throat meets Scully at Mulder's apartment	May 10, 6:30 A.M.
Deep Throat killed	May 10, night or May 11, early A.M.
Mulder phones Scully X-Files shut down	thirteen days later, 11:21-22 P.M.

2.01 "LITTLE GREEN MEN"

Arceibo receives signals	July 5 (Tues.), 6:30 A.M.
Matheson meets with Mulder, promises to delay the Blue Beret for twenty-four hours	July 6
Mulder flies to San Juan	July 7
Scully being followed at Miami International	July 7, 5:45 P.M.
Scully buys ticket to San Juan	July 7, 6:30 P.M.
Bright light (aliens?) at Arecibo	July 7, 10:30 P.M.
Scully finds Mulder; Blue Beret arrive	July 8, day (probably early A.M.)

2.05 "DUANE BARRY"

Mulder and Krycek go to hostage scene	Aug. 7 (Sun.), day
Duane Barry shot	Aug. 7, night, or Aug. 8, early A.M.
Kazdin speaks with Mulder at hospital	Aug. 8

Note: Barry's escape from the hospital, and his kidnapping of Scully, took place anywhere from one to several days following his shooting, surgery and at least partial recuperation. Scully is wearing different clothes the night of her kidnapping than at either the previous office scene, or at the hostage site.

2.06 "ASCENSION"

Mulder hears Scully's message	date NA, 11:23 P.M.
Mulder finishes examining crime scene	same night, 11:40 P.M.
Skinner takes Mulder off case	next day, 8:03 A.M.
Barry kills Virginia police officer	same day, 11:23 A.M.
Mulder views police-car video of scene	same day, 3:11 P.M.
Mulder listens to tape of Barry	same day, 4:03 P.M.
Mulder and Krycek drive to Skyland	same day, 5:43 P.M.
Mulder reaches summit	night of the same day
Barry being questioned at summit	same night, 8:46 P.M.

Barry autopsy performed	next day, morning
Skinner meeting; Krycek backs up Mulder	same day, 10:36 A.M.
Mr. X meets Mulder near Matheson's office	same day, 11:45 A.M.
Skinner meets Mulder, promises to reopen X-Files	next day, 8:11 A.M.

2.07 "3"

X-Files reactivated; Mulder flips calendar from May to present	November 1994

2.08 "ONE BREATH"

Note: The date of Scully's return is not specified in episode; though her hospital chart is dated Jan. 3, 1994, this is a continuity error, based on the time-stamps of the previous and following episodes. She was evidently missing from August to November 1994.

2.09 "FIREWALKER"

Date of events, per Mulder's report	Nov. 11-13
Post-episode: In quarantine for next month	Nov. 13-c. Dec. 13

2.13 "IRRESISTIBLE" (SEE FOLLOWING NOTE)

Agents meet Moe Bocks at cemetery	Nov. 12 (Sat.)
Agents meet Bocks in his office	Nov. 13
Scully performs autopsy on streetwalker	Nov. 14, 11:14 A.M.
Mulder phones Scully to announce arrest	Nov. 14, 11:21 P.M.

Note: These dates are continuity errors, since per Mulder's report last episode, the agents were still in Washington state on the "Firewalker" case from Nov. 12-13, and were in quarantine immediately afterward until mid-December. The previous episode's time-stamps are the more reliable, since much dialogue concerns the nearness of Scully's recent, November return. These episodes likely take place in December.

1995

2.14 "DIE HAND DIE VERLETZT"
Pre-episode, possibly by only hours: Jan. 16 (Mon.)
  Dave Duran checks out occult library
  book

2.16 "COLONY" (EVENTS BELOW ARE FLASHBACKS)

Mysterious aircraft appears in Arctic	date NA
Pilot kills Dr. Prince in Scranton	two days later
Mulder tells Scully of murdered doctors	two weeks from first death

2.17 "END GAME" (EVENTS BELOW ARE FLASHBACKS)

Samantha speaks to Mulder before Skinner arrives and Scully phones	date NA, 12:38 A.M.
Exchange on Old Memorial Bridge	approx. one hour later
FBI drags water for bodies	next day
Mulder breaks news to father; drives to Rockville clinic	same day

2.19 "DOD KALM"

Food and water depleted	March 11 (Sat.), approx. 4:30 A.M.
Rapidly aged Mulder loses consciousness	March 12, 4:30 A.M.

2.23 "SOFT LIGHT"

Pre-episode: Wysnecki disappearance	March 17
Newirth disappearance at hotel	March 31 (Fri.), night
Agents meet with Ryan at hotel	April 1, morning
Police confront Banton at train station	April 1, 11:50 P.M.
Agents and Ryan at train station	April 2, morning
Agents interview Dr. Davey	same morning
Agents find Banton at train station	same morning, 11:14 A.M.

Mulder meets with Mr. X	April 3 (Mon.), 2:19 A.M.
Mr. X tries to abduct Banton	April 3, 3:24 A.M.
Agents captured by Dr. Davey, whom X Kills	April 3, day

2.25 "ANASAZI"

Earthquake; Eric Hosteen finds boxcar	April 9 (Sun.), day
The Thinker hacks into government E.T. Files	April 10, day
Multinational cabal learns of break-in	April 10, night
Lone Gunmen go to Mulder's apartment	April 11, day
Mulder meets the Thinker, Botanic Gardens	April 11, night
Mulder shows Scully files, brawls with Skinner	April 12
Scully meets with Skinner and senior agents	April 13, day*
Cigarette-Smoking Man visits William Mulder	same day
Mulder visits William, whom Krycek kills	night of April 13 or early A.M. April 14
Mulder awakens in Scully's apartment	April 14, day
Mulder confronts Krycek, is shot by Scully	April 14, night
Agents in New Mexico after "two-day" drive	April 16 (Sun.)
Albert Hosteen brings Mulder to reservation; Smoking Man orders boxcar afire	same day

228

* A senior agent asks Scully, "Weren't you originally assigned to agent Mulder to debunk his work?" Scully replies, "Yes, sir, a year-and-a-half ago," even though she was teamed with Mulder March 21, 1992, over three years ago. Blame it on the stress of the moment.

3.01 "THE BLESSING WAY"

Soldiers brutalize Hosteen family	April 16 (Sun.)

Kenneth Soona's body discovered   same day
Soldiers take Scully's hard copy files   April 16, night
OPC meeting   April 17
Scully walks to mother's   April 17, night
Albert finds Mulder buried beneath   April 18, morning
    rocks
Frohike shows Scully newspaper article   April 18
Scully sees Skinner, sets off metal   April 19
    alarm
Third day of Blessing Way ritual   April 21
Mulder recuperates; does not   for four days
    change clothes   following end of
                                                   ritual

3.06 "2SHY" (EPISODE OUT OF ORDER IN CONTINUITY)

Incanto kills Lauren   Aug. 28
                                                   (Mon.), night

Cop finds Lauren's remains   Aug. 29, morning
Scully attempts autopsy   Aug. 29, 4:15 P.M.
Incanto kills streetwalker   Aug. 29, night
Mulder arrives with FBI skin analysis   Aug. 30,
                                                   10:13 A.M.

Incanto kills canvassing Cross   same day
Incanto has dinner with Ellen; kills   that night
    landlady; is captured
Incanto confesses to forty-seven   one week later
    murders

3.03 "D.P.O."

Darren gets high score on arcade game   Sept. 12 (Tues.),
                                                   11:41 P.M.

Hammond's body found   Sept. 13,
                                                   12:17 A.M.

Darren electrocutes cows   Sept. 13, night
Teller and agents find cows and   Sept. 14, morning
    fulgarite
Frank Kiveat admitted to hospital   Sept. 14,
                                                   10:25 A.M.

Darren kills Teller; is captured   Sept. 14, night,
                                                   or Sept. 15,
                                                   early A.M.

3.04 "CLYDE BRUCKMAN'S FINAL RESPONSE"

Note: The September 16 and September 21 on-screen time-
stamps are directly contradicted by an on-screen artifact
(Lotto ticket with October date).

"Puppet" kills Madame Zelma	Oct. 4, night
Agents, police, and Yappi at doll-collector crime scene	Oct. 7
Agents question Bruckman, bring him to doll-collector crime scene	Oct. 8
Agents find body in lake	Oct. 9, morning
Lotto drawing	Oct. 9 (Mon.)
Agents and Bruckman find Dukenfield	Oct. 9
Havez killed	Oct. 10, morning

X-HUMATION

The Nitpick File

hile *The X-Files'* writers and producers do an exceptionally good job of avoiding glaring lapses in logic, fans nonetheless love to nitpick. And since *The X-Files* presents so much action and scientific evidence, it provides a rich lode. Here are some of the most glaring bloopers and inconsistencies.

• 1.01 Pilot: "The X-Files" •

Scully can't accept that they "lost" nine minutes; time, she says, is "a universal invariant," to which Mulder replies, "Not in this Zip code." But as an undergrad physics-major, Scully should know that only *the speed of light* is a universal invariant, or constant.

And if Mulder, Scully, and the car lost nine minutes, why didn't Mulder's watch?

This episode takes place March, 1992. The next time-stamped episode, 1.03 "Squeeze," takes place July 1993. Is there a year of "Untold X-Files: The Early Mulder and Scully"?

• 1.06 "Shadows" •

Graves's headstone gives a different middle name (Patrick) than in the newspaper account (Thomas). Also, his headstone dates are March 4, 1940–October 5, 1993—though Lauren's ATM attack took place Sept. 22, when Graves had been dead "two weeks." It's possible the security camera was set to the wrong month, and she was attacked *Oct.* 22.

• 1.07 "Ghost in the Machine" •

The COS computer had Scully's home phone number with which to call up her home computer. But how did it switch on Scully's turned-off computer?

David Duchovny, getting caught in the X-Files.

• 1.08 "Ice" •

After Bear dies, the others discover that though all the victims have had the worm-like organism, only Bear's remains alive. But later, Scully places an ammonia jar with one live "worm" next to a jar with another live "worm" to see them each respond aggressively. Where did the second worm come from?

• 1.10 "Fallen Angel" •

Scully agrees with Mulder that there are no railroad tracks near the town on which a railcar of "toxic cargo" could've derailed. So how come the local reporters didn't discover this, but just blithely reported on *an entire railroad line* nobody had ever heard of in this area? That government claim would've been ridiculously easy to check. Anyone ever hear of maps?

The crash and fire began at 12:57 A.M., DAY 1—yet it's *still* 12:57 A.M., Day 1, the next night, when Mulder watches a news report of the evacuation that took place that day, hours *after* the crash. And Mulder's *flashback* has Deep Throat telling him about the crash occurring "last night." Clearly, the wrong subtitle was used in the motel establishing shot.

An additional error: It's 12:57 A.M., and we see Mulder getting ready to investigate. Yet when next we see him, it's daytime. Shortly afterward, when he sneaks into Falcon, it's a half-hour before nightfall—making it over *forty hours* since Falcon went into effect! This might have all been avoided by, for instance, showing the motel in daylight, and marking the time as, say, 12:57 P.M., Day 1.

233

• 1.12 "Fire" •

At Boston Mercy Hospital, Bob/Cecil is in a hyperbaric chamber with "fifth- and sixth-degree burns." The rating only goes up to fourth-degree, in which flesh is burned down to the bone.

• 1.15 "Lazarus" •

Since *The X-Files's* fictional continuity roughly follows real-life time, and since episode 1.18, "Miracle Man," takes place March 7–8, it can't be two months before Scully's February 23 birthday. Unless, of course, this whole episode is a flashback.

• 1.17 "E.B.E." •

How is it trained UFOlogist Mulder can't tell that Deep Throat's photo is a fake, and Scully gets it by just a quick visual examination?

• 1.20 "Darkness Falls" •

The sun has just recently risen when Spinney returns with the Jeep, and it's only a four-hour drive down the mountain. So since they leave right away, how is it night already on the drive back down? Did they stop for a long picnic?

Mulder lets eco-terrorist Spinney leave the cabin—and custody—and take with him precious gasoline and a battery. Why does Mulder simply let him go at his word, without having himself, armed fellow agent Scully, or the armed park ranger accompany him to make sure he kept his word?

Why did Spinney get killed by the light-avoiding bugs when he was standing in the headlights of the car?

• 1.21 "Tooms" •

Why would Tooms defy his animalistic genetic instincts to *frame* Mulder rather than just eat his liver?

The care used in filling out an official police report would seem to confirm Scully's address as 107 E. Cordova, but the outside of her building shows the number 1419 (in episode 2.06, "Ascension") though her apartment looks the same.

• 1.22 "Born Again" •

Mulder, an Oxford-trained psychologist, confuses Multiple Personality Syndrome with schizophrenia.

• 1.24 "The Erlenmeyer Flask" •

Chloroplasts aren't plant cells.

How did Scully just pick up an apparent alien fetus—which looked too large for a briefcase—and just walk off with it? They're willing to kill, but not to check inside your bag?

• 2.01 "Little Green Men" •

The pay phones at Miami International Airport require more than 20 cents.

• 2.02 "The Host" •

EMS workers load the strapped-in creature to a U.S. Marshal's van, with a single Marshal and no one else. It's extremely unlikely that this scientific marvel would be treated so casually, but let's give benefit of doubt and say the Justice Department genuinely believed it was a normal man, self-mutilated.

• 2.07 "3" •

How does Mulder get into the closed Hollywood Blood Bank at night, in a presumably legal way that won't get the case thrown out of court?

There *is* no fifty-second chapter of John—what Mulder accurately quotes is John 6:54. God'll get *somebody* for that.

• 2.08 "One Breath" •

Byers misspeaks when he says he "downloaded" Scully's chart to The Thinker. Actually, he "uploaded" it—to download is to receive, and to upload is to send.

The previous episode had confirmed this episode takes place in November 1994 at the earliest; the following episode takes place Nov. 11–13, 1994. These facts together contradict the January 1994 date on Scully's chart.

• 2.09 "Firewalker" •

If 130°F temperature is so hot that Pierce says nothing can long survive there, how did Trepkos do so?

• 2.14 "Die Hand Die Verletz" •

Mulder cites the Coriolis Effect as dictating that water must flow down a drain counterclockwise (whereas in the fountain here it goes clockwise). But The Coriolis Effect only concerns large systems like hurricanes and tornadoes. And even so, only 80 percent of tornadoes rotate counterclockwise.

In the early scene with the high school kids in the woods, the girl who is later referred to as Shannon is called Kate—both audibly and in closed captioning.

• 2.16 "Colony" •

Scully runs to escape from "Chapel" at the warehouse, and then goes hide in her apartment—where "Chapel" knows the address!

The exterior of Scully's apartment house, previously shown as a brownstone with stone steps, is here a red-brick building with a large blue front door.

• 2.17 "End Game" •

Scully fallaciously brands the events "paranormal" even though the apparent aliens have been *using* science.

The scene of the perplexed USS *Allegiance* finding some mysterious craft is inserted between the Pilot's arrival at Scully's hotel room and, moments later, the Pilot's abducting Scully—by all the laws of film editing, this absolutely shows it was happening concurrently. Yet the spacecraft had crash-landed more than two weeks before the Pilot appeared at Scully's room, and was so widely reported by TV news that the *Allegiance* would *certainly* have known what they'd found. The only explanation otherwise is that the *Allegiance* scene occurred immediately after the crash, before news could be disseminated. *However*, Mr. X tells Mulder—over two weeks *after* the crash—that the *Allegiance* found the craft "five days ago." And since Mulder (and the rest of the world within TV-news earshot) knew about the craft two weeks ago, it'd be ridiculous for X to be lying now.

There's no evident way to plug these chronology holes; the best possible explanation is that the *Allegiance* events took place just over two weeks prior and was a flashback—which as a bonus helps explain how the Pilot could have been there to murder the crew. (Automatic defenses are another possibility.)

236

• 2.22 "F. Emasculata" •

If Dr. Torrence was worried enough about contagion to put on surgical gloves, why not also a surgical mask? Plotwise, he *still* could have been spurted on and infected with just part of his face exposed.

• 2.23 "Soft Light" •

RE: The lightbulb prints not matching those of any hotel employee or guest: Since hotels don't keep fingerprints of guests on file—and not usually employees either, for that matter—we have to assume the Richmond P.D. had simply gotten a list of names and then run them through the national fingerprint database. But there's no way that every person in the hotel would have a criminal, immigration, or other sort of record requiring fingerprinting.

So what the heck *was* Chester doing outside Margaret Wysnecki's home?

• 2.24 "Our Town"•

Sheriff Arens has to drag the lake since he doesn't want the FBI to do it. So why didn't he conveniently "not find anything?"

Why, after the outbreak of the evidently food-transmitted Creutzfeldt-Jacob disease that probably involves Chaco Chicken, does Scully risk eating from a bucket of chicken?

• 3.01 "The Blessing Way" •

In one of the series's most disappointing anti-climaxes, there's no explanation of how Mulder escaped the boxcar after Eric shut the hatch. *How* could be possibly have gotten out?

• 3.02 "Paper Clip" •

Scottish mathematician John Napier (1550–1617), who invented logarithms and introduced the decimal point in math, devised a base number for all natural logarithms. This Napier's Constant is 2.71828—yet, somehow, the agents opened the five-digit coded door by entering not 27182, but 27828. Oops.

Skinner confirms that whoever downloaded the files (e.g., Soona) copy-protected them against either digital or hard copies. So how did they print out a hard copy in the first place for Scully to have the Navajo woman in Washington look at, and which the soldiers retrieved?

• 3.04 "Clyde Bruckman's Final Repose" •

Bruckman's Lotto ticket is dated Monday, Oct. 9, 1995 (which is probably the date of the drawing and not of the purchase). Since this is the only on-screen artifact relating to the date, it holds more credence than the date-and-place subtitles, which place the events in mid-September.

• 3.05 "The List" •

Would a prison guard *really* leave a woman alone in a maximum-security, death-row cell block? Even an FBI agent?

• 3.06 "2Shy" •

Scully says its 4:15 P.M. when she's about to do the autopsy, yet the morgue clock, while blurry, definitely doesn't read 4:15: It's either 11:05 or 1:55. Of course, it's possible the clock's broken. . . .

Trained FBI agent Scully leaves her gun behind in the bedroom when going to get first-aid stuff from the bathroom?

Scully, tape-recording her autopsy notes, give the date as Aug. 29. This episode, then, would have to have taken place before episode 3.03, "DPO," which demonstrably takes place Sept. 12–14, 1995.

Though Ellen's handle is Huggs, Mulder tells Scully and the computer tech it's Friend.

• 3.07 "The Walk" •

Callahan (who from the way he checks outside the door has never encountered the phantom before) tells the agents the phantom knows his name. Yet the phantom never uttered Callahan's name, calling him only "Killer."

• 3.08 "Oubliette" •

Mulder, spotting Easton on the map, says Lucy was taken fifteen years ago. Yet earlier he'd said she's thirty now, and was kidnapped at eight—that's twenty-two years ago. Even if Mulder were talking about how long ago she'd escaped—she was said to be thirteen then—that's seventeen years ago.

IND-X

UNCREDITED ONSCREEN:

Andaluz, Michael 3.05 *
Bermel, Pat 3.07
Bourne, Lindsay 3.06
Brookstone, Peta 3.02
Carter, Chris 2.25
Cunningham, Cavan 3.03
Cutshall, D. Harlan 3.07
Dickson, Paul 3.07
Dinunzios, Aurelio 2.25
Evans, Martin 3.01
Frazier, Guyle 2.07 *
Hay, Bonnie 3.03
Kotowich, Brennan 3.07
Malebranche, Adrien 2.15
Mardon, Alexa 3.08

Mattia, Jan Bailey 3.06
McDonald, Michael 2.16 *
McIntyre, Capper 2.16
McKay, Don 3.05 *
McKenzie, Dean 3.06
Moon, Byron Chief 2.25 **
Moore, John 3.01
Pinard, Bruce 3.05
Prinsloo, P. J. 3.06
Rands, Doris 3.04
Sparks, Carrie Cain 3.09
Takeuchi, Warren 3.09
Walsh, Stanley 3.01–3.02
Wattum, Brad 3.06
Wilde, Bob 3.09
Williams, Steven (voice only) 2.02

* No speaking lines or prominent presence on-screen, but listed in print sources, with scene(s) likely cut in editing.
** Role credited in print sources to Tim Michael in 3.01–3.02, though performer is the same in all three episodes.

ABOUT THE AUTHOR

FRANK LOVECE has covered film, TV and news media as a regular contributor to such publications as *Entertainment Weekly*, *The Los Angeles Times*, *Newsday*, *Penthouse* and *TV Guide*. A former nationally syndicated columnist for United Feature/NEA, he's also the author of *The Brady Bunch Book* (with Andrew J. Edelstein), *Hailing TAXI: The Official Book of the Show*, *The Television Yearbook 1990–91* and *Thirty Years of Television*.